THE
MITOTIC CYCLE

THE CYTOPLASM AND NUCLEUS DURING
INTERPHASE AND MITOSIS

By

ARTHUR HUGHES, M.A., Ph.D.

University Demonstrator in Anatomy, University of Cambridge

Formerly Sir Halley Stewart Research Fellow
Strangeways Research Laboratory, Cambridge

LONDON
BUTTERWORTHS SCIENTIFIC PUBLICATIONS
1952

2692

BUTTERWORTH   PUBLICATIONS   LTD
BELL YARD . TEMPLE BAR . LONDON . W.C.2

BUTTERWORTH & CO (AFRICA) LTD . DURBAN
BUTTERWORTH & CO (AUSTRALIA) LTD . SYDNEY
MELBOURNE . BRISBANE . WELLINGTON . AUCKLAND
BUTTERWORTH & CO (CANADA) LTD . TORONTO

U.S.A. Edition published by
ACADEMIC PRESS INC., PUBLISHERS
125 EAST 23rd STREET
NEW YORK 10, NEW YORK

First Edition   January 1952

Set in Baskerville type
Printed in Great Britain by J. W. Arrowsmith Ltd., Bristol

THE MITOTIC CYCLE

CONTENTS

FOREWORD

EVEN at the risk of beginning with an unnecessary remark, it may be worth stating that this is not a text-book of cytology. The readers' acquaintance with the elements of the subject has been assumed. The intention of this book has been rather to review recent progress in the study of the dividing cell, and to relate it where possible to the history of the subject. It cannot be claimed that precisely equal justice is done to all branches and in common with most cytological works, a larger share of attention has been paid to those topics with which the researches of the author have been concerned. The centre of gravity lies more towards the physiological than to the descriptive aspects of the subject, though the attempt has been made, however imperfectly, to view the subject as a whole. In recent years there has been a marked growth of interest in the dividing cell, though for several reasons it is impossible yet to assess the extent of the permanent contributions to knowledge which are now being made. One cannot forecast for how long the present trends in research will be maintained, though their momentum is still high. Caution in any estimates of this kind is suggested by the previous reviews of this field, from which the contemporary reader may well have gained the impression that the way was clear for substantial progress in promising directions, though not always would such hopes have subsequently been fulfilled. For instance, in Professor FAURÉ-FREMIET's classical *Cinétique du Développement* the approach is from the standpoint of energetics, which has since been found more applicable to the wider embryological aspects of growth than to the study of the single cell in division. Again, Professor GRAY's *Experimental Cytology*, to which the writer in common with many others owe their interest in the problems of the cell, has the unifying theme of cell mechanics which is there expounded with masterly grace and penetration. It is a sobering experience to realize how little the past twenty years can add to the treatment of some topics on cell division to be found in that book. There can be no doubt that the single living cell in mitosis is one of the most difficult objects which the experimental biologist has ever attempted to analyse.

The present author has been fortunate in enlisting the help of two colleagues, Dr Charity WAYMOUTH and Dr Michael SWANN, each with special and indeed unique experience in their own fields; their contributions appear on pages 163-182 and 119-134 respectively. He is further indebted to them for the help which they have given in advice and criticism elsewhere in the book, though their responsibility is here entirely restricted to their own respective sections.

He is further indebted for much advice and assistance to Dr Honor FELL, Dr Michael WEBB, and other colleagues at the Strangeways Laboratory; to Dr GRAY and to DR PELC of the M.R.C. Radiotherapeutical Research Unit, to Dr C. D. DARLINGTON and his colleagues at the John Innes Horticultural Institution, to Dr R. A. BEATTY of the Department of Animal Genetics, Edinburgh, and to Dr Ivor CORNMAN of Washington who generously allowed him to make use of his unpublished survey of the effects of aromatic compounds on dividing cells, and to his publishers for their interest in this book and their promptitude in its publication.

Cambridge, October, 1951

'Les méthodes nouvelles de l'anatomie microscopique qui permettent de saisir la matière vivante aux differentes périodes de son évolution, de la fixer dans sa forme, de différencier, au moyen de réactifs chimiques, les éléments qui entrent dans sa constitution, les perfectionnements apportés aux objectifs des microscopes qui font apercevoir des détails qui devaient fatalement échapper aux anciens observateurs, ont montré que la structure et la vie d'une cellule sont plus complexes qu'on ne le pensait. Nous sommes loin aujourd'hui du temps où l'on considérait la cellule comme une petite masse de substance homogène, sarcode ou protoplasma, entourée ou non d'une membrane d'enveloppe et renfermant un petit corps réfringent, le noyau, contenant lui-même un corps plus petit, le nucléole.'

L. F. HENNEGUY, 1896.

'From the extensive investigations on the mechanism of cell division it must be concluded that there is as yet no full understanding of the physical and chemical mechanisms which bring forth this process.'

E. S. G. BARRON, 1949.

'We have learned many things about cell division, but we do not know much in the end.'

W. D'ARCY WENTWORTH THOMPSON, 1942.

THE NUCLEIC ACIDS

BEFORE we attempt to discuss the behaviour of the cell and of its microscopically appreciable components, there should be given some account of those macromolecules the changes in which, at a lower order of magnitude, are now known to relate to the visible events within the cell, and are believed in some way to initiate and govern the course of the whole complex of biological events which results in the production of two cells from one.

HISTORICAL

The history of this branch of biology is an interesting one, for it may be said that it began in the seventies and eighties of the last century with studies on the chemistry of the cell nucleus, which only in recent years have been resumed. Then, as now, there are two general methods which could be used for such investigations. Under the microscope one can study the behaviour of cells and tissues towards stains and reagents, or alternatively cell components such as nuclei can be separated from gross quantities of tissue and then analysed in bulk by chemical methods.

By the eighteen-sixties the affinity of cell nuclei for colouring agents such as carmine was well known (MANN,[1] BAKER[2]), and the recognition that the invariable presence of the nucleus pointed to its essential role in the life of a cell led MIESCHER, a pupil of HIS, to attempt its investigation by the second of these general methods, for which he needed a source of one type of cell in large quantity.* He first used pus from surgical bandages, plentiful in the pre-Listerian era, a material from which, although *nicht tadelfrei*, MIESCHER found that he could free the degenerating leucocytes, and after further trials could separate these as we should now say, into nuclear and cytoplasmic fractions. MIESCHER describes the isolated nuclei as 'vollkommen reinen Kernen, mit glatter Contour, homogenen Inhalt, scharf gezeichnetem Nucleolus, im Vergleich zur ihren ursprunglichen Volumen etwas verkleinert' (MIESCHER[5]). From these isolated nuclei, MIESCHER proceeded to prepare a substance which he termed 'nuclein' with stronger acidic properties than any organic cell constituent then known, and which was soluble in weak alkali, but not in dilute acid. It contained a high

---

* An admirable account of MIESCHER's life and work is given by GREENSTEIN.[3]

percentage of phosphorus; it was only very slowly attacked by gastric juice. An account of this research was submitted to HOPPÉ-SEYLER in 1869, but so startling were the nature of these conclusions that MIESCHER's[5] paper was not published until 1871, by which time other colleagues had confirmed these observations on different types of material. In that year, MIESCHER returned to his native city of Basle and became interested in the biology of the Rhine salmon, the sperm of which provided new material for investigations on nuclear chemistry. The acid nuclein of the sperm head was shown to be united with a nitrogenous base, to which MIESCHER gave the name protamine. He did not regard this as a protein, for it gave no reaction with the Millon reagent.

The first instance in which the results of MIESCHER were applied to a histochemical investigation is provided by the work of ZACHARIAS,[6] who sought to determine whether the nuclei of several types of cell consisted of nuclein, by testing if they were resistant to peptic digestion, and whether they would swell or gelate in strong sodium chloride, as did MIESCHER's nuclein. ZACHARIAS applied these tests to a number of animal and plant cells and found that the behaviour of their nuclei suggested that they also contained nuclein. This research FLEMMING[7] had in mind when in his classical *Zellsubstanz, Kern und Zelltheilung* he gave a definition of the substance which forms the 'framework' of the nucleus:

> which, in virtue of its refractile nature, its reactions, and above all, its affinity for dyes, is a substance which I have named chromatin. Possibly chromatin is identical with nuclein, but if not, it follows from ZACHARIAS' work that one carries the other. The word chromatin may serve until its chemical nature is known, and meanwhile stands for 'that substance in the cell nucleus which is readily stained'.

Although this definition was framed with respect to the resting nucleus, FLEMMING clearly describes in the following section of the book how the 'Kerngerüste' of the resting nucleus is directly transformed into the 'chromatischen Kernfigur' during mitosis, the individual loops of which were not given a special name until WALDEYER[8] first used the term 'chromosome'.

By the eighteen-seventies, there were available a number of the azo dyes which are still used by histologists, and FLEMMING in 1882 lists those which he had employed in studying the nucleus throughout its stages. It was not long afterwards that EHRLICH drew attention to the difference in staining properties between those dyes in which the colour group was acidic or basic (see for instance EHRLICH[9]).

Meanwhile, advances in the chemical study of the nucleus were in progress and the presence was being recognized of one type of constituent unit, the purine bases, then known as the 'alloxuric bases'. Such investigations were begun by PICCARD, and continued by KOSSEL. At first it was not clear whether nuclein or protamine was the source of these bases. KOSSEL[10] had by 1881 inclined more to the former opinion, and continued to work on these substances from this point of view. In 1889, however, ALTMANN[11] first described a method for preparing nucleic acids which were free from protein, from both animal tissues and yeast, and within a few years KOSSEL and NEUMANN[12] were able to isolate thymonucleic acid from the thymus gland. These advances in the study of the structure of the nucleic acids did not lead to any immediate comparable progress in histochemistry. By means of double staining methods, LILIENFELD[13] attempted to distinguish between nucleoproteins and free nucleic acid in the nuclei of resting and dividing cells, but similar efforts by HEINE[14] led this author to the conclusion that such a distinction could not be made by the staining methods then available. When FISCHER[15] wrote his classical monograph on the *Fixierung, Färbung und Bau des Protoplasmas* the subject of biological staining was already in the complex state in which it has largely remained. In this work, he discussed the influence on the results obtained of such factors as the nature of the fixative, and the order in which stains are applied, both with tissue sections and with films of proteins and nucleic acids. It was recognized that methyl green has a special affinity for thymonucleic acid, although FISCHER pointed out that proteins, when fixed by heavy metal salts, can also absorb this stain. In a series of papers at this time (MANN[16]), the question was debated whether the affinity for dyes depends upon chemical factors or whether physical effects are alone involved. In the end, future progress depended not only on the further development of micro-chemical staining methods, but also on the use of specific enzyme preparations on tissue sections under the microscope. The first histo-chemical researches which related to the nucleoclastic enzymes were studies on autolysis. Such experiments indicate the presence of tissue ferments only when conducted in the presence of antiseptics, which SALKOWSKI[17] first used for this purpose. ZALESKI[18] demonstrated that purine bases were liberated on prolonged autolysis of plant material at 30° C. while OËS[19] [20] showed that a few hours' incubation under these conditions was sufficient to break up and dissolve the chromosomes in dividing cells of both plants and animals.

The investigations of VAN HERWERDEN[21] [22] differed in both methods and results. By means of the method described by SACHS[23] a nuclease was prepared from beef pancreas or spleen. The expressed juice of these organs was precipitated with saturated ammonium sulphate, and the washed product was subsequently dissolved in water and dialysed. Sections of echinoderm eggs were incubated for 24 hours in this preparation, and were then stained in haemalum. On comparing them with control sections incubated in water, VAN HERWERDEN found that the basophil granules of the cytoplasm, the 'chromidia', had disappeared. These bodies must therefore be related in composition to nuclein. A similar treatment of sections of the intervertebral ganglia of the cat resulted in the dissolution of the Nissl granules. The demonstration that nucleic acid is found in the cytoplasm is thus nearly forty years old.

In VAN HERWERDEN's experiments, the changes within the oocyte nucleus, either in the chromatin or the nucleolus were very much less marked. He returned to this subject in a further study (VAN HERWERDEN[22]) of the effects on the sperm head of both nuclease and 1 per cent hydrochloric acid. He found that in both fishes and echinoderms the basophily of the sperm nucleus was decreased after hydrolysis by the latter reagent in the cold, but that the mammalian sperm was resistant to this treatment. The same result was obtained in each case by digestion with nuclease. VAN HERWERDEN saw in his results an illustration of the observations of KOSSEL[24] and KOSSEL and EDLBACHER[25] that the linkage between the basic protein and nucleic acid was broken with particular ease in the sperm nucleoprotein of fishes and echinoderms. He further observed that the unripe mammalian sperm head was attacked by the agents which he employed.

We now know that it is the difference between the nucleic acids of the sperm head and of the egg cytoplasm which is primarily responsible for VAN HERWERDEN's results. At the time, the conclusion was drawn from these results that the 'nuclease test' could not be used as a reliable index of the presence of chromatin. The verdict of WILSON[26] on this matter, still to be found in the third edition and its reprints is that 'it must be admitted, therefore, that we have no certain means of identifying "chromatin" in the cell apart from its morphological history'.

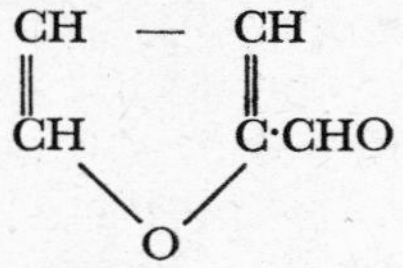

$$CH = CH$$
$$CH \quad C \cdot CHO$$
$$\diagdown \; O \; \diagup$$

(i) Furfural

$$CH_3—CO—CH_2—CH_2 \cdot COOH$$

(ii) laevulinic acid

$$HO—CH_2—CO \cdot CH_2—CH_2 \cdot CHO$$

(iii) ω. hydroxy laevulinic aldehyde

Figure 1—STRUCTURAL FORMULAE

The recognition of two classes of nucleic acids preceded this cytochemical work of VAN HERWERDEN by many years, but until long after this period it was believed that one was found in plants and the other in animals. In 1893 KOSSEL[27] had shown that although nucleic acids from both yeast and animal sources contained the same purine bases, the

parent substances differ in that in the former there is a reducing carbohydrate which produces furfural on hydrolysis (Figure 1) and is thus
a pentose. A further difference between the two groups is found in
respect to the second category of constituent basic groups, the pyrimi-
dines, the presence of which was recognized in 1893 by KOSSEL and
NEUMANN.[28] In a series of papers published in 1903, LEVENE[29] showed
that the pyrimidine cytosine was common to both plant and animal
nucleic acids, but that uracil was only found in the former, and thymine
only in the latter. MANDEL and LEVENE,[30] however, found uracil and
not thymine in their analysis of the nucleic acid of fish eggs. In Table I
the main points of difference between the two types of nucleic acid are
summarized. The admirable reviews of SCHLENK[31] and DAVIDSON[32]
should be consulted for further information in the chemical field.

TABLE I

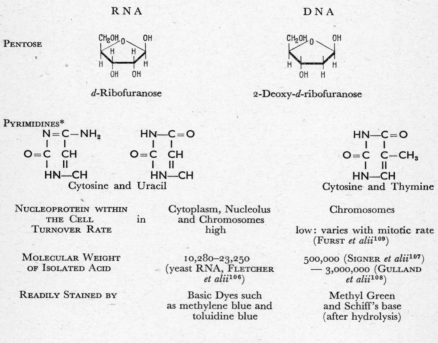

	RNA		DNA
PENTOSE			
	d-Ribofuranose		2-Deoxy-d-ribofuranose
PYRIMIDINES*	Cytosine and Uracil		Cytosine and Thymine
NUCLEOPROTEIN WITHIN THE CELL in TURNOVER RATE	Cytoplasm, Nucleolus and Chromosomes high		Chromosomes low: varies with mitotic rate (FURST et alii[109])
MOLECULAR WEIGHT OF ISOLATED ACID	10,280–23,250 (yeast RNA, FLETCHER et alii[106])		500,000 (SIGNER et alii[107]) — 3,000,000 (GULLAND et alii[108])
READILY STAINED BY	Basic Dyes such as methylene blue and toluidine blue		Methyl Green and Schiff's base (after hydrolysis)

FEULGEN REACTION

The carbohydrate of thymonucleic acid, corresponding to the pentose
of yeast nucleic acid was believed by Kossel and Neumann[28] to be a
hexose, on the grounds that on hydrolysis laevulinic acid was formed,

*There have been several reports of the occurrence of 5-methyl cytosine in DNA's of
different sources, the most recent of which is by WYATT.[110]

a known breakdown product of these sugars. This was believed for a number of years although certain observations did not accord therewith, notably the unstable nature of the sugar of thymonucleic acid, and the fact that elementary analysis gave an empirical formula for this acid which did not suggest that the molecule contained a hexose. In 1914, FEULGEN[33 34] drew attention to these discrepancies; three years later he showed that among the products of gentle hydrolysis is a substance which gives the Schiff's test for an aldehyde, namely the re-appearance of coloured fuchsin in a solution of dye decolorized by sulphur dioxide. This is the basis of the now famous Feulgen reaction, the application of which to microscopical preparations was subsequently described (FEULGEN and ROSSENBECK[35]). In this classical paper these authors apply the test to a number of tissues and organisms, including the wheat germ, from which triticonucleic acid had been prepared (OSBORNE and HARRIS[36]) similar in nature to that of yeast. They did not therefore expect to find, as they did, that sections of the wheat embryo gave a positive reaction with the test:

> This gave us a great surprise, for the nuclei of the wheat embryo gave the nucleal reaction more intensively than we have ever seen in any animal tissues. This was confirmed in other plants, and so it was demonstrated that the plant nucleus contains nucleal bodies. The old dualism of yeast and thymonucleic acids is thus set aside. . . .

It now seems remarkable that it took several years from the publication of this paper before biologists began to make use of the means which had been put into their hands to follow up this demonstration of a fundamental property common to both plant and animal nuclei. At the time, however, it was uncertain whether Feulgen's test related to the sugar of thymonucleic acid or was due to traces of furfural formed by hydrolysis of pentose nucleic acid (STEUDEL and PEISER[37]). Possibly, also there was confusion between Feulgen's nucleal reaction, and the 'plasmal' test for cytoplasmic aldehydes, liberated after a prolonged hydrolysis (FEULGEN and VOIT[38]), which also uses decolorized fuchsin as a reagent.

The proof that the carbohydrate of thymonucleic acid is indeed responsible for the Feulgen reaction was given by LEVENE and LONDON.[39] They were able to separate the constituent nucleosides, units consisting of base plus sugar, and later to isolate the latter component itself. LEVENE et alii[40] proved it to be d-2-deoxyribose. By this time, biologists had begun to use the Feulgen reaction (e.g. COWDRY[41]). The growth of the ensuing literature followed a sigmoidal curve; in 1938, MILOVIDOW[42] could list over 450 papers in this field. In recent years, discussion of the Feulgen reaction has centred round two points; one, whether the distribution of the liberated dye within a microscopical preparation indicates the precise localization of the DNA when the cell was alive;

6

secondly, if so, whether the reaction can be used quantitatively to measure this substance in absolute amounts.

All are agreed that aldehyde groups in the hydrolysis products of deoxyribose are responsible for the production of the purple colour; according to STACEY et alii,[43] it is w-hydroxy-laevulinic aldehyde which reacts with the fuchsin-sulphurous reagent (Figure 1). The question is whether the coloured substance formed by this reaction stays precisely at the site of formation, or whether it can diffuse into and stain neighbouring zones of the section. STEDMAN and STEDMAN[44] point out that this dye is water-soluble, but is readily adsorbed by chromosomin, the non-basic protein of the nucleus which these authors have discovered. The Feulgen reaction according to these authors indicates the position of the chromosomin stained by a dye liberated in a reaction in which deoxyribose took part.

The STEDMANS' argument is not demolished by the demonstration that a granule of DNA* when fixed, embedded in gelatin and sectioned, is Feulgen-positive (BRACHET[45]), for the liberated dye has then no chromosomin to which it may become attached. It would be useful to compare the result of this experiment with one in which a similar mass of DNA was embedded in gelatin to which chromosomin had been added. At the moment, the most cogent argument which can be brought forward to support the validity of the Feulgen reaction is the constancy of the results obtained when a standard procedure is adopted. For instance, the small Feulgen-positive heterochromatic granules of the interphase nucleus are seen in a constant relationship to the residual chromosome threads (FELL and HUGHES;[46] p 33). If in such instances there is diffusion of the liberated dye, it must be restricted to a radius little greater than the limits of resolution of the microscope.

The subject which we have just discussed is clearly antecedent to the further question of whether the Feulgen reaction can be made the basis of a quantitative microcolorimetric method. Several workers have assumed that all the necessary conditions are satisfied, and their results will be discussed in a further section (p 35). LESLER[47] has made a series of model experiments which relate to this question. He prepared a series of mixtures of gelatin with DNA at various concentrations, on which the Feulgen reaction was performed, and the results were judged subjectively. They did not suggest a uniform relationship between the concentration of DNA and the depth of colour produced.

Comparable debates on the validity of the methods used and the results obtained have occurred in other branches of cytochemistry. It must be borne in mind that the search for methods which will estimate

* In this book, the usual abbreviations of 'DNA' for deoxyribonucleic acid and 'RNA' for ribonucleic acid have been employed. The latter term is used loosely for all cytoplasmic nucleic acids; some authors prefer to speak of pentose nucleic acids (PNA), for it has not been proved that d-ribose occurs in them all.

7

or even recognize particular constituents within an area of a complex mixture of the order of a few square microns goes beyond the exactitude demanded of any analytical procedure elsewhere in microchemistry. However, rather than sit with folded hands until fully adequate methods are available, students of cellular biology have chosen to make use of the present inadequate procedures although the results obtained have often only a provisional status. To allow the tentative generalizations which emerge to harden into dogma by frequent reiteration is nevertheless an avoidable impediment to the development of the subject. Furthermore, it must be remembered that much of our knowledge of intracellular physiology is still well within the early phase of the development of a science at the qualitative level.

With these considerations in mind we must now turn to the discussion of two major developments in research relating to the cytochemical localization of the nucleic acids, namely the development of ultra-violet microspectrometry by CASPERSSON and his school, and secondly the isolation of separate nucleoclastic enzymes in approximate states of purity, exclusively affecting the two types of nucleic acid.

NUCLEOCLASTIC ENZYMES

It will be convenient here to discuss first the latter of these two developments. Following the usual nomenclature which uses the name of the appropriate substrate, these enzymes are now known as ribonuclease and deoxyribonuclease respectively. Both have been prepared from the pancreas, by which they are secreted for the digestion of nucleic acids liberated by the stomach acid from dietary nucleoproteins. The intracellular nucleases in other tissues are probably not identical with these pancreatic enzymes.

Ribonuclease proved much the easier enzyme to prepare, thanks to its remarkable stability towards both temperature and pH (JONES,[48] DUBOS and THOMPSON[49]). It was crystallized first by KUNITZ[50] in 1940, and found to be an albumen-like protein, with a molecular weight of approximately 15,000.

The method described by KUNITZ and NORTHROP[51] for the separation of chymo-trypsin from the pancreas was found to be of service also for the nucleases. The tissue is extracted in cold 0·25N sulphuric acid and by this means the activation of the tryptic enzymes is prevented. Ribonuclease is resistant to trypsin, but deoxyribonuclease is readily attacked thereby. From the filtered acid extract, the various enzyme proteins can be fractionally precipitated with different concentrations of ammonium sulphate; first deoxyribonuclease at a saturation of 0·4 and ribonuclease between 0·6 and 0·8. Deoxyribonuclease was prepared in this way by FISCHER *et alii*[52] in 1941, and by McCARTY[53] in 1946.

It was crystallized by KUNITZ in 1948. McCARTY developed a method for estimating the activity of a preparation of the enzyme, by making use of the high viscosity of sodium thymonucleate in solution. The rate of decrease is measured when the substrate is incubated with de-oxyribonuclease. By this method, it was shown that the enzyme is activated by magnesium ions. One group of inhibitors are substances which remove this ion (Figure 2).

Numerous papers have been published on the cytochemical use of these enzymes. It is necessary to incubate a control series of sections in the buffer solution used to dissolve the enzyme, and then to compare the sections exposed to the latter with those treated with buffer alone. After ribonuclease digestion, either basophilia or absorption in ultra-

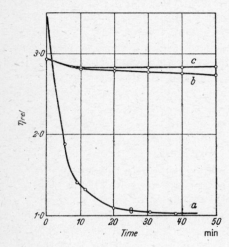

Figure 2 Relative viscosity curves of DNA **a** in the presence of desoxyribonu-clease and o·oo2 M MgSO$_4$ Magnesium, **b** with o·oo2 M Sodium arsenate, **c** with o·oo2 M Sodium citrate. (*By courtesy of Dr Michael Webb.*)

violet light is compared in the two series of preparations. Among the earliest papers in this field are those of BRACHET[54] in 1941, who used the methyl green-pyronin staining method of UNNA-PAPPENHEIM as the test for the effects of the enzyme. BRACHET found that in a number of cells and tissues, such as exocrine glands and oocytes in which there occurs a rapid synthesis of material, their basophilia was much re-duced by treatment with ribonuclease.

DAVIDSON and WAYMOUTH showed that in the cytoplasm of rat liver cells, digestion with ribonuclease decreased both the affinity for tolui-dine blue[55] and the absorption of ultraviolet light.[56] In the nucleolus, the results were partly masked by the outer zone of heterochromatic deoxynucleoprotein. Although there are a number of apparently successful instances of the cytochemical use of ribonuclease, some authors including DAVIDSON[57] himself have drawn attention to diffi-culties in its use. STOWELL and ZORZOLI[58] have shown how much the final results depend upon the nature of the fixative which was used, and conclude that 'with our present limited knowledge and technics, it would seem advisable to use the ribonuclease technic only crudely to confirm observations made by other methods'. DAVIDSON[57] believes that the main difficulty resides in the contamination even of the crystalline enzymes with traces of proteolytic ferments*. It has been suggested that certain inorganic reagents can remove ribonucleic acid from tissue sections more effectively than the enzyme. ERICKSON *et alii*[59] suggest perchloric acid for this purpose, while VENDRELY-RANDAVEL[60] and PONYET[61] advise the use of normal hydrochloric acid for ten minutes.

This difficulty of proteolytic contamination is even more marked with deoxyribonuclease, which does not share the heat-stable nature of the former enzyme, thanks to which it can be mainly freed of impurities. Several workers have added a very small amount of gelatin to their preparations of deoxyribonuclease which they have used for the digestion of sectioned biological material; WEBB and JACOBSON[62] have used small concentrations of tryptic inhibitors in the digestion mixture.

The extent to which deoxyribonucleic acid can be removed from the nucleus by digestion again depends among other factors upon the fixative originally used. Formalin should be avoided (STOWELL,[63] SANDERS[64]); chilled acetone is recommended by DAVIDSON.[65] Nuclei in the digested sections are sometimes still faintly Feulgen-positive (STOWELL, DAVIDSON, op. cit.), although a completely negative reaction following digestion is reported by CATCHESIDE and HOLMES[66] in the bands of salivary chromosomes, and by WEBB and JACOBSON[62] in smears of mouse and human cells. CATCHESIDE and HOLMES find that thymonuclease prepared from the spleen does not act on bean-root nuclei unless ribonuclease is used at the same time, while pancreatic deoxynuclease is effective alone.

DANIELLI[67] has criticized the use of these enzymes in cytochemistry with some severity, on the grounds of their probable impurity. He further suggests that a nuclease entirely free of proteolytic activity might fail to act if even a monolayer of protein surrounded the substrate within the tissue section. It is possible, however, that the recent successful use of nucleases in the presence of proteolytic inhibitors by WEBB and JACOBSON[62] have diminished the force of these criticisms.

But for the use of ribonuclease in cytochemistry there would have been no advance in the microscopical identification of ribonucleic acid subsequent to the recognition of its affinity for basic stains. Why such dyes as methylene and toluidine blue should be adsorbed more readily by RNA than by DNA is still not known, though it is surmised that free phosphate groups at the surface of the molecule are more

* McDONALD[4] has prepared ribonuclease free of all proteolytic activity.

abundant in the former type of nucleic acid. MICHAELIS[68] has shown that basic stains adsorbed on RNA are in the form of single molecules, but that the metachromatic staining of cartilage matrix, for instance, involves polymerization of the dye. In this interesting paper the author touches on a fundamental topic in this field. The living nucleus is not stained by methylene blue. When the stain is absorbed, the nucleus is dead; MICHAELIS believes that the dye has then displaced the protein from nucleic acid. In living cells are the whole nucleoproteins; their free components are produced by fixation. MONNÉ,[69] however, claims to have demonstrated a transient vital staining of the nucleus in *Amoeba* by micro-injecting dyes into the cytoplasm. These penetrated the nuclear membrane. The coloration within the nucleus soon disappeared; the cycle was more rapid with acid dyes than with basic.

SPECTROPHOTOMETRIC METHODS

Our final topic in the discussion of recent advances in the cytochemistry of the nucleic acids is the most important of the developments in this field, and is mainly responsible for the interest aroused in this subject in recent years. We refer to the development of spectrophotometric methods applied to the microscope, very largely by CASPERSSON and his school, which they use mainly in the ultraviolet range. At 2,600 Å, which corresponds to the resonance frequency of the pyrimidine and purine ring structure, the absorption of the nucleic acids is far more intense than that of other cell constituents in which these configurations are not found (Figure 3). The absorption band at this wavelength is equally a property not only of both DNA and RNA and their constituent nucleotide units, but also of the other adenylic acids and the co-enzymes. Thus ultraviolet techniques like any other cytochemical procedures are not alone sufficient to study the location of the nucleic acids within the cell.

A number of workers have demonstrated by photomicrography the presence of ultraviolet-absorbing substances within the cells and tissues; the special contribution of the Stockholm school is the development of quantitative methods by which, it is claimed, the extinction coefficient of an area one micron in diameter within a biological preparation can be measured to an accuracy of 1 per cent (CASPERSSON[70]). Such precision goes much beyond that obtainable by photographic methods; it is necessary to make direct photo-electric measurements through a range of wavelengths at a series of points within one single cell.

From a complete ultraviolet absorption curve, information can be obtained concerning the presence not only of nucleic acids but also of proteins which contain the aromatic amino acids, namely tyrosine, tryptophane, and phenylalanine. These show an absorption maximum in the ultraviolet between 2,700 and 2,900 Å. The position of that of tyrosine is shifted to the upper limit of this range at high pH's (HOLIDAY[71]) and also according to CASPERSSON[72 73] by the presence of histones. A shift in the protein maximum to this region of the ultraviolet absorption curve is used as evidence by the Stockholm workers for the presence of basic proteins. CASPERSSON and THORELL[74] claim that a protein peak in this region is seen very clearly in embryonic cells at stages when the proportion of histone to non-basic protein is high. HYDEN[75] has devised an independent cytochemical test for basic proteins which depends on their capacity for binding acid dyes at low pH's and claims that the results obtained by these two methods on nerve cells are consistent. Little use seems yet to have been made of

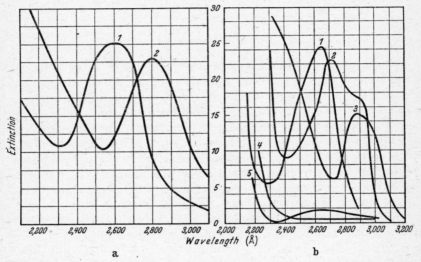

Figure 3 **a** Absorption curves of (1) polynucleotides and (2) serum globulin, and **b** of (1) adenine (2) tryptophane (3) tyrosin (4) histidine (5) phenylalanine. (Adenine ⅓%, all others 1%; 1 cm thickness of layer.) From CASPERSSON[78] (*By courtesy of W. W. Norton & Company*).

this method of Hyden's. The effect of the presence of histones on these ultraviolet absorption curves is still in some doubt; POLLISTER and RIS[76] quote the observations of MIRSKY and POLLISTER[77] that the peak for relatively pure histones is in the usual protein region, and not shifted towards 2,900 Å; CASPERSSON[73] however, says that the displacement only occurs in the presence of nucleic acids in addition. An illustration of the uncertainty which thus still surrounds the recognition of histones within the cell is that different workers do not agree on the question of their distribution within the chromosomes during mitosis (p104). On this subject, CASPERSSON[78] has recently admitted that 'the absorption of the nucleic acids is . . . in these dense structures so very large that even with the highest possible precision in the absorption measurement it is not possible to make an exact determination of the amount or character of the proteins.' There is some doubt whether the absorption spectrum of a mixture of protein and nucleic acid is entirely the sum of that of each component. FERKHMIN[79] claims to have shown that those of adenylic acid and tyrosine are non-additive; I have been informed by BRACHET that the same is true of nucleic acid in the presence of the protein edestin. It is here of interest that RUDALL[80] reports that in the x-ray diffraction pattern of 'the fibrous product of combination between nucleic acid and edestin . . . neither nucleic acid structure nor protein structure can be recognized'. If interaction between proteins and nucleic acids, or between their constituent units may influence their ultraviolet absorption, microspectrometric measurements on cells will be affected by the extent to which these constituent substances are combined within the specimen under test. It is generally believed the linkage between nucleic acids and proteins is destroyed when tissues are fixed; it would be highly desirable to know whether this is always wholly true of dead cells, even when the freeze-drying technique has been used. Such technical matters relating to the validity of microspectrometric research methods may well be of greater importance to those which have recently been raised on optical grounds (COMMONER[81]). They are peculiarly relevant to the question of the relationship between protein synthesis and the nucleic acids, the evidence for which we shall now attempt to discuss.

NUCLEIC ACIDS AND PROTEIN SYNTHESIS

The general thesis that nucleic acid is abundant in cells which are synthesizing proteins at a comparatively rapid rate is due both to CASPERSSON[72][82] and to BRACHET,[83] who were working simultaneously by different methods, and came independently to the same conclusion. BRACHET used the Unna-Pappenheim staining technique, and studied the effect of ribonuclease on the basophilia towards the pyronin component of this mixture. Instances of cells and tissues in which both workers have observed this correlation of nucleic acid content and synthetic activity are the exocrine glands, keratinizing epithelia, embryonic tissues in which mitosis is frequent and also the developing oocyte. The neurone was also included in this scheme when it was realized (HYDÉN[75]) that here also proteins are produced and are used up during functional activity. A further example is that of the silk glands of the Arachnida (BRADFIELD[84]), and the available evidence is by no means confined to the cells of Metazoa (DAVIDSON[32]).

The accumulation of nucleic acids within the cells of a tissue may anticipate growth and protein production (CASPERSSON[78]). In tumour cells approaching necrosis, a high content of nucleic acids is said to persist after the mechanism for protein production has broken down (CASPERSSON[78]).

In the normal growth of the cell, CASPERSSON maintains that the nucleoli and the adjacent heterochromatic chromosomal material are particularly concerned with protein synthesis; this thesis is supported in his paper in 1941 by the following assertions:

1. Nucleoli are large in all the basophilic protein-forming cells which we have listed above, and also in rapidly growing malignant cells.

2. That 'heterochromatin' is involved is shown by the fact that the amount of cytoplasmic nucleic acid in an egg cell of *Drosophila* is

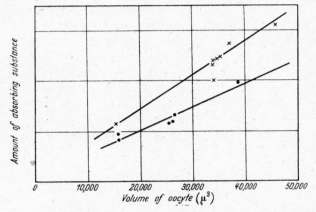

Figure 4 Comparison of the amount of substances absorbing ultraviolet light at 2,570 A in the oocytes of an XX and an XXY female of *Drosophila melanogaster* for varying volumes of these cells. Crosses represent the values from XXY; points, those from XX ovaries. From CASPERSSON and SCHULTZ[85] (*By courtesy, Nature*).

increased when an extra Y-chromosome has been incorporated into the nucleus (CASPERSSON and SCHULTZ[85]) (Figure 4). Whether this argument, however, can be generally applied depends on how far 'heterochromatin' is a constant entity (p 47).

3. In some cells a zone of high nucleic acid content surrounds the nuclear membrane. CASPERSSON's view of the bearing of this on the function of the nucleolus may best be given in his own words taken from a later review.[73]

A certain part of the chromatin, we call it the nucleolus-associated chromatin, secretes substances of a protein nature. These are very strong indications that they contain considerable amounts of diamino acids. These substances accumulate and form the main bulk of the large nucleolus. From the nucleolus they diffuse towards the nuclear membrane, on the outside of which an intensive production of ribose nucleotides takes place. At the same time the amount of cytoplasmic proteins increases. Their synthesis is apparently in some way linked with the nucleic acid changes.

This perinuclear region of high ultraviolet absorption has been demonstrated for two types of cells in both of which it may be said that the cytoplasm is highly absorbing, namely the sea-urchin oocyte (CASPERSSON and SCHULTZ[86]) (Figure 5), and the ovarian nurse cells in *Drosophila* (SCHULTZ[87]). In the egg of the toad (PAINTER and TAYLOR[88]), there is a zone of cytoplasm next to the nucleus which stains

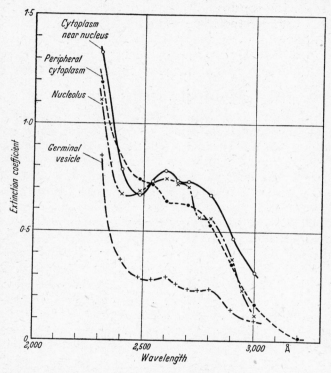

Figure 5 Ultraviolet absorption spectra of different parts of an ovarian egg of the sea urchin, *Psammechinus miliaris*. From CASPERSSON and SCHULTZ[85] (*By courtesy, Proc. Nat. Acad. Sci.*).

strongly with pyronin. CASPERSSON and SCHULTZ themselves did not observe such a perinuclear zone in root-tip cells of the spinach, nor was it found by LUDFORD *et alii*[89] in their ultraviolet photomicrographs of living malignant cells.

BRACHET[83] has cited evidence from his embryological experience which suggests that not always is there an immediate relationship in development between nucleoli and cytoplasmic basophilia. In the amphibian embryo, nucleoli are absent in early cleavage stages and are first detectable at the morula stage. They are everywhere well developed in the gastrula. The cells of the presumptive endoblast do not become basophilic until much later, while on the other hand, those of the neural ectoderm early show a marked basophilia, which is later lost, but the nucleoli then remain equally prominent. It was suggested by POLLISTER and LEUCHTENBERGER[90] that the high proportion of oligo-nucleotides which they found in the nucleoli of pollen mother-cells of *Zea mais* indicated that synthetic activity was in progress therein, though it could equally well be argued that this fact suggests depolymer-ization heralding the approaching break-up of the nucleolus. It would be valuable to compare the proportion of oligonucleotides in nucleo-proteins at other sites where they are believed to be actively concerned in synthesis, such as the cytoplasmic nucleoproteins, and the hetero-chromatic regions of the salivary chromosomes of the *Drosophila* larva.

Isotopic methods

By the use of isotopic methods, evidence has been obtained which suggests that the ribonucleoproteins of the cell can originate within the nucleus. Living cells and tissues have been treated in various ways with phosphates in solution, containing P^{32}; these cells have been subse-quently fractionated and the specific radioactivities of the various fractions compared. MARSHAK and CALVET[91] and JEENER and SZAFARZ[92] have used mammalian liver for such experiments, while the two latter authors have also worked with mice embryos, and cul-tures of the flagellate *Polytomella*. All agree that at first the activity of the nuclei is greater than that of the cytoplasm. JEENER and SZAFARZ separated their cytoplasmic material into fractions of graded sizes of particles, and found that the smallest took up radiophosphorus more quickly than did larger particles. Their conclusion is that in the nucleus is synthesized at least an important part of the RNA of the cell, and that this passes through the nuclear membrane in an extremely fine form (unsedimentable at $60,000 \times g$), and then 'spreads into the rest of the cytoplasm by integrating itself with cytoplasmic particles of large dimensions'.

While more remains yet to be learnt regarding the interrelationships in both space and time within the cell between basic and non-basic proteins and the two types of nucleic acid, the general thesis that some connexion exists between the function and formation of these substances in all cells may meanwhile be accepted, although nothing is yet known of the steps by which proteins are synthesized in the living cell. It has been suggested that nucleic acids may furnish phosphate groups to an intermediate substance in which energy-rich phosphate bonds are built up, which in its turn could provide the necessary calories for the synthesis of peptide bonds by phosphorylation. The association of phosphatases both with the sites of protein synthesis, particularly of a fibrous nature (JEENER,[93] BRADFIELD[84]), and also with concentrations of nucleic acids suggests this possibility. Whether the transpeptidation reactions of FRUTON[94] and HANES, HIRD and ISHERWOOD[95] are consonant with this mechanism is not yet clear. Chromosomes give a strongly alkaline phosphatase reaction, and in the salivary glands of *Drosophila* it has been shown that the enzyme is concentrated in the Feulgen-positive bands (DANIELLI and CATCHESIDE,[96] KRUGELIS[97]). In the intermitotic nuclei of chick cultures, the nucleoli and the heterochromatic granules are also Gomori-positive, and the strength of this reaction has been shown by CHÈVREMONT and FIRKET[98] to be correlated with the growth rate of the culture.

BRACHET and JEENER[99] have also shown that the intensity of the Gomori reaction in several types of nuclei is paralleled both by their frequency of mitosis and by their DNA turnover rates as measured isotopically (HEVESY and OTTESEN,[100] [101] HAMMARSTEN and HEVESY[102]). Thus fowl erythrocytes are Gomori-negative, they have a negligible DNA turnover-rate, and do not undergo cell division, whilst on the other hand in the cells of the intestinal crypts the opposite is true in each instance, although the function of the alkaline phosphatase elsewhere within the mucosal cells, and possibly in the nucleus as well is related to the transport of metabolites. Moreover, in nuclei from the cerebral cortex where the mitotic index is *nil*, RICHTER and HULTIN[103] report that both acid and alkaline phosphatases are there present in higher concentrations than in the cytoplasm.

As one surveys the general state of this subject at the moment it must be admitted that the extent of our knowledge about what JONES[104] termed the 'physiological conduct' of the nucleic acids within the cell is still restricted to the barest outlines. In recent years, there has been a tendency to explain every cellular change in terms of nucleic acids, much as the Peripateticks once used to interpret all natural phenomena in terms of the four elements. However, as WILLEY[105] so lucidly expounds, the real purpose of all explanations is to satisfy mental needs. In science such satisfaction can come finally from factual knowledge alone.

REFERENCES

[1] MANN, G., *Physiological Histology*, Oxford, 1902
[2] BAKER, J. R., *J. Quekett micro. Soc.*, 4 (1943), 256
[3] GREENSTEIN, J. P., *Sci. Mon.*, 57 (1943), 523
[4] McDONALD, M., *J. Gen. Physiol*, 32 (1948), 39
[5] MIESCHER, F., *Hoppe-Seyl. med-chem. Untersuch.*, 4 (1871), 441
[6] ZACHARIAS, E., *Bot. Zeitung Jahrg.*, 39 (1881), 169
[7] FLEMMING, W., *Zellsubstanz, Kern, und Zelltheilung*, Leipzig, 1882
[8] WALDEYER, W., *Arch. mikr. Anat.*, 32 (1888), 1
[9] EHRLICH, P., *Z. Klin. Med.*, 1 (1880), 553

[10] KOSSEL, A., *Hoppe-Seyl-Z.*, 5 (1881), 152
[11] ALTMANN, R., *Arch. Anat. Physiol.* (Physiol. Abt.), (1889), 524
[12] KOSSEL, A., and NEUMANN, A., *Ber. dtsch. chem. Ges.*, 27 (1894), 2215
[13] LILIENFELD, L., *Arch. Anat. Physiol.* (Physiol. Abt.) (1893), 391
[14] HEINE, L., *Z. Hoppe-Seyl. Z.*, 21 (1895), 494
[15] FISCHER, A., *Fixierung, Färbung und Bau des Protoplasmas*, Jena, 1899
[16] MANN, G., *Physiological Histology*, chap. 24, Oxford, 1902
[17] SALKOWSKI, E., *Z. Klin. Med.* Suppl., 17 (1890), 77
[18] ZALESKI, W., *Ber. dtsch. Bot. Ges.*, 25 (1907), 349
[19] OËS, A., *Bot. Ztg.*, 66 (1908), 89
[20] —, *Z., Bot.*, 2 (1910), 39
[21] VAN HERWERDEN, M. A., *Arch. Zellforsch*, 10 (1913), 431
[22] —, *Arch. Néerl. Phys.*, 1 (1916), 101
[23] SACHS, F., *Hoppe-Seyl. Z.*, 46 (1905), 337
[24] KOSSEL, A., *ibid.*, 88 (1913), 163
[25] —, and EDLBACHER, S., *ibid*, 94 (1915), 264
[26] WILSON, E. B., *The Cell in Development and Heredity*, 3rd Ed., New York, 1925
[27] KOSSEL, A., *Arch. anat. Physiol.* (Physiol. Abt.) (1893), 157
[28] —, and NEUMANN, A., *Ber. dtsch. chem. Ges.*, 26 (1893), 2753
[29] LEVENE, P. A., *Hoppe-Seyl. Z.*, 39 (1903), 4, 133 and 479
[30] MANDEL, S. A., and LEVENE, P. A., *J. biol. Chem.*, 1 (1905), 425
[31] SCHLENK, F., Chemistry and Enzymology of Nucleic Acids, *Advanc. Enzym.*, 9 (1949), 455
[32] DAVIDSON, J. N., *The Biochemistry of the Nucleic Acids*, London, 1950
[33] FEULGEN, R., *Hoppe-Seyl. Z.*, 92 (1914), 154
[34] —, *ibid.*, 100 (1917), 241
[35] —, and ROSSENBECK, H., *ibid.*, 135 (1924), 203
[36] OSBORNE, T. B., and HARRIS, I. F., *ibid.*, 36 (1902), 85
[37] STEUDEL, H., and PEISER, E., *ibid.*, 132 (1924), 297
[38] FEULGEN, R., and VOIT, K., *Arch. ges. Physiol.*, 206 (1924), 389
[39] LEVENE, P. A., and LONDON, F., *J. biol. Chem.*, 81 (1929), 711; 83 (1929), 793
[40] —, MIKESKA, L. A., and MORI, T., *ibid.*, 85 (1930), 785
[41] COWDRY, E. V., *Science*, 68 (1928), 40
[42] MILOVIDOW, P., *Protoplasma*, 31 (1938), 246
[43] STACEY, M., DERIAZ, R. E., TEECE, E. G., and WIGGINS, L. F., *Nature*, 157 (1946), 740
[44] STEDMAN, E., and STEDMAN, E., *Symp. Soc. Exp. Biol.*, 1 (1947), 232
[45] BRACHET, J., *ibid.*, 1 (1947), 207
[46] FELL, H. B., and HUGHES, A. F., *Quart. J. micro. Soc.*, 90 (1949), 355
[47] LESLER, M. A., *Science*, 108 (1948), 419
[48] JONES, W., *Amer. J. Physiol.*, 52 (1920), 203
[49] DUBOS, R. J., and THOMPSON, R. H. S., *J. biol. Chem.*, 124 (1938), 501
[50] KUNITZ, M., *J. gen. Physiol.*, 24 (1940), 15
[51] —, and NORTHROP, J. H., *ibid.*, 18 (1935), 433
[52] FISCHER, F. G., BÖTTGER, I., and LEHMANN-ECHTERNACHT, H., *Hoppe-Seyl. Z.*, 271 (1941), 246
[53] McCARTY, M., *J. gen. Physiol.*, 29 (1946), 123
[54] BRACHET, J., *Enzymologia*, 10 (1941), 87
[55] DAVIDSON, J. N., and WAYMOUTH, C., *Proc. Roy. Soc. Edin.*, 62 (1944), 96
[56] —, —, *J. Physiol.*, 105 (1946), 191
[57] —, *Ann. Rev. Biochem*, 18 (1949), 155
[58] STOWELL, R. E., and ZORZOLI, A., *Stain Technol.*, 22 (1947), 51
[59] ERICKSON, R. O., SAX, K. B., and OGUR, M., *Science*, 110 (1949), 472
[60] VENDRELY-RANDAVEL, C., *C.R. Acad. Sci.*, Paris, 228 (1949), 606
[61] PONYET, J., *ibid*, 228 (1949), 608
[62] WEBB, M., and JACOBSON, W. In the press, 1951
[63] STOWELL, R. E., *Stain Technol.*, 21 (1946), 21
[64] SANDERS, F. K., *Quart. J. micro. Soc.*, 87 (1946), 203
[65] DAVIDSON, J. N., *Symp. Quart. Biol.*, 12 (1947), 50

[66] CATCHESIDE, D. G., and HOLMES, B., *Symp. Soc. exp. Biol.*, 1 (1947), 225
[67] DANIELLI, J. F., *ibid.*, 1 (1947), 101
[68] MICHAELIS, L., *Symp. quant. Biol.*, 12 (1947), 131
[69] MONNÉ, L., *Proc. Soc. exp. Biol. Med.*, 32 (1935), 1197
[70] CASPERSSON, T., *Quart. J. micro. Soc.*, 60 (1940), 8
[71] HOLIDAY, E., *Biochem. J.*, 30 (1936), 1715
[72] CASPERSSON, T., *Chromosoma*, 1 (1940), 562
[73] —, *Symp. Soc. exp. Biol.*, 1 (1947), 127
[74] —, and THORELL, B., *Chromosoma*, 2 (1941), 132
[75] HYDÉN, H., *Acta. physiol. Scand.*, 6 (1943), Suppl. 17
[76] POLLISTER, A. W., and RIS, H., *Symp. quant. Biol.*, 12 (1947), 147
[77] MIRSKY, A. E., and POLLISTER, A. W., *Trans. N.Y.Acad. Sci.*, Ser. II. 5 (1943), 187
[78] CASPERSSON, T., *Cell Growth and Cell Function*, New York, 1950
[79] FERKHMIN, A. A., *C.R. Acad. Sci. U.S.S.R.*, 59 (1948), 945
[80] RUDALL, K. M., *Prog. Biophys.*, London, 1950
[81] COMMONER, B., *Science*, 110 (1949), 31
[82] CASPERSSON, T., *Die Naturwiss.*, 29 (1941), 33
[83] BRACHET, J., *Arch. Biol.*, 53 (1942), 207
[84] BRADFIELD, J. R. G., *Exp. Cell Res.* Supp., 1 (1949), 338
— *Quart. J. micro. Soc.*, 92 (1951), 87
[85] CASPERSSON, T., and SCHULTZ, J., *Nature*, 142 (1938), 294
[86] —, —, *Proc. Nat. Acad. Sci.*, 26 (1940), 507
[87] SCHULTZ, J., *Symp. quant. Biol.*, 9 (1941), 55
[88] PAINTER, T. S., and TAYLOR, A. N., *Proc. Nat. Acad. Sci.*, 28 (1942), 311
[89] LUDFORD, R. J., SMILES, J., and WELCH, F. V., *J. Roy. micro. Soc.*, 68 (1948), 1
[90] POLLISTER, A. W., and LEUCHTENBERGER, C., *Nature*, 163 (1949), 360
[91] MARSHAK, A., and CALVET, F., *J. Cell Comp. Physiol.*, 34 (1949), 451
[92] JEENER, R., and SZAFARZ, D., *Arch. Biochem.*, 26 (1950), 54
[93] —, *Biochem. Biophys. Acta*, 2 (1948), 439
[94] FRUTON, J. S., *Yale J. Biol. Med.*, 22 (1950), 263
[95] HANES, C. S., HIRD, F. J. R., ISHERWOOD, F. A., *Nature*, 166 (1950), 288
[96] DANIELLI, J. F., and CATCHESIDE, D. G., *ibid.*, 156 (1945), 294
[97] KRUGELIS, E. J., *Biol. Bull.*, 90 (1946), 220
[98] CHÈVREMONT, M., and FIRKET, H., *Arch. de Biol.*, 60 (1949), 441
[99] BRACHET, J., and JEENER, R., *Biochem. Biophys. Acta*, 2 (1948), 423
[100] HEVESEY, G. and OTTESEN, J., *Acta. Physiol. Scand.*, 5 (1943), 237
[101] —, —, *Nature*, 156 (1945), 534
[102] HAMMARSTEN, E., and HEVESEY, G., *Acta Physiol. Scand.*, 11 (1946), 335
[103] RICHTER, D., and HULTIN, R. P., *Abstracts. Int. Biochem. Congress*, Cambridge, 1949
[104] JONES, W., *Nucleic Acids*, 2nd Ed., London, 1920
[105] WILLEY, B., *The Seventeenth Century Background*, London, 1946
[106] FLETCHER, W. E., GULLAND, J. M., JORDAN, D. O., and DIBBEN, H. E., *J. chem. Soc.* (1944), 30
[107] SIGNER, R., CASPERSSON, T., and HAMMARSTEN, E., *Nature*, 141 (1938), 122
[108] GULLAND, J. M., JORDAN, D. O., and TAYLOR, H. F. W., *J. Chem. Soc.* (1947), 1131
[109] FURST, S. S., ROLL, P. M., and BROWN, G. B., *J. biol. Chem.*, 183 (1950), 251
[110] WYATT, A. R., *Nature*, 166 (1950), 237

2

THE INTERPHASE CELL AND THE CYTOPLASM

In this chapter will be described the appearance and structure of one particular type of cell; the nature and composition of its component structures will be discussed with reference to other cells for which evidence is available. A flattened 'fibroblast' in the outgrowth of a culture of skeletal or connective tissue of a chick or mammal will serve as a representative type of cell for our purpose. Such living cells in the outgrowth of cultures photographed by phase-contrast are illustrated in Plate I. The fibroblasts from cultures of bone should be more strictly called osteoblasts for under appropriate conditions in culture they may again take part in the formation of bone in the outgrowth of the culture. From a number of explanted tissues, cells of the general fibroblastic form will grow out in a partially de-differentiated condition; they are then not necessarily identical, for differences in the metabolism between races of such cells have been demonstrated (PARKER[1]). Thus the word fibroblast is used loosely, and as WILLMER[2] says: 'The use of this term arose not because the cells necessarily have any connection with the formation of fibres, although some of them may show this property, but because they are similar in appearance to the cells in the body which are believed to function in this manner.'

CYTOPLASMIC INCLUSIONS

The cytoplasmic structure of such cells in tissue culture has been studied many times. Among studies of this kind are those of LEWIS and LEWIS,[3] STRANGEWAYS and CANTI,[4] and LUDFORD.[5] CLAUDE et alii[6] [7] have reported on the electron micrography of cells in tissue culture, while observations with the phase microscope are described by ZOLLINGER[8] and HUGHES.[9] RICHARDSON[10] and HILL[11] have been specially concerned with the Golgi body. All are agreed that the cytoplasm contains granular or filamentous mitochondria and also granules and vacuoles. As with other cells, the existence and the nature of the Golgi body has been disputed, and not all authors mention whether a central body is to be observed. Since tissue culture fibroblasts include several sorts and conditions of cells, it is not remarkable that descriptions of them can differ in detail. The inclusions are set in an apparently clear and homogeneous cytoplasm, seen best at the margin of the cell, near which the mitochondria are seen most distinctly (Plate I (1)). Further inwards, the granules become denser and occasional vacuoles are to be seen. Next to the nucleus is usually an area of darkish cytoplasm, the cytocentre or centrosphere. It is free of large granules, though its structure is not homogeneous; there may be some vacuoles within it. The distinction between this body and the surrounding cytoplasm is a variable one; sometimes there is almost a sharp boundary, in other cells the whole structure can easily be overlooked. STRANGEWAYS and CANTI[4] describe it as follows: 'The centrosphere is seen as a distinct area lying as a cap over one side of the nucleus and contains a number of faint granules or filaments'.

In phase-contrast micrographs of malignant cells of a mouse sarcoma, LUDFORD and SMILES[12] have shown that here also the centrosphere ranges in size and distinctness from cell to cell. It has no special absorption in the ultraviolet. Generally it consists of a finely granular mass, but occasionally within it these authors state that there is a suggestion of a canalicular system. They are doubtful whether this corresponds to the reticulate structure of impregnated preparations, because such an appearance within the central body of the living cell is but rarely seen. The centrosphere is clearly shown by dark-ground illumination in a photomicrograph of a rat heart fibroblast published by LUDFORD in 1935, who says that this body corresponds 'to the Golgi apparatus of silver and osmic impregnation preparations'. A continuous and lobulated body of impregnated material is seen by the side of the nucleus in cells of a hepatic epithelium in culture described by RICHARDSON.[10] Similar preparations of HILL[11] of chick osteoblasts show only a number of discrete impregnated granules near the nucleus, arranged so as to suggest that the cytocentre includes, or is closely surrounded by this osmophilic material.* Some recent investigations by PALADE and CLAUDE[14] have still further increased the probability that in the living cell the Golgi material is represented solely by globular elements, a view for which BAKER[15 16] has already assembled much evidence. It appears, however, that in living cells of the pancreas, the Golgi bodies are in the form of 'clear canals' (BENSLEY[17]).

PALADE and CLAUDE isolated cells from a number of mammalian and embryonic chick tissues. They found that their lipoid inclusions, unlike the mitochondria, were stable in form when the cells were suspended in various media; but that when ethyl alcohol was added thereto, these droplets within the cells began to swell and to form myelin figures, which 'duplicate faithfully the numerous and different forms ascribed at various times to the Golgi apparatus'. Experiments with model substances showed that a high proportion of phospholipines was necessary to give this effect. They then went on to inquire whether

---

* LASFARGUES and DI FINE[13] have recently shown by vital staining methods that the Golgi zone in cells in tissue culture is composed of granular elements.

the fixation mixtures used in cytological investigations on the Golgi body would give the same result when discs of liver pulp were immersed in them. Again myelin figures appeared within the cells, but their formation was found to depend on a sequence of changes which follow as the various ingredients of the mixture diffuse into the tissue at differing rates. First the pH is gradually lowered, and then the electrolyte concentration slowly rises. Next, the myelin figures are formed and are finally stabilized by slowly diffusing molecules such as OsO_4. These authors suggest that the necessity for comparatively slow fixation in order to produce a typical Golgi network explains why tissue cultures have not proved to be easy material in which to demonstrate such structures. In living cells in tissue culture, and elsewhere (BAKER[15]), no lipoidal network can be seen by phase-contrast. Yet owing to its high refractive index, fatty material is revealed by this method more readily than is any other cell component.

Vacuoles within cells

The number of cytoplasmic vacuoles within cells in tissue is very variable. Sometimes cells with none are seen close to others which show numerous vacuoles among the lipoidal inclusions. Where the cell boundary consists partly of an undulating membrane, vacuoles can there be seen to enter the cell by the process which LEWIS[18] has called 'pinocytosis' (Plate II (3)).

Mitochondria

The mitochondria of rabbit and mouse spleen cells in culture are thin regular filaments, seldom more than 10μ long. Chick mitochondria are less uniform, and sometimes bend into loops; their estimated thickness from both the electron micrographs of PORTER et alii[6] and from phase pictures is approximately $0.25-0.40\mu$. The mitochondria of the toad Xenopus are larger and much more variable in form (HUGHES and PRESTON[19]). When a chick or mammalian culture is observed with the phase or the dark-field microscope at $37°C$, one occasionally sees a granule or mitochondrial filament move with an immediately appreciable velocity (Plate I (1)), but continuous observation over some minutes is necessary to follow the movement of most of them. In a 'speeded-up' film in which the time scale is shortened by a factor of about ten times, the movement of all the cell inclusions becomes immediately obvious.

The two facts that are known about this kind of intracellular activity are that it is something more than Brownian movement and is a function of living protoplasm. If the cell is poisoned by any of a number of agents, the normal slow movements can be inhibited, while Brownian motion

of small granules may then be seen by direct observation. Mitochondria exhibit a very complex example of protoplasmic streaming,
the customary theories about which have been suggested as explanations for this motion; but no real attempt to analyse it has yet been
made. Some of the possible ways in which mitochondria can change
their form is illustrated by a sequence of photographs of a cell of
Xenopus in culture in Plate I (2). In this example, within a few minutes
one filament rolled up and rotated; it then divided into two blobs, one
of which elongated and later became Y-shaped. The extreme mobility
of the mitochondria in these Amphibian cells suggests that they are of a
liquid nature. SCHNEIDER and HOGEBOOM[54][55] believe that at the surface
of rat liver mitochondria is a semi-permeable membrane, one reason for
this view being the osmotic behaviour of the isolated elements. The mitochondria of mammalian cells in culture are much less mobile than are
those of XENOPUS. If the latter are enveloped by a membrane, it must
have great plasticity.

The movement of mitochondria suggests that they are not moved
passively by the surrounding cytoplasm; sometimes two nearby filaments
will move quite quickly relative to each other. A single granule may
suddenly migrate alone for a distance of ten microns or more.

RASHEVSKY and his school have developed the theory that protoplasmic streaming in general is caused by diffusion forces which result
from continually varying concentrations of metabolites in the neighbourhood of centres of chemical change within the cell (RASHEVSKY[20]);
there is now good evidence that in some cells enzymes are associated
with mitochondria and so continuous molecular changes at their surfaces may be inferred. It would be very desirable to test this hypothesis
by applying the equations of RASHEVSKY to data derived from observation of mitochondrial movement. Another and not necessarily incompatible suggestion is that electrical potentials are involved.

It has long been considered that mitochondria play some special
role in cell metabolism; the general evidence from work in this field
is summarized by BOURNE.[21] They can be stained in the living cell by
Janus green; according to LAZAROW and COOPERSTEIN,[22] this is due
both to the reduction of the dye to a colourless leucobase by the
surrounding cytoplasm, and also to the action of the cytochrome system
of enzymes within the mitochrondria which keep it there in the oxidized
form. In tissue cultures, the vital staining of mitochondria by this dye
(LEWIS and LEWIS[23]) and by methylene blue (LUDFORD[5]) has been
shown by these authors to be inhibited by cyanide. LEWIS and LEWIS
were able to demonstrate that the effect was reversible.

Methods of isolation—Within recent years, methods have been
developed for isolating mitochondria and other cell fractions by

differential centrifugation of a homogenate obtained by mechanical disintegration (CLAUDE[24] [25] [26]); the literature in this field has recently been reviewed by BRADFIELD[27] (1950) and by SCHNEIDER and HOGE-BOOM.[55] It seems now quite certain that with due precautions, mitochondria can be isolated unchanged in form and in affinity for Janus green (HOGEBOOM, SCHNEIDER and PALADE[28]), and with much of their enzymic activity still intact. The mitochondria of the frog's eggs have been shown by RECKNAGEL[29] to contain cytochrome oxidase and adenosine triphosphatase. Further researches in which these and other enzymes of the cyclophorase system have been found to be associated with mitochondrial fractions are described by SCHNEIDER[30] and by HAR-MAN.[31] In a succeeding chapter, Dr WAYMOUTH (p. 179) refers to the use of fractionation procedures for the isolation from the cytoplasm of particulate material of lower orders of size. It is not yet certain how far the 'microsomes' prepared by these methods correspond with constituents of living cytoplasm. In electron micrographs of cells, either of tissue cultures or thin sections of liver, the cytoplasm has a granular texture, in which particles of the order of 100mμ in diameter can be discerned. CLAUDE has suggested that these correspond with the microsomes of this range of size sedimented at the appropriate speed from cytoplasmic fractions.

Although no heterogeneity in 'clear cytoplasm' has yet been revealed by optical methods, it is not impossible for particles of the size of 100mμ to be revealed by light microscopy. If there were sufficient difference in refractive index in the living cell between microsomes and their cytoplasmic background, they should be visible in the ultraviolet phase microscope which has recently been developed (TAYLOR[32]). Such observations would be of great interest and importance.

FINE STRUCTURE

The nature of the sub-microscopical structure of protoplasm has been discussed from several points of view. We will first consider the evidence from what have been known as the so-called 'structure proteins' which have been isolated from cells. These substances are fibrous in nature, with properties analogous to those of myosin. In solution they are highly viscous. The literature in this field has been reviewed by SCHMITT.[33] BENSLEY[34] extracted 'plasmosin' from liver with 10 per cent sodium chloride, while BANGA and SZENT-GYÖRGI[35] prepared 'renosin' by extraction of kidney tissue with 30 per cent urea. It has been subsequently shown that neither of these products is exclusively cytoplasmic in origin, for deoxyribonucleoproteins are found in both, as was shown by LAZAROW[36] for plasmosin, and by BRACHET and JEENER[37] for renosin. In these tissues, therefore, it has not yet been proved that fibrous proteins analogous to myosin occur in the cytoplasm. However, the evidence for cytoplasmic long-chain particles has not rested only on the properties of these 'structure proteins'. POLLISTER[38] pointed out that a sub-microscopical pattern of order may affect the orientation of cell inclusions at the microscopical level. Study of elongated fibroblastic cells in tissue culture supports this suggestion, for both the arrangement and motion of the mitochondria and granules is generally parallel to the axis of a cell process. Elongated fibroblasts generally show a slight cytoplasmic birefringence (SWANN and MITCHISON[39]). It is not known, however, whether this is due to orientation of the fluid interior of the cell or within the gelated cell wall.

It has been claimed by PFEIFFER[40] [41] that certain physical phenomena characteristic of long-chain particles in solution can be exhibited by living cytoplasm. By forcing isolated portions of cells or of slime-mould plasmodium through capillary tubes he appears to have demonstrated both streaming birefringence due to molecular orientation by shearing forces, and a high viscosity which varies with the rate of flow. Such experiments, however, do not necessarily reveal properties of fluid endoplasm, for a new external gel may form round isolated cytoplasm or even more serious changes may occur. KAMIYA[42] says: 'it is impossible to make slime mould protoplasm flow through a glass capillary without fatal results'.

Estimations of viscosity

The evidence from measurements and estimates of endoplasmic viscosity in various types of living cell is by no means uniform. Although the contents of some differentiated cells apparently are gelated or highly viscous (CHAMBERS and RENYI,[43] SEIFRIZ,[44] RENYI,[45] SPEIDEL,[46]), the cytoplasm of a number of marine eggs stratifies in the centrifuge at rates which correspond to viscosities of only a few times that of water (HEILBRUNN[47]). Moreover, HOWARD[48] has shown that the viscosity of the internal cytoplasm in the unfertilized sea-urchin egg is independent of the rate of shear, and thus behaves as a true liquid. She observed the stratification of the granules of the egg when centrifuged at different speeds, and found that when allowance was made for the opposing tendency of these inclusions to return to their normal random distribution, the rate of movement was directly proportional to the force applied.

One method which has been used to estimate protoplasmic viscosity has been to introduce magnetic particles into the cytoplasm and to observe them in motion within the cell under the influence of external magnetic fields. This method was first used by HEILBRONN[49] in a study of the plasmodium of a slime mould, and has been applied by CRICK and HUGHES[50] to cells in tissue culture, by taking account of the

c

fact discovered by FELL that solid particles 1μ or more in diameter can slowly be phagocytosed by fibroblastic cells, the growth of which is not impaired by the presence of these foreign inclusions. Once within a cell,

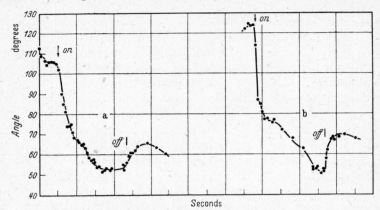

Figure 6 Angular displacement of a magnetic particle in the cytoplasm of a chick osteoblast in culture when magnetic fields of **a** 8 oersteds, **b** 16 oersteds were applied for the intervals indicated. From CRICK and HUGHES[50] (*By courtesy, Academic Press Inc. New York*).

a magnetic particle can be rotated by two magnetic fields at right angles to each other in the apparatus used by CRICK and HUGHES. First one field is used to orientate the particle, and then the other is applied for a variable interval. Cells containing particles were rigorously selected to minimize disturbing influences by neighbouring structures and inclusions.

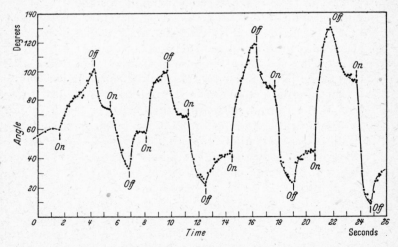

Figure 7 Increase in angular displacement of a magnetic particle in the cytoplasm of a chick osteoblast in culture when a magnetic field of 24 oersteds was applied alternately in opposite directions. From CRICK and HUGHES[50] (*By courtesy, Academic Press Inc., New York*).

The particle at first rotates rapidly; but the resistance offered by its surroundings increases and the early rapid phase of rotation gives place to a slower one in which movement then involves the breakdown of protoplasmic structure by shearing (Figure 6). When the field is switched off, there is at once an elastic recoil which is small in comparison with the original deflection. The endoplasm of cells in tissue cultures is thus a weakly elastic fluid. It also shows another property characteristic of some colloids, known as thixotropy, which is an increase in fluidity during mechanical agitation. During repeated movement of a magnetic particle within a cell, the deflection due to a magnetic field of constant strength was shown to increase (Figure 7). It has already been shown qualitatively by CHAMBERS[51] that the protoplasm

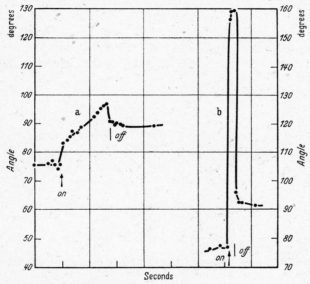

Figure 8 Angular displacement of a magnetic particle in a solution of sodium oleate when magnetic fields of **a** 3 oersteds, **b** 24 oersteds were applied for the intervals indicated. From CRICK and HUGHES[50] (*By courtesy, Academic Press Inc., New York*).

of an *Amoeba* tends to liquefy on mechanical agitation with a microdissection needle.

A further experiment of CRICK and HUGHES suggests that the physical properties of the cytoplasm of fibroblastic cells is not necessarily due to an ultra-microscopic structure of long molecules, for if magnetic particles are suspended in a highly elastic liquid, such as a solution of sodium oleate, and are rotated as in the experiments on the living cell, the recoil which results when the magnetic field is switched off is then almost as large as the initial deflection (Figure 8). This contrast in the magnitude of the elastic recoil in the two instances suggests that the

27

ultimate structure of living protoplasm is not exclusively or even mainly fibrous in nature, and that 'models' based on this conception such as those of SEIFRIZ[52] and FREY-WYSSLING[53] are misleading. A fresh approach to the problems of cytoplasmic ultrastructure is being made by KOPAC[56] [57] based on observation of the 'Devaux effect', which is the increase in area on denaturation of a protein film absorbed at an oil-water interface. Thus the surface of oil droplets, microinjected into a sea-urchin egg, wrinkles when the egg is cytolysed.

Although any strictly quantitative investigation of protoplasmic consistency and movement must wait on progress in the study of the physics of elastic fluids, yet much could still be done empirically by combining different techniques. For instance, it would be valuable to know how far the physical properties of cytoplasm could be matched by a mixture of cell fractions of varying particle size, and whether mitochondria isolated by the method of HOGEBOOM and his colleagues show any movement under the influence of electric fields, or in the presence of substrates appropriate to the enzymes which they are known to contain.

REFERENCES

[1] PARKER, R. C., *J. exp. Med.*, 55 (1932), 713; 58 (1933), 97, 401
[2] WILLMER, E. N., *Tissue Culture*, London, 1935
[3] LEWIS, M. R., and LEWIS, W. H., *Amer. J. Anat.*, 17 (1915), 399
[4] STRANGEWAYS, T. S. P. and CANTI, R. G., *Quart. J. micro. Sci.*, 71 (1927), 1
[5] LUDFORD, R. J., *Arch. exp. Zellforsch*, 17 (1935), 339
[6] PORTER, K. R., CLAUDE, A., and FULLAM, E. F., *J. exp. Med.*, 81 (1945), 233
[7] CLAUDE, A., PORTER, K. R., and PICKELS, E. G., *Cancer Res.*, 7 (1947), 421
[8] ZOLLINGER, H. U., *Mikroskopie*, 3 (1948), 1
[9] HUGHES, A. F., *Brit. Sci. News*, 2 (1949), 367
[10] RICHARDSON, K. C., *Arch. exp. Zellforsch*, 16 (1934), 100
[11] HILL, J. C., *ibid*, 18 (1936), 496
[12] LUDFORD, R. J., and SMILES, J., *J. Roy. micro. Soc.*, 70 (1950), 186, 194
[13] LASFARGUES, E., and DI FINE, J., *Anat. Rec.*, 106 (1950), 29
[14] PALADE, G. E., and CLAUDE, A., *J. Morphol*, 85 (1949), 35, 71
[15] BAKER, J. R., *Quart. J. micro Sci.*, 85 (1944), 1
[16] —, *ibid*, 90 (1949), 293
[17] BENSLEY, R. R. *Exp. Cell Res.*, 2 (1951), 1
[18] LEWIS, W. H., *Bull. J. Hopk. Hosp.*, 49 (1931), 17
[19] HUGHES, A. F., and PRESTON, M. McE., *J. Roy. micro. Soc.*, 69 (1949), 121
[20] RASHEVSKY, N., *Mathematical Biophysics*, Chicago, 1938
[21] BOURNE, G., in *Cytology and Cell Physiology*, Ed by Bourne, 2nd ed. Oxford, 1951
[22] LAZAROW, A., and COOPERSTEIN, S. J., *Biol. bull.*, 99 (1950), 322
[23] LEWIS, W. H., and LEWIS, M. R., in *General Cytology*, Ed by E. V. Cowdry, Chicago, 1924
[24] CLAUDE, A., *Symp. quant. Biol.*, 9 (1941), 263
[25] —, *Science*, 97 (1943), 451
[26] —, *J. exp. Med.*, 80 (1944), 19; 84 (1946), 51
[27] BRADFIELD, J. R. G., *Biol. Rev.*, 25 (1950), 113
[28] HOGEBOOM, G. H., SCHNEIDER, W. C., and PALADE, G. E., *J. Biol. Chem.*, 172 (1948), 619
[29] RECKNAGEL, R. O., *J. Cell. Comp. Physiol.*, 35 (1950), 111

[30] SCHNEIDER, W. C., in *Respiratory Enzymes*, Ed by H. A. Lardy, Minneapolis, 1949

[31] HARMAN, J. W., *Exp. Cell Res.*, 1 (1950), 382, 394

[32] TAYLOR, E. W., *Proc. R. Soc. Lond.*, B 137 (1950), 332

[33] SCHMITT, F. O., *Adv. Prot. Chem.*, 1 (1944), 26

[34] BENSLEY, R. R., *Anat. Rec.*, 72 (1938), 351

[35] BANGA, I., and SZENT-GYÖRGYI, A., *Science*, 92 (1940), 514

[36] LAZAROW, A., *Biol. Symp.*, 10 (1943), 9

[37] BRACHET, J., and JEENER, R., *Biochem. Biophys. Acta.*, 1 (1947), 13

[38] POLLISTER, A. W., *Physiol. Zool.*, 14 i(1941), 268

[39] SWANN, M. M., and MITCHISON, J. M., *J. exp. Biol.*, 27 (1950), 226

[40] PFEIFFER, H. H., *Physics*, 7 (1936), 302

[41] —, *Cytologia*, Fujii Jub., 2 (1939), 701

[42] KAMIYA, N., in *The Structure of Cytoplasm*, Ed by W. Seifriz, Iowa, 1942

[43] CHAMBERS, R., and RENYI, G. S., *Amer. J. Anat.*, 35 (1925), 385

[44] SEIFRIZ, W., *Arch. exp. Zellforsch*, 6 (1928), 341

[45] RENYI, G. S., *J. Comp. Neurol.*, 53 (1931), 497

[46] SPEIDEL, C. C., *Amer. J. Anat.*, 62 (1938), 179

[47] HEILBRUNN, L. V., *J. exp. Zool.*, 44 (1926), 255

[48] HOWARD, E., *J. Cell. Comp. Physiol.*, 1 (1932), 355

[49] HEILBRONN, A., *Jb. wiss. Bot.*, 61 (1922), 284

[50] CRICK, F., and HUGHES, A. F., *Exp. Cell. Res.*, 1 (1950), 37

[51] CHAMBERS, R., *Proc. Soc. exp. Biol. Med.*, 19 (1921), 87

[52] SEIFRIZ, W., *Protoplasm*, New York, 1936

[53] FREY-WYSSLING, A., *Submicroscopic Morphology of Protoplasm*, Amsterdam, 1948

[54] SCHNEIDER, W. C., and HOGEBOOM, G. H., *Nature*, 166 (1950), 302

[55] — — *Cancer Res.*, 11 (1951), 1

[56] KOPAC, M. J., *Ann. N.Y. Acad. Sci.*, 50 (1950), 870

[57] —, *ibid*, 51 (1951), 1541

3

THE INTERPHASE NUCLEUS

NUCLEUS OF CHICK AND MAMMALIAN CELLS IN LIVING TISSUE CULTURES

THE interphase nucleus is bounded by the nuclear membrane which is sharply outlined in the living cell. Within, the most obvious structures are the nucleoli, either one or two in cells of the chick and more numerous in those of mammals. Scattered at intervals throughout the nucleus are a larger number of smaller bodies, which are sometimes referred to as the 'chromocentres'. They differ in composition from the nucleoli, for whereas the latter mainly consist of ribonucleoproteins, the chromocentres are made of deoxyribonucleoproteins, and so are Feulgen-positive (Plate II (4)). They are small segments of the chromosomes which persist apparently unchanged into interphase; and are termed 'heterochromatic' (p 43); their surface is apparently adhesive, for as VANDERLYN[1] has observed, they stick either to the nuclear membrane, or to the surfaces of the nucleoli, or to each other in aggregates. The non-heterochromatic parts of the chromosomes in this type of nucleus are represented by extremely fine threads, the chromonemata, of which there may be more than one to each chromosome. In well fixed nuclei, a uniform groundwork of chromonemata can be seen throughout the nucleus, and some of these threads can occasionally be seen in life by phase-contrast (Plate XII (18)). It is probable that the chromonemata line the inside of the nuclear membrane, because in prophase when they become more visible, they are then seen in this position. In time-lapse films of cells in interphase, no movement within the nucleus can be seen, whereas in the cytoplasm there is ceaseless activity. The nucleus as a whole is a structure of some rigidity, though evidence from micro-dissection (CHAMBERS and FELL[2]) suggests that the nuclear sap is a fluid.

In succeeding pages, each of these nuclear components will be further discussed.

CHROMOSOMES AND THE DEOXYNUCLEOPROTEINS

During the prophase of mitosis, chromosomes are formed within the nucleus identical in number with those which were present in the daughter group during the later phases of the preceding division. During the intervening period, the chromosomes are not usually recognizable as such, and it is clearly a question of much importance from several points of view to inquire what happens to these bodies in the interphase nucleus. Nobody since the advent of the chromosome theory of heredity has doubted that the chromosomes in the interphase nucleus are 'there' in some sense, although with WHITE[3] one might regard them as 'unfixable'.

Until recently, it seemed unlikely that any general answer would be possible to the question of the form of the chromosomes in interphase, for the differences between the fixed and the living nucleus seemed irreconcilable. Usually in fixed preparations, the interior of the nucleus is occupied by a complex network; while at the other extreme, the nucleus of the living *Echinus* oocyte contains a fluid little more viscous than water through which the nucleolus falls readily under gravity (GRAY[4]).*

Such a comparison served to encourage scepticism on the subject of the detail seen in the fixed nucleus, which was further reinforced by reports of the apparent 'optical emptiness' of the nuclei of living cells in tissue cultures, when seen either in the bright-field or the dark-field of the microscope (LEWIS and LEWIS,[5] STRANGEWAYS and CANTI[6]). Insufficient weight was then accorded to descriptions of visible texture in plant nuclei in life (p 72) and the observation of FLEMMING[7] was long forgotten that the 'Gerüststränge' seen in a living amphibian nucleus are only brought out more sharply on the addition of a fixative.

The conclusion that the detail seen in the nuclei of tissue cultures after fixation was spurious was reinforced by the observations of LEWIS (M.R.)[8] that a 'mass of granules' appeared within them when an acid was added to the culture medium. This gelation was reversible and the usual appearance and behaviour of the cell was resumed when the normal pH was restored.

We now know that the failure to detect structure within the nucleoplasm of such cells lay with the method of observation, and that in fact the nucleoplasm of such nuclei is not a 'perfect and absolute blank'. The ordinary bright-field microscope is insufficiently sensitive to fine detail; the dark-ground method which brilliantly illuminates sharp discontinuities at surfaces and boundaries, does not scatter light in regions where there are only fine gradations in refractive index. Observations by phase contrast of the living nucleus of cells in tissue cultures in which such fine detail is revealed have been described by FELL and HUGHES.[9] Comparison of the appearance of the same nucleus in life and after fixation should be extended to other material. Such observations were first made by TELLYESNICZKY[10] who observed how much the texture of the fixed nucleus can vary with the nature of the

---

* If the chromonemata of the *Echinus* oocyte line the inside of the nuclear membrane, as is true of other nuclei, they would not impede the fall of the nucleolus through the nuclear sap.

fixative used, though his claim that the living nucleoplasm is homogeneous needs to be examined by further investigations with the use of modern optical methods.

Chromonemata—The visibility of the chromonemata in the living intermitotic plant nucleus is variable, and can be altered by treatment of the cell with media of differing tonicity (SHINKE[11]). Both the osmotic pressure of the guard cells of stomata (WIGGANS[12]) and the appearance of their nuclei (WEBER[13]) alter when these structures open and close. The differences in refractive index between chromonemata and nuclear sap are thus influenced by the water content of the whole nucleus.

The chromosomes of the interphase nucleus, as we have said, are represented by two components, the heterochromatic granules, which are segments of the chromosomes which persist apparently unchanged, together with the 'backbone' threads, the chromonemata. Animal nuclei, in which the latter can be demonstrated are regarded by SERRA[14] as characteristic of secretory cells and of tissues in which frequent cell division is occurring. He finds that in an immature snail oocyte, before meiotic prophase begins, chromonemata are not so readily visible. It would be of great interest to extend such studies on interphase nuclei from this point of view. SHIWAGO[15] was able to demonstrate slowly moving threads within intermitotic leucocytes of the frog, visible in a bright-field microscope.

The chromonema is the residual part of most of the chromosome after the greater part of its nucleoproteins have been dispersed in telophase. The first stage in the process is that the chromosomes in late anaphase swell into vesicles. This can most readily be seen where one or two chromosomes lie apart from the main daughter group. The early telophase nucleus can thus be regarded as a mass of chromosomal vesicles. The nuclear membrane is formed from those sectors of their walls which form the interface between cytoplasm and nucleus. Elsewhere, their adjoining walls do not persist intact, but in the embryo of the fish *Fundulus* (RICHARDS[16]) the vesicles are separately distinguishable throughout interphase (Figure 9). According to KATER, in resting nuclei both of the frog[17] and of the rat[18] the intervesicular boundaries can still be traced though it must be admitted that the author's illustrations of this are not entirely convincing. LEWIS[19] supports the view that the interphase nucleus is morphologically vesicular.

It is clear that as the chromosomes swell in telophase chromatinic material is detached from their 'backbone' threads. RIS and MIRSKY[20] speak of the chromosomes as then being in the 'extended state', though these authors overlook the persistence of the chromonemata in some nuclei, and consider that the deoxynucleoproteins of the chromosomes are evenly spread throughout the living interphase nucleus. The usual methods of fixation, they assert, precipitate the Feulgen-positive material into artefactual aggregates, though the original disperse condition can be maintained by suspension of the nuclei in 10 per cent sucrose.

Heterochromatic granules—In nuclei of the mouse in tissue culture, FELL and HUGHES[9] have shown that the heterochromatic granules which are Feulgen-positive after fixation can also be identified by phase-contrast in the living nucleus, in the same position and form. The chromonemata are also faintly Feulgen-positive, and some threads, slightly denser than the rest, can be recognized in the living nucleus. It is possible to maintain that the entire Feulgen-positive charge on such heterochromatic granules and chromonemata is precipitated thereon during fixation and that their contrast in life is due to their constituent proteins or perhaps to lipoidal material in addition, but if this were true, then the living nucleus should show no detail when

Figure 9 Blastomere nucleus of *Fundulus heteroclitus* in early prophase. Chromatin condensing on walls of chromosomal vesicles ($\times$ 1800+). From RICHARDS[16] (*By courtesy, Biol. Bull.*).

photographed at 2,600 Å, except for the nucleoli. Now in the ultraviolet photomicrographs of sarcoma cells published by LUDFORD *et alii*,[22] and by LUDFORD and SMILES[23] it is clear that absorbing granules smaller than the nucleoli are abundantly present within the nucleus, (Plate III (7)), which has a very similar appearance both in the ultraviolet and by phase-contrast. On the other hand, the ultraviolet photomicrographs of isolated nuclei suspended in sucrose which RIS and MIRSKY[24] have published show no internal structure, and suggest that the nucleoli and perhaps other constituents have been dissolved as a result of the procedure to which they have been submitted. Although BROWN, CALLAN and LEAF[25] found no trace of nucleic acid in the nuclear sap of *Xenopus* oocytes, one would not expect the same necessarily to be true of somatic nuclei; for their structure is very different. It may well be that there is no uniform state of aggregation of the DNA in the interphase nucleus.

DNA content in nuclei—It would probably not be realized from the inspection of stained preparations that the amount of DNA in the nucleus greatly outweighs that of RNA, for the nucleoli seem at least as prominent as the Feulgen-positive material. However the analyses of isolated nuclei by VENDRELY and VENDRELY[26] and DAVIDSON and McINDOE[27] suggest ratios of DNA/RNA of 3–30 times. It is probable that if the DNA were not scattered in small aggregates throughout the nucleus it would appear to be much greater in amount. In the rat liver nucleus, however, DOUNCE *et alii*[28] find more RNA than DNA.

Within the last two years results of much interest have been obtained by estimation of the absolute quantity of deoxyribonucleic acid in the nucleus. Where bulk chemical methods have been used, nuclei has been isolated either by the citric acid procedure or by the anhydrous technique of BEHRENS (DOUNCE *et alii*[28]). Their density in a suspension

TABLE II. DNA CONTENT OF NUCLEI IN mg $\times$ 10^9

Material	Amount	Author
Bull sperm	2·82	MIRSKY and RIS[30]
	3·4	VENDRELY and VENDRELY[26]
	4·5	ZITTLE and O'DELL[31]
Calf somatic nuclei	6·22–7·15	MIRSKY and RIS[30]
	6·5±10%	VENDRELY and VENDRELY[26]
	6·0–7·0	KURNICK[32]
Fowl sperm	1·26	MIRSKY and RIS[30]
Fowl erythrocytes	2·34	MIRSKY and RIS[30]
	2·62	DAVIDSON and McINDOE[27]
	1·6–1·8	KURNICK[32]
Frog erythrocytes	15·0	MIRSKY and RIS[30]
Toad erythrocytes	7·33	MIRSKY and RIS[30]
Tradescantia somatic nuclei	5·5–12·0	SCHRADER and LEUCHTENBERGER[33]
Arbacia sperm	0·67	VENDRELY and VENDRELY[26]
Arbacia egg	220	VENDRELY and VENDRELY[26]
	700	SCHMIDT *et alii*[34]

is measured by counting on a haemocytometer slide, and the preparation is then analysed in bulk for DNA. BOIVIN, VENDRELY and VENDRELY, [26] [29] MIRSKY and RIS[30] and DAVIDSON and McINDOE[27] have all made measurements of this kind on various types of nucleus; some of the values obtained are here reproduced in *Table II*, together with estimates made by other methods which will shortly be described.*

The agreement between the results obtained on vertebrate tissues by the different authors at first was considered to be sufficient to support these generalizations:

1. The DNA content of a nucleus is characteristic of the species and is constant from tissue to tissue.

2. Diploid and somatic nuclei have approximately twice the DNA content of the haploid sperm nucleus.

* MIRSKY and RIS[30a] have recently published a further series of estimations of nuclear DNA, in both vertebrates and invertebrates.

MIRSKY and RIS[30] state that 'observations on egg nuclei show that the quantity of deoxyribonucleic acid in the egg nucleus corresponds very closely to that in the sperm', though no details relating to this alleged equality are given. For the sea-urchin egg this conclusion is not supported by the available data (SCHMIDT et alii,[34] VENDRELY and VENDRELY[35]) which suggests that the fertilized egg of *Arbacia* contains several hundred times the amount of DNA contained in the single sperm. The VENDRELYS do not attach much significance to their result for the DNA content of the egg; but the importance of this question would warrant an extended comparison of eggs and sperms in different animals in this respect. MIRSKY and RIS[30a] are of opinion that analysis of the sea-urchin egg for DNA by the customary method of SCHMIDT and THANNHAUSER must give fallacious results, for a very intense Feulgen reaction would be given if the DNA content were as high as chemical analysis suggests. They state, moreover, that the egg nucleus of *Echinometra* is Feulgen-negative, and that in *Ascaris megalocephala* the reactions given by egg and sperm are equal in intensity. It is not clear at present whether this apparent incertitude of chemical assay for DNA is confined to the sea-urchin egg. No adult tissue of the sea-urchin has yet been analysed for the nuclear content of DNA, so diploid and haploid nuclei cannot yet be compared in the way which MIRSKY and RIS have done for several vertebrates. The immature gonad would probably be the most suitable material for this assay. In relative measurements on Feulgen-stained eggs and larvae of *Paracentrotus lividus*, LISON and PASTEELS[35a] find that the DNA content of the nuclei vary with their stage of development and from tissue to tissue. Up to the blastula stage, the embryonic nuclei contain 4-5 times as much DNA as does the sperm nucleus. In *Sabellaria*, PASTEELS and LISON[39] find that the egg and sperm do not contain the same amount of DNA, and that in the fertilized egg, the DNA content of both pronuclei increases markedly prior to their fusion.

Measurement of DNA content

One method of measuring the DNA content of a nucleus is to make micro-colorimetric estimations in sections of tissues, either in the ultra-violet, or at visual wavelengths after staining by suitable cytochemical methods. The measured coefficient of extinction can be related to DNA content by an empirical calibration based on the results of bulk estimations. POLLISTER and RIS[36] claimed that a very similar result for the nucleic acid content of the nucleus of the calf thymocyte was obtained both by ultraviolet measurements and by bulk chemical analysis. Their value for this, however, was less than one-sixth of that of later measurements, and RIS has subsequently admitted that an error was made in calculations from the data for bulk analysis (LEUCHTENBERGER[37]).

To calibrate a cytochemical method independently of bulk analyses, it is necessary to establish that there is some constant stoichometrical relationship in the amount of dye absorbed or liberated by a given quantity of DNA. It might be expected that for this purpose the Feulgen reaction could only be used empirically, for so many factors influence the density of the staining. However, by measuring the rate at which the constituents of deoxyribonucleoproteins are removed from frog cartilage nuclei during Feulgen hydrolysis, DI STEFANO[38] claims to have shown that the optimal point in this procedure corresponds with the removal of half the bases, and that this result can serve as a basis for micro-colorimetric estimations. DI STEFANO's assumptions have been criticized by LEUCHTENBERGER[37] and found not to be valid in practice by RIS and MIRSKY.[40] These authors have calibrated their measurements on Feulgen-stained nuclei from their previous chemical estimations for isolated nuclei of the same kind. LISON and PASTEELS calibrate their Feulgen preparations by including a fragment of rat testis tissue to serve as a standard. This is fixed, sectioned and stained at the same time as the material on which microphotometric measurements are to be made. The results are expressed in relative terms. SWIFT[41] has also made relative measurements of the DNA content of nuclei in a range of tissues by microcolorimetry of Feulgen-stained material.

The reaction of DNA with methyl green has been used as a basis for such estimations (KURNICK,[32] [42] KURNICK and MIRSKY[43]). In the well known method of UNNA for distinguishing between RNA and DNA, methyl green is used to stain the latter component. KURNICK has shown that a positive reaction with methyl green is given by highly polymerized nucleic acids, irrespective of the nature of the constituent pentose; and that DNA is sufficiently greater in molecular weight than RNA to make the reaction specific for the former. After treatment of a section with hot water, the Feulgen-positive material no longer stains in methyl green (POLLISTER and LEUCHTENBERGER[44]) for there has then been some depolymerization. KURNICK[32] found that after removal of histones by 0·1N hydrochloric acid one molecule of dye reacts with 10 atoms of phosphorus in highly polymerized DNA, a figure which he subsequently revised to 13. KURNICK's figures for the DNA content of mammalian nuclei come within the range of those obtained by other means, though his value for the chick erythrocyte is low.

In comparing somatic nuclei of the same species from different tissues, for example liver and erythrocyte nuclei, RIS and MIRSKY found that a close approximation to the same value for DNA content was obtained only when the DNA was evenly dispersed throughout the nucleus. This condition is attained by isolation of the nuclei in 30 per cent sucrose, followed by fixation in formalin; but some DNA is said to be lost when hypertonic sucrose alone is used for this purpose (ARNESON *et alii*[45]).* For quantitative estimations on Feulgen-stained material, LISON and PASTEELS[35a] aim at an even dispersion of DNA by using a fixative which would be unsatisfactory from the cytological standpoint. To quote these authors, 'Les tissus ont été fixés a l'alcool-formol qui a pour effet d'homogénéiser les noyaux dans une certaine mesure'. SCHRADER and LEUCHTENBERGER[33] measured the absorption of Feulgen-stained nuclei of different issues of *Tradescantia* without even dispersion of the DNA, and found a range of apparent DNA content in various interphase somatic nuclei of the same diameter of more than twofold. SCHRADER and LEUCHTENBERGER calculated the absolute amounts of DNA by means of the procedure of DI STEFANO, but apart from the possible errors involved in these computations their results can be considered as relative values. It might be expected that the nuclei of mammalian cells on which most of these estimations have been made would contain less Feulgen-positive material than those of *Tradescantia* in which the chromosomes are much larger, and so differences in DNA content between somatic nuclei would be there more readily revealed. In *Lilium*, OGUR *et alii*,[46] have found by using methods of bulk analysis that in the nuclei of the pollen grain, the content of DNA is very much higher than in any animal nuclei so far assayed.

SWIFT[41] used formalin-fixed material for his absorption studies on Feulgen-stained sections of animal tissues, principally from mice and Amphibia, with no previous treatment with sucrose. His results were reproducible to within 15 per cent. In mouse tissues he found three classes of nuclei with respect to their relative DNA content, the ratios between which were approximately 1:2:4, which suggest that these differences were due to heteroploidy. The relative DNA content of nuclei of the smallest class in different tissues was approximately the same.

When nuclei of the mammalian liver are isolated and analysed in bulk, the figure for the DNA content per nucleus does not stand for a diploid value and must be an average for the various size classes and degrees of heteroploidy. In the adult rat liver, estimates of the proportion of diploid nuclei present range from about 10–60 per cent (p 61). SWIFT found that his second class of nuclei were most abundant in the liver of the adult mouse. RIS and MIRSKY[24] also find twofold relationships between the DNA contents of rat liver nuclei of three size classes; although SWIFT[41] states that the volume of a nucleus is not necessarily related to its DNA content. In the regenerating rat liver, the proportion of polyploid nuclei is markedly increased; accordingly, it has been found that the average nuclear DNA content then rises nearly twofold (PRICE and LAIRD[47]).

* SCHNEIDER and HOGEBOOM[45] have recently criticized this assertion.

Even if further work should show that adult nuclei with equal numbers of chromosomes always contain a constant amount of DNA, this probably does not generally apply to the early embryo. The nucleus of the fertilized egg is larger than those of the blastomeres (p 63); in the sea-urchin the DNA content of the nuclei decreases during cleavage, but is not apparently directly proportional to nuclear size. The DNA content of embryonic echinoderm nuclei has been studied by BRACHET,[48] SCHMIDT *et alii*,[34] VILLEE *et alii*,[49] and by MAZIA.[50] The latter author has clearly summarized the results in this field which have so far been obtained. The DNA content of the echinoderm embryo increases steadily, but at a rate much slower than that of cell multiplication, so that in *Arbacia* at the tenth hour, the nuclei contain only one twentieth to one thirtieth of the DNA of the fertilized egg. The frequency of cell division then decreases slightly and so by the fortieth hour this fraction has increased to about one tenth. It would be very desirable to follow the subsequent course of events towards the adult condition in these respects.

ALFERT[51] finds that the range of relative DNA content of the nucleus of the mouse egg apparently remains constant during early cleavages, and approximate to that of the primary oocytes.

Until the varying relationships of the DNA content of nuclei with age and size are better understood, it may be unsafe, as DAVIDSON and LESLIE[52] have done, to base work on the growth and development of tissues on an assumed fixity of this quantity. The evidence for the synthesis of DNA between mitotic periods is increasing. This subject is developing very rapidly, and it may be that fresh observations will have appeared before the publication of this book.

THE NUCLEOLI

In general, the nucleoli are the most obvious feature of resting nuclei, though sometimes in early stages of development they are absent (LUDFORD,[53] BRACHET[54]). In the history of microscopical study, the first trace of the nucleolus is to be found in 1781, in a book by FONTANA,[55] mainly concerned with the viper and its venom. In one section of this work are described a number of rather miscellaneous observations; within an epithelial cell or 'vesicule' from the slime of an eel, he tells us, 'on observe un corps oviforme, ayant une tache dans son milieu'. The nucleus, FONTANA's egg-shaped body, was first described by LEEUWENHOEK in 1702 (BAKER[56]).

Distinction between true nucleoli and chromosome-nucleoli

Many papers in all have been written on the nucleolus; among reviews on this subject may be mentioned those of MONTGOMERY,[57]

WALKER and TOZER,[58] LUDFORD,[53] and GATES.[59] [60] One of the main questions has been the distinction between the true nucleolus or plasmosome, and the residual 'heteropycnotic' chromatin of what has been termed the chromosome-nucleolus. The two are usually closely associated. The difference in staining reactions of these two nuclear components was recognized as early as 1883 by OGATA.[61] For those who accept its validity, the Feulgen reaction clearly distinguishes between chromosomal material and the main body of the nucleolus, which in the opinion of most authors is Feulgen-negative. WERMEL,[62] one of the earliest users of the test, found this negative reaction to be particularly distinct in mammalian neurones in which there was little residual chromatin in the nucleus. In a series of insect oocyte nuclei BAUER[63] found but two instances of Feulgen-positive nucleoli, in which it may be presumed that heterochromatic material was incorporated. In the nucleolus of the mammalian liver cell (DAVIDSON[64]) there is an outer zone of this Feulgen-positive material.

Composition of true nucleolus

The nucleolus proper is composed mainly of ribonucleoproteins. Treatment with ribonuclease has been shown to decrease both the ultraviolet absorption of this body (DAVIDSON and WAYMOUTH[65]) and also its affinity for basic dyes (BRACHET,[54] GERSCH and BODIAN,[66] DAVIDSON et alii[67]). It is now usual to regard the basophilia of the nucleolus as its most characteristic feature, though in the older literature, an affinity for acidic dyes is often described (LUDFORD,[53] WILSON[68]). Ribonucleic acid is basophilic, but the basic proteins to which it is bound within the nucleolus (CASPERSSON[69]) can take up acidic dyes at low pH's (HYDEN[70]). Both these reactions are as yet insufficiently understood. In developing oocytes, the nucleolus may exhibit regions of different affinity (*Limnea*, LUDFORD[53]; *Asterias*, GATES[60]); this condition is related to active changes within the nucleolus, at the time when yolk is being deposited within the cytoplasm of the developing oocyte. In *Limnea*, acidophilic material is then extruded by the nucleolus through the nuclear membrane into the cytoplasm; numerous nucleolar buds are formed at the same time (Figure 10). Again, HOGBEN[71] describes how the yolk granules of the cockroach oocyte may be traced back to material from nucleolar vacuoles. A remarkable example of another kind of secretory activity which apparently originates in the nucleolus is provided by the slime glands of the skin of Myxine (SCHREINER[72]) which produce immense quantities of material in all.* According to this author, fuchsinophilic

---

* The statement in PARKER and HASWELL's *Text-book of Zoology* that 'two specimens of Myxine thrown into a bucket of water are capable of gelatinizing the whole with their secretion' is well known.

granules arise from the nucleoli of the secretory cells and are transformed within the cytoplasm into spiral threads of mucus.

Synthetic activity

The thesis of CASPERSSON and his school that the nucleolus is a centre of protein production, which we have discussed in a previous section of this book (pp 13–17), like other recent developments in cell biology, is thus a modern version of an older conception. It would be of great interest to apply modern techniques to these extreme instances of synthetic activity in which nucleoli are involved. BRADFIELD[73] has studied the silk-glands and oocytes of the spider from this point of view; the nucleoli of the latter are very large, they contain much ribonucleic acid, and give a strongly positive phosphatase reaction. BALBIANI[74] in

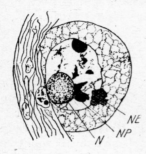

Figure 10 Young oocyte of *Limnae stagnalis* attached to wall of ovotestis. Material from the nucleolus (N) is being extruded into the cytoplasm (NP, NE). From LUDFORD[53] (*By courtesy, J. Roy. micr. Soc.*).

1864 observed movements in these same nucleoli, which continued for some hours in a preparation of the living material under the microscope. An amoeboid motion of the whole nucleolus was seen, together with dilation of vacuoles within, which BALBIANI compared with the action of the Protozoan contractile vacuole. Movement of nucleolar vacuoles was also observed by BÖHM[75] in the oocyte of *Petromyzon*. Again, a study of the relationship of such movements to the synthetic activities of the nucleolus might be of value.

Changes in form of this body are not apparently confined to the oocyte. Extrusion of nucleolar material into the cytoplasm of cells in tissue culture has been described by LEWIS[76] and by LUDFORD,[77] who observed the process in living material and did not regard it as abnormal. STRANGEWAYS[78] describes how the nucleoli repeatedly joined together and separated when such cells were observed over a period of several hours. Movements of the nucleoli of cells in culture is greatly enhanced both when prophase approaches and during the first hour or so of interphase. Sometimes vacuoles are seen in the nucleoli of both normal and malignant cells (LEWIS[79]). LASNITZKI and WILKINSON[80] have observed them in chick cells in culture treated with acridine derivatives. ZOLLINGER[81] has shown that when tissue cultures are treated with distilled water, all structure within the nucleus is dissolved, and that this change is reversible when the culture is returned to a normal saline medium. The nucleoli then reappear, though not in their original outline. HUGHES[82] observed that the nucleoli of cells in chick tissue cultures are rapidly affected by treatment with the nucleoside adenosine (Plate II (5)), or the purine analogue benzimidazole. These substances cause the nucleoli to break up into granules which may ultimately be scattered throughout the nucleus. This effect again is readily reversed by washing the culture with fresh physiological saline.

Coacervation

It has been suggested that the nucleolus is of the nature of a co-acervate (HYGÉN,[83] EHRENBERG,[84] DURYEE[85]). Under certain circumstances, it is possible for two aqueous solutions of the same colloid, one dilute and the other concentrated, to be immiscible with each other. This phenomenon was called coacervation by BUNGENBERG DE JONG and KRUYT[86] because of the 'heaping together' of the constituent micelles in the concentrated phase. A general account of the phenomenon has been given by DERVICHIAN.[87] It is greatly influenced by inorganic ions, and the evidence for a coacervate nature of the nucleolus rests mainly on the effects upon it of various salts. HYGÉN observed that the nucleoli of the egg nucleus in *Micrasterias* fuse under the influence of KNO_3, while DURYEE reports that a number of reagents will dissolve the nucleoli of the oocyte nucleus of the frog. Temperature is also a factor of importance in coacervation. EHRENBERG[84] found that the nucleolus in *Salix* decreases in volume with increase of temperature and drew the inference that this phenomenon was involved. It may well be that the concept will prove to be widely relevant in biology; but its application to the nucleolus depends on whether this body is in fact a liquid. Very probably, the physical state of the nucleolus varies in different organisms; in vertebrate cells in tissue culture, the nucleoli appear to be solid; when they disappear in such cells treated with distilled water, as ZOLLINGER[81] has described, it is probable that simple solvation is involved. GERSCH[88] finds that the solubility in water of the nucleoli of the oocyte nucleus of the frog increases as its development proceeds.

Nucleoli and chromosomes

In recent years, morphological interest in the nucleoli has centred mainly round the thesis that they have a definite relationship to particular chromosomes, in association with a special segment of which they are formed in telophase. The development of this view has been traced by GATES.[59] In plants, the relationship is so well established that, as GATES[60] says: 'the number of nucleoli arising in the nuclei at telophase can now be regarded as characteristic of the species'. The various types of relationship of chromosomes to nucleoli have been summarized by DARLINGTON[89]; they imply that the number of nucleoli in the early normal diploid telophase nucleus is constant. The greater part of the literature on this particular topic refers to plant material; of the few corresponding papers on animal nucleoli, we may instance those of DEARING[90] on *Ambystoma tigrinum* (Figure 11); KAUFMAN[91] on the salivary gland nuclei of *Drosophila melanogaster*; and CHEN[92] on the primitive ciliate *Zelleriella intermedia*. In the nuclei of heteroploid Amphibia, the nucleoli have been found to be related to the degree of ploidy. FANKHAUSER and HUMPHREY[93] have used the number present as an index of heteroploidy, while BEATTY[94] finds that the sum of the areas of the nucleoli in a nucleus is proportional to the number of chromosomes. KAWAGUCHI[95] has shown that in nuclei of polyploid silkworms, there is an equality between the number of nucleoli and the

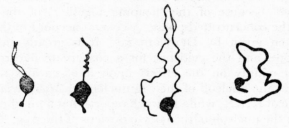

Figure 11 The nucleolus bearing chromosome in *Ambystoma tigrinum* in larval epithelial nucleoli; from very early to late prophase. × 2,000. From DEARING[90] (*By courtesy, J. Morph.*).

number of the 'Z' chromosomes, which are one of the two types of sex chromosome. DURYEE[85] has shown that the cloud of nucleoli which are formed during the 'lamp-brush' stage in the oocyte nucleus of the frog all arise from nucleolar organizers in particular chromosome pairs (Figure 12).

In Mammalia, the evidence for relationships between nucleoli and chromosomes is somewhat conflicting. SCHULTZ and LAWRENCE[96] find that in human spermatocytes there are two nucleoli, one borne on the sex chromosome, the other on an autosome to which these authors have devoted particular study. On the other hand, ANDREASSI[97] finds that the nuclei of the human foetal liver contains three or more nucleoli, which tend subsequently to fuse together. In the rat, the maximum number of nucleoli in diploid nuclei is six (BIESELE[98]), and in the mouse is four (BIESELE[99]). In studies on fibroblastic cells of these animals in tissue culture, neither LEWIS[100] nor FELL and HUGHES[101] were able to observe any constancy in number or arrangement of the nucleoli in telophase nuclei. In the early interphase nucleus, there is much re-arrangement of the nucleolar material, but even when the nucleoli are first recognizable, their number is variable. LEWIS states that this is true both of mother and daughter nuclei and of the daughter pairs. According to FELL and HUGHES nucleoli seem first to form where chromosomes are most densely clumped together in the early telophase nucleus. It may be that a number of chromosomes are concerned in nucleolar formation, and that their several individual contributions may be

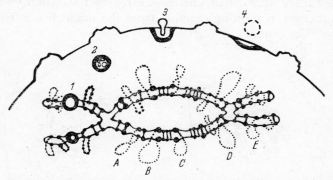

Figure 12 Diagram of chromosome pair in the half-sized ovarian eggs of Amphibia (compare *Figure* 35e). Paired granules are shown imbedded in 'plastic cylinder'. Letters indicate various lateral loops, formed as outgrowths of the granules. Numbers indicate successive stages in formation of a nucleolus at a definite locus, and its passage through the nuclear membrane. From DURYEE[85] (*By courtesy, University of Pennsylvania Press*).

indistinguishably fused from the very first. In the nuclei of malignant cells with a diploid number of polytene chromosomes, the number of nucleoli is increased (BIESELE *et alii*[102]). The duplicated chromonemata must therefore each carry separate nucleolar organizers.

HETEROPYCNOSIS

It was observed by HENKING[103] that a 'peculiar chromatin element' could be seen in both resting and dividing stages of the spermatocytes of the Hemipteran *Pyrrhocoris*. During the anaphase II of meiosis, this element passed undivided to one pole, and was thus to be found in half the resulting spermatids. Similar observations in the following years were made on other insects; this body was regarded by most authors as chromosomal in nature, although HENKING had regarded it as a nucleolus. The suggestion that their distribution to half the spermatids was related to sex determination was due to McCLUNG[104]; the term 'heterochromosome' for such bodies was first used by MONTGOMERY[105] in 1904. In the spermatogonial mitoses, the heterochromosomes do not lose their chromatin at telophase at the same rate as do the other chromosomes; they are visible within the interphase nucleus.

43

The name 'heteropycnosis' was suggested by GUTHERZ[106] for this general type of behaviour. It was first shown to apply to segments of the autosomes by HEITZ[107] in 1928, who studied resting and dividing nuclei in a number of liverworts and mosses. Those 'heterochromatic' parts of the chromosomes which persist unchanged during telophase can be traced into the resting nucleus where mostly they are associated with the nucleolus. Such bodies in the interphase nucleus had long been recognized; they were called 'chromocentres' by BACCARINI.[108] In plants their distinction in staining reaction from the nucleoli was recognized by ROSEN[109] in 1892.

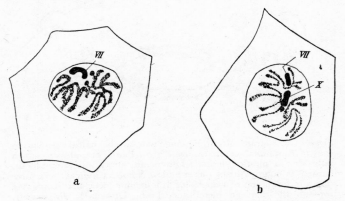

Figure 13 Second spermatocytes of *Mecostethus grossus* in interphase **a** without X– **b** with X-chromosome. The heteropycnotic autosome (VII) is visible in both. From WHITE[110a] (*By courtesy, Proc. roy. Soc. B*).

This condition in which part or all of a chromosome is still loaded with chromatin when elsewhere in the 'euchromatic' regions the charge has been partly lost is now known as positive heteropycnosis. Examples of the contrary negative condition are known, and have been described by WHITE[110] in the early spermatogonial divisions in the short-horned grasshoppers and crickets, where at metaphase the X-chromosome is less charged than are the autosomes (Figure 13). The reverse is true at diakinesis. Thus this example may be looked on as a difference in phase during the cycle of the migration of chromatin to and from the two types of chromosome. This aspect of heteropycnosis has been termed 'allocycly' by DARLINGTON and LA COUR.[111] These authors find that negatively heterochromatic segments of the metaphase chromosomes in *Paris* and *Trillium* are found in plants kept at 0° C. and claim that the chromocentres of the resting nuclei represent the same chromosomal regions as those in which the phenomenon of 'nucleic acid starvation' is found at low temperatures. Similar observations on animal cells have been made by CALLAN[112] in the newt. In the spermatocytes of the toad,

Bufo arenarum, SAEZ *et alii*[113] find that one autosome in metaphase I normally is negatively heteropycnotic (Figure 14).

Such are perhaps the main facts concerning this question which descriptive cytology has so far provided, although SCHULTZ[114] is of opinion that all the various features of heterochromatin in different organisms when added together 'come pretty close to including all the possible aspects of chromosome behaviour'. To mould this subject into a presentable form, it has been found necessary to mix in a large proportion of theoretical matrix, within which it is not always easy to discern other ingredients. It is believed that there are special features of heterochromatin in its genetical properties (SCHULTZ[114]), in its high susceptibility to breakage by mutagenic chemicals (LOVELESS and

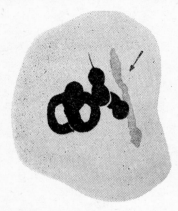

Figure 14 Negative heteropycnosis of an autosome in metaphase I of meiosis in the toad *Bufo arenarum*. After SAEZ *et alii*[113] (*By courtesy, Z. Zellsforsch.*).

REVELL[115]), and also in its chemical composition. Some of these generalizations are based on observations in *Drosophila*; in the larval salivary gland nucleus next to the nucleolus there is a single chromocentre made up of all the heterochromatic regions near the centromeres (Figure 15), it includes the whole of the Y-chromosome of the male. CASPERSSON[116] concluded from a comparison of the ultraviolet absorption spectra of this and the adjacent structures in the salivary nucleus, that basic proteins are characteristic of the heterochromatic regions. There is, however, some doubt whether nucleoproteins can be characterized by this method alone (p 12). In the nuclei of the spinal ganglion cells of the rabbit, HYDÉN[117] has shown that both the nucleolus and the chromocentre have a strong affinity for acidic dyes. It is not yet certain, however, whether the euchromatic regions at metaphase differ in this respect.

In *Drosophila*, variation of the total amount and arrangement of the heterochromatin have been shown to be correlated with changes elsewhere within the cell. CASPERSSON and SCHULTZ[118] showed that where a Y-chromosome was included in the oocyte nucleus, cytoplasmic nucleic acids were increased in amount (Figure 4). SCHULTZ *et alii*[119] found that genetical rearrangements of heterochromatin in the X-chromosome were reflected in differences in the absorption spectra of the nucleoli. These observations have assumed a prominent part in the

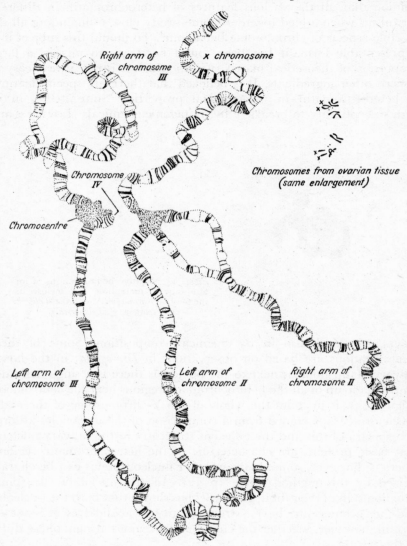

Right arm of chromosome III

x chromosome

Chromosomes from ovarian tissue (same enlargement)

Chromosome IV

Chromocentre

Left arm of chromosome III

Left arm of chromosome II

Right arm of chromosome II

Figure 15 Chromosomes of salivary gland nucleus of *Drosophila melanogaster* together with those of oogonial nucleus to same scale. In the salivary nucleus the synopsis of homologous elements is everywhere complete except for the proximal part of the 2nd chromosome. The 4th chromosomes are partly covered by the chromocentral mass common to all the chromosomes, here shown in two portions. From PAINTER[114a]
(*By courtesy, J. Hered.*).

thesis of the Stockholm school that the site of protein synthesis of the whole cell is the nucleolus and its associated heterochromatin, for SCHULTZ[114] in speaking of this genetical change in nucleolar composition, says 'this is the cardinal fact which lies at the base of the theory that the heterochromatic regions have to do with cytoplasmic synthesis in general, by way of precursors deriving from the nucleoli'. How far this theory can generally be applied to all types of cell depends among other considerations on whether the nucleoli are invariably associated with heterochromatic regions of chromosomes. In plants, the satellite threads connecting nucleoli and chromosomes are often Feulgennegative (RESENDE[120]). Indeed the term SAT-thread (Sine Acido thymonucleinico) was first used by HEITZ[121] to indicate the absence of DNA therein.

BAKER and CALLAN[122] have suggested that the term 'heterochromatin' should be abandoned because such a noun suggests a chemical entity. This argument applies equally to 'chromatin' itself which still serves an indispensable purpose as a general term in FLEMMING's original sense (p 2). However, it is possible that if the use of the word 'heterochromatin' were relinquished, there might be some decrease in the tendency to generalize from the salivary nucleus of *Drosophila* to all other cells.

PROTEINS OF THE NUCLEUS

It has long been known that in the nucleus, proteins of small molecular weight with basic properties are associated with nucleic acids. MIESCHER[123] isolated an organic base from the heads of salmon sperm which he termed protamine, the molecular weight of which is now known to be intermediate between those of polypeptides and proteins; ten years later, KOSSEL[124] found a basic protein of more complex structure in bird erythrocytes which he termed histone. The evidence for the existence of basic proteins in the nucleus still depends mainly on bulk chemical analysis, for cytochemical observations on this subject do not point to conclusions of the same clarity. Some of the difficulties which beset the identification by ultraviolet microspectometry of proteins in the presence of nucleic acids have been discussed in previous pages (p 12). A cytochemical method for the recognition of arginine (SERRA[125]) has been claimed by this author[126] to demonstrate the presence of basic proteins in the nucleus. All proteins, however, contain arginine, and although the proportions of this amino acid are high in protamines and histones, a positive reaction for arginine still might be given by a non-basic protein present in large amounts. Results of great interest and possible significance on differences between the histones of nuclei in different tissues in the same animal are beginning to emerge in the work of STEDMAN and STEDMAN.[127] These authors

47

have already shown that nuclear histones are composite and consist of one main and one or more subsidiary components. The latter vary greatly in arginine content, whereas the proportion of this amino acid in the main histone seems almost constant throughout a number of vertebrates.

Fractionation

Not all the proteins of the cell nucleus are basic. STEDMAN and STEDMAN[128] have prepared from various types of nucleus a protein which is neither a protamine nor a histone, which they regard as the main protein of the chromosomes, to which they gave the name 'chromosomin'. This substance is prepared by first extracting with acid the basic material from dry lipoid-free nuclei and then fractionating the residual material with dilute alkali. The heads of fish sperm may contain up to 30 per cent of chromosomin. This substance gives strongly positive reactions for tryptophane, tyrosine, arginine and contains sulphur; histones give negative or only very faint reactions for tryptophane. A non-basic protein containing tryptophane has also been identified in the nucleus by MIRSKY and POLLISTER.[129] By extraction of nuclei with molar sodium chloride these authors separated a complex fibrous product, consisting of nucleic acid, histone and this non-histone protein. To the whole of this they give, not without the risk of confusion, the name of 'chromosin'. The tryptophane containing protein ('Tr. Pr.') is freed from histone and partially from nucleic acids by methods similar to those employed by the STEDMANS.

The isolated 'chromosomes' prepared by MIRSKY and RIS[130] (p 64) can also be fractionated into the same three components. Molar sodium chloride causes these threads to swell, and to lose their histone and most of their nucleic acid into solution. The residue which is still microscopically recognizable as a thread, consists mainly of a protein which these authors identify with their 'Tr. Pr.' prepared from whole nuclei. Apart then from differences in nomenclature and their rival claims of priority, the STEDMANS agree with the MIRSKY group both over the non-basic protein of the nucleus, and also in the view that the DNA is evenly spread throughout the resting nucleus, in which they may well both be wrong.

Although there is this evidence for the existence of non-basic proteins in the cell nucleus, we do not know whether they belong equally to the chromonemata and to the nuclear sap. The chromatographic analysis of the nuclear sap of *Xenopus* oocytes which we owe to BROWN *et alii*[131] clearly indicates that a complex non-basic protein is present in this material (Figure 16).

The proportion of tryptophane-containing protein to DNA in the interphase nucleus which POLLISTER and LEUCHTENBERGER[132] calculate from microcolorimetric measurements is higher than that derived by the bulk analysis of isolated nuclei. These authors concluded that their observations demonstrate that protein is lost from nuclei during their isolation. The comparison rests, however, on the validity of the cyto-chemical procedures which were used. Their figures for the DNA nuclear content were calculated according to DI STEFANO's method, which has subsequently been found inadequate, notably by one of the above authors herself (p 36).

Some part of the non-basic proteins of the interphase must be enzymic. In isolated nuclei a number of enzymes have been shown to be present, although the possibility that some of their activity is due to

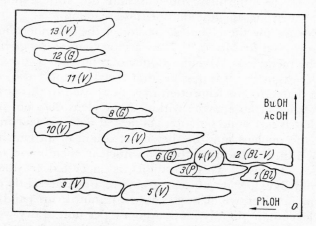

Figure 16 Paper chromatogram of acid hydrolysate of the sap of the oocyte nucleus of *Xenopus laevis*. (1) aspartic acid; (2) glutamic acid; (3) glycine; (4) serine; (5) lysine; (6) threonine; (7) alanine; (8) tyrosine; (9) arginine (histidine, if present); (10) proline; (11) valine; (12) phenylalanine; (13) leucine and isoleucine. The colour differentiation indicated by letters in parenthesis (Bl, blue; V, violet; P, pink; G, grey; Y, yellow) was produced by 5% collidine in the ninhydrin spray. From BROWN et alii[131] (*By courtesy, Nature*).

contamination by cytoplasmic material is always present; where, however, enzymes are present in relatively high concentration in isolated nuclei this source of error is less probable. DOUNCE[133] found that a number of enzymes were conspicuous in rat liver nuclei, and that they were not removed by washing, as was the adsorbed haemo-globin. Among them were both acid and alkaline phosphatases, which have also been identified in isolated nuclei of the cerebral cortex by RICHTER and HULTIN,[134] who found that the latter enzyme was more abundant in the nucleus than in the cytoplasm.*

* DOUNCE[135] has reviewed the various methods which are used for the isolation of nuclei.

Phosphatase distribution

By means of the well-known cytochemical methods of GOMORI[136] [137] the distribution of phosphatases within the nucleus has been examined, though the customary debates concerning the validity of methods for cytochemical localization extend also to these procedures (DANIELLI,[138] JACOBY and MARTIN[139]). WOLF et alii[140] have investigated the acid phosphatase of a number of types of cell, while several studies have been devoted to the alkaline enzyme, such as those on chick cells in tissue culture (WILLMER,[141] CHÈVREMONT and FIRKET[142]), on salivary gland chromosomes (DANIELLI and CATCHESIDE,[143] KRUGELIS[144] [145]), and on mouse spermatocytes (KRUGELIS[146]). Both the nucleoli and the heterochromatin of the interphase nucleus and the chromosomes during mitosis give a strong alkaline phosphatase reaction.

The evidence for the chemical nature of the alkaline phosphatases has been reviewed by MOOG.[147] They are proteins of the globulin type, activated by metal ions. Alkaline kidney phosphatase is strongly bound to zinc (CLOETENS[148]); it is possible that the zinc reported by HEATH[149] in isolated deoxyribonucleoprotein may be related to this enzyme.

The presence of an enzyme within the nucleus does not necessarily indicate that it has some function connected with nuclear metabolism per se, for the nucleus may be the site of origin of an enzyme, which may then diffuse outwards from the nuclear membrane to operate within the cytoplasm. This possibility is suggested by the work of DOUNCE and BEYER[150] on nuclear arginase, a characteristic enzyme of the mammalian liver, which breaks down arginine to urea and ornithine. Liver nuclei contain slightly more arginase per unit of dry weight than does the cytoplasm, while kidney nuclei contain little or none. In a further paper, DOUNCE et alii[151] have confirmed that this enzyme is present in rat liver nuclei.

LIPOIDS OF THE NUCLEUS

Both chemical analysis of isolated nuclei and microscopic techniques have been used in the few studies which have been devoted to this subject. In the original paper describing the citric acid method of isolating nuclei STONEBERG[152] used this technique for studying the lipoids. It was found that in a number of organs there was a somewhat greater lipoid content in the nuclei than in the whole tissue; phospholipine and cholesterol were the main substances of this class to be found within the nucleus. It has been found that in the nuclei of the mouse liver, the percentage of phospholipines is equal to that of ribonucleic acid, namely 3·4 (BAVAUM et alii[153]). WILLIAMS et alii[154] studied the effect on the nuclear lipoids of the liver of feeding the carcinogen butter yellow and found that the proportion of cholesterol present was thereby increased. In the intact nucleus, the lipoids are bound to protein, and so the difficulty of demonstrating their presence by cytochemical methods is greatly increased. COHEN[155] has shown that the hetero-chromatin in the interphase nuclei of the plants *Allium* and *Phaseolus* responds to the powerful lipoid colorant Sudan black (LISON[156]), the use of which in nuclear cytology should be extended. GATES[157] denied that lipoids were present in the nucleolus; in some marine eggs, however, SHINKE and SHIGENAGA[158] and MENSINKAI[159] report their presence while SERRA[126] states that in the nucleolus of snail oocytes there are 'peripheral inclusions which give a coloration of middle intensity with BZL blue'. It seems therefore that both in mitochondria and the nu-cleoli, ribonucleic acid is associated with lipoproteins, though the proportion of each constituent in the two types of structure are probably widely different. The possible functions of the phospholipine within the cell have been discussed by CLAUDE.[160]

NUCLEAR MEMBRANE

The debates on the validity of the detail seen in the fixed and stained cell have included each of its main constituents, the nuclear membrane among them. PISCHINGER,[161] for instance, argued that this was an artefact, since its prominence in sections of mouse liver varied with the fixative used; furthermore he was unable to identify it in the unfixed cell. First, therefore, we must consider the question whether the nuclear membrane has a real existence.

It must be admitted that the presence of an interface between nucleus and cytoplasm does not necessarily prove that a physical membrane is there, for BUNGENBERG DE JONG[162] has shown how two aqueous colloidal solutions may be immiscible, if one of them is a coacervate (p 41). The argument that a nuclear membrane is not visible in life is unlikely to survive the introduction of the phase contrast microscope. The phase photomicrographs of living intermitotic cells in culture (Plate I(1)) show how clearly this structure stands out, particularly where nuclear sap and the adjacent cytoplasm are of about the same refractive index. A vacuole within the cytoplasm has no such definite border. In binucleate cells, the two nuclei are usually in contact, and the apposed membranes usually appear thicker than the single layer elsewhere on the circumference of the nucleus. Such cells have been observed for several hours with their nuclei in apposition. In the divid-ing cell, the disappearance of the membrane at the end of prophase is immediately noticeable as the nuclear area then suddenly contracts. Even before these particular observations were available, the evidence from micro-dissection studies (CHAMBERS and FELL[163]) had already pro-vided a clear proof of the presence of this structure within the cells of tissue cultures.

Structure and composition

Several lines of research have given information on the structure and composition of the nuclear membrane. It has been shown in several instances that it bears a positive charge (DAHLGREN;[164] CHURNEY and KLEIN,[165]) and that the isoelectric point of its proteins is far to the alkaline side of the physiological *p*H (CHURNEY[166]). The reverse is true in both instances for chromatin. The nuclear membrane must therefore in part consist of a protein-anion complex, with a high proportion of basic amino acids. An observation on cultivated chick and mammalian cells in mitosis may be related to this. It is striking that at the end of prophase, the nucleoli and the nuclear membrane suddenly disappear, always at exactly the same moment. The nucleoli are known to contain basic proteins (p 39); probably some event within the nucleus, perhaps the liberation of an enzyme, causes similar material in both structures to be dissolved at the same time.

CHURNEY[166] has found that unlike the cell membrane, a torn nuclear membrane is not 'repaired' in the presence of calcium because a calcium-proteinate cannot be formed on the acid side of an isoelectric point. It is thus improbable that the ash which is seen at the site of the nuclear membrane in cells submitted to micro-incineration (SCOTT[167]) can mean that the living structure has a high mineral content. The location of cations within the cell is all too readily disturbed by fixation, and it is probable that the positive reaction for potassium in the nuclear membrane found by BUREAU[168] is also an artefact.

Some experiments of LUYET and ERNST[169] have shown that the nuclear membrane of the cells of the onion root has marked plastic properties. These authors centrifuged whole roots at a force of 30,000 x g for periods of from 10 minutes to 2 hours, and found that the nuclei moved to one wall of the cells, against which they were flattened, while their opposite surfaces were drawn out into bottlenecks. These changes must have involved a considerable increase in nuclear surface. The fine structure of the nuclear membrane has been investigated both by the polarizing and the electron microscope. The sign of its birefringence is that of fibrous protein; BAUD[170] was able to observe this by precipitating on the nuclear membrane antimony sulphide in the same orientation. CALLAN[171] found that the membrane of germinal vesicles of *Triton* became strongly birefringent when dilated. CALLAN and TOMLIN[172] have published an elegant study of the oocyte nuclear membrane of *Triturus* and *Xenopus* by electron micrography. It consists of an outer porous layer, and an inner one, apparently continuous, which is the thinner of the two. The porous layer apparently contains some lipoidal material. It would be of very great interest to compare the structure of this membrane with those of normal somatic nuclei, because it appears that the Amphibian germinal vesicle has a particularly high permeability. Both salts (ABELSON and DURYEE;[173] CALLAN[171]) and sugars (CALLAN[171]) are able to traverse it, whereas the osmotic properties of other nuclei suggest that they are permeable to water and not to solutes. Among these are Amphibian epithelial nuclei (HAMBURGER[174]) and the germinal vesicle in the egg of *Arbacia punctulata* (BECK and SHAPIRO;[175] CHURNEY[166]).*

It is probable that various cells differ widely from each other in this respect. It does not appear from the photographs of ZOLLINGER[176] that the nucleus of cells in tissue cultures swells when distilled water is added to the medium; MONNÉ[177] observed a transitory vital staining of the nucleus in *Amoeba* when dyes were injected into the cytoplasm. In these experiments acidic dyes penetrated the nuclear membrane more rapidly than did basic ones.

SIZE OF THE INTERPHASE NUCLEUS AND OF THE CHROMOSOMES

Not all the nuclei in one type of cell in an individual are of the same size. Generally, the size of the nucleus is related to that of the whole cell, and most of the literature of this subject is concerned with this proportionality, to which HERTWIG (R.)[178] gave the well-known name of 'karyoplasmic ratio'. On the theoretical developments associated with this idea, the verdict of WILSON[179] is that they were 'undoubtedly carried too far', but in these days probably too little is heard of the subject. However, interest in the nuclear size, *per se*, has survived in respect to its relationship to the number and size of the constituent chromosomes. The early observations bearing on this subject indicated a close and fixed proportionality; but as one might expect, other factors have since emerged which modify and complicate it.

Production of haploid and tetraploid larvae in Echinoderms

The classical experiments in this field are those of BOVERI[180] who employed the methods discovered as early as 1887 by HERTWIG (O. and R.)[181] for the production of haploid and tetraploid larvae of sea-urchins. If unfertilized eggs are suitably shaken, they can be separated into two parts, one with, the other without, the nucleus†; these halves then round off and both can be fertilized and subsequently undergo cleavage. The phenomenon was called 'merogony'. Both diploid and haploid larvae result from this procedure, the chromosomes of the latter being solely derived from the sperm nucleus. A tetraploid larva can be produced by shaking a normal fertilized egg near the time

---

* CHAMBERS and POLLACK[175a] found that phenol red penetrated into the germinal vesicle of the starfish egg.

† It is now customary to employ the centrifuge to effect this operation (HARVEY[182]).

of the first division; a 'monastral' mitosis results where one nucleus is formed containing both daughter sets of chromosomes. Haploid, diploid and tetraploid sea-urchin larvae at the same stage of development are all of the same size. The individual nuclei and cells are related in size to their chromosome content, and so it follows that a tetraploid larva has about one quarter the number of cells of a haploid one. Clearly some regulative process during development must limit the number of cell divisions so that the standard size of the organism is maintained.

Among other observations, BOVERI compared the size of the interphase nuclei of haploid and diploid merogenous plutei of *Echinus*, and of tetraploid and diploid gastrulae of *Strongylocentrotus*, and found a simple proportionality between the squares of their mean nuclear diameters. If the nuclei are assumed to be approximately spherical their surface area must be directly proportional to their number of chromosomes.

Polyploidy in other animals

In recent years the most extensive investigations on animal polyploidy have been those of FANKHAUSER *et alii* on the Amphibia, which provide great scope for such research (FANKHAUSER[183]). Haploid and polyploid individuals not only occur spontaneously but their frequency may be increased experimentally by treatment such as the application of heat or cold to the eggs. In Amphibia, as in echinoderm larvae, polyploid individuals are of the same size as diploid; but here, haploid ones are somewhat smaller.* FANKHAUSER makes use of measurements of nuclear size in cells of the tail fin as a means of determining the degree of heteroploidy in his larvae; the area of the flattened epidermal nuclei is found to be proportional to the number of chromosomes. In other amphibian tissues HERTWIG (G. and P.)[184] claim that this is more closely related to the volume of the nucleus. From the data of FANKHAUSER[183] and FANKHAUSER and HUMPHREY[185] nuclear areas of larval epidermal cells are plotted against their ploidy in Figure 17. It can be seen that the range in nuclear areas increases at each step.

Among the Arthropods, there are polyploid races of certain species which reproduce by parthenogenesis. Of these, the best known is the brine shrimp *Artemia*, which has been studied by ARTOM[186] [187] [188] and by BARIGOZZI.[189] The bisexual race is diploid, while there are separate parthenogenetic races which are diploid, tetraploid and octoploid respectively. The cytology of their germ cells is described by WHITE.[190] The relationship between chromosomal status and body size seems to vary in *Artemia* according to ARTOM,[187] who investigated the ratio of

* Recent evidence suggests that in mammals, the relationships between degree of ploidy, the size of the nuclei and of the whole body are more complex.

the areas of nuclei from different tissues in tetraploid and diploid strains, and found considerable deviation from a 2:1 relationship. Moreover these aberrant ratios themselves vary from tissue to tissue. BARIGOZZI[189] measured nuclear areas in epithelial cells of the gut of an octoploid race of *Artemia* and found the range of variation to be nearly fourfold. It is clear that factors other than their content of chromosomes can affect the size of interphase nuclei. BARIGOZZI suggested that some of these may be hereditary, for he found much less variation in nuclear size between mother and sister individuals in the octoploid *Artemias*. Thus in polyploid individuals, in every cell of which there is the same multiple of the haploid number of chromosomes, measurement of nuclear size alone is not always a sufficient guide in deciding the value

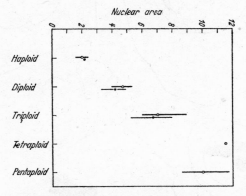

Figure 17 Relative nuclear areas of epidermal nuclei in polyploid amphibia, for each degree of ploidy. Plotted from the data of FANKHAUSER and HUMPHREY[185] and FANKHAUSER.[183] (circles, *Triturus*; dots, *Ambystoma*. Where given, the range and the mean of each degree are indicated.

of this multiple. BOWEN[191] and SCHRADER[192] have shown that in the Bug *Arvelius albopunctatus* the size of the spermatocyte nuclei in different lobes of the testis may vary by as much as 4:1, yet in all these cells the chromosomes which appear in the subsequent stages of meiosis are similar in size and number (Figure 18)*. In Amphibia, BEATTY and FISCHBERG[193] state that 'large significant differences in mean nuclear size can be found between diploid frog tadpoles, even of the same batch'. It follows, therefore, that where the degree of heteroploidy is not constant in the various cells and tissues of a single individual, statistics of nuclear dimensions must be interpreted with reserve.

*SCHRADER and LEUCHTENBERGER[192a] have shown that the DNA content of *Arvelius* spermatocytes of different sizes is approximately constant, but that their content of RNA and protein is proportional to their size.

Growth in interphase

One of the factors which influence the nuclear size in rapidly growing tissues is the stage which a nucleus has reached in its period of growth in interphase. According to CONKLIN,[194] in the embryo of the mollusc

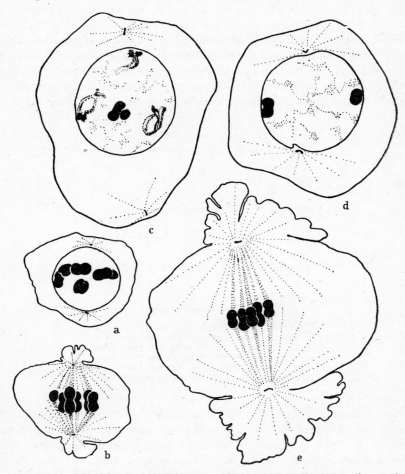

Figure 18. Various sizes of spermatocyte nuclei in *Arvelius albopunctatus* (**a**, **c** and **d**) all form chromosomes of the same number and size (**b** and **e**). Diakinesis and metaphase I in 4th lobe of testis (**a** and **b**); in 5th lobe (**c**, **d** and **e**) × 1500. From SCHRADER[192] (*By courtesy, Chromosoma*).

Crepidula the interphase nucleus enlarges most rapidly as the next mitosis approaches, while in cells of the mouse spleen in tissue culture (FELL and HUGHES[195]) two-thirds of the full interphase size is reached within three hours of telophase (Figure 19). A number of authors believe that the growth of resting nuclei is discontinuous and rhythmic.

Their evidence for this is indirect, and is based on studies of the distribution of size of large numbers of nuclei. Thus, if the nuclei in a tissue remain at one size for some time and then rapidly grow to another at which they again halt, then the histogram of nuclear size will show peaks corresponding to these values, provided that the errors involved are not large enough to obscure the result. The best known of such numerical investigations are those of JACOBJ[196] [197] who measured nuclear diameters in a series of mammalian tissues, and displayed the calculated volumes in this form; the peaks were identified as modal values which, JACOBJ claimed, bore to each other ratios of 1:2:4 and

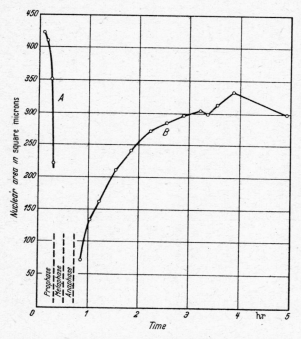

Figure 19 Nuclear area of a mouse spleen cell in tissue culture during mitosis; (A) that of the parent cell in prophase, (B) that of one daughter cell in telophase and early interphase. From FELL and HUGHES[195] (*By courtesy, Quart. J. micr. Sci.*).

so forth. Before discussing the author's conclusions, we must first examine the evidence on which they are based.

In the first place it is necessary to say that simple inspection of a histogram is not adequate to decide whether or not a distribution is discontinuous, for the irregularities may be due merely to sampling errors. However, a simple test may be applied to JACOBJ's data by plotting his result on probability paper, in the manner described in a recent paper by HARDING.[198] It is better to use the measured data for nuclear diameter rather than the cubed values for volumes, for the errors involved in measurements under the microscope from serial sections which have been shrunk in dehydration and embedding are already formidable enough without being raised to higher powers. Figure 20 shows that JACOBJ's data for nuclear diameter in a mouse embryo when plotted on probability paper suggests a normal distribution about a single mode, for the points may approximately be joined by a straight line. HARDING[198] showed that a bimodal distribution when plotted in this way gives a sigmoidal curve, and the abscissa of the point of inflection indicates the approximate proportion of the representatives

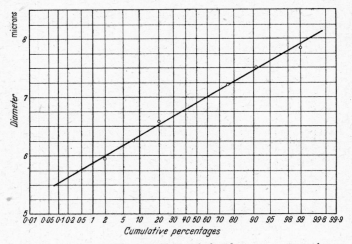

Figure 20 Nuclear diameter in kidney tubules of 20 mm. mouse embryo. Data taken from JACOBJ[196] and plotted as cumulative percentages on probability paper. The distribution is unimodal, as the points may approximately be represented by a straight line.

of each mode. Such a distribution is exemplified by the results of BEAMS and KING[199] for the nuclear diameter of mononucleate cells in the normal adult rat liver* (Figure 21). The data for the mouse liver is less easily interpreted. In addition to JACOBJ's observations, nuclear diameter in this tissue has also been investigated by HEIBERG,[200] VOSS[201] and MÜLLER[202] and the data of all these authors for mononucleate cells is plotted in Figure 22 in the same manner which has been described. It is clear that the points for each set of data could only very approximately be represented by a straight line, and one cannot point to any sigmoidal inflections with confidence; nor are there any constant features in the shape of the curve for each set of points. Nuclear size in the adult mouse liver is therefore too complex an example to be analysed in this way from the existing data.

* The corresponding data of JACOBJ also suggests a bimodal distribution, but is curiously divergent from that of BEAMS and KING in absolute size.

JACOBJ's procedure has been followed by a number of other workers. Several of these, however, have found that their modes of nuclear volume were not related in the ratios of powers of 2 (WERMEL and

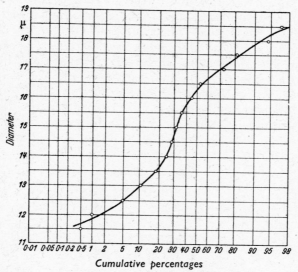

Figure 21 Nuclear diameter of uninucleate cells in normal rat liver, plotted on probability paper as in Figure 20. Data taken from BEAMS and KING.[199] The sigmoidal curve indicates a bimodal distribution.

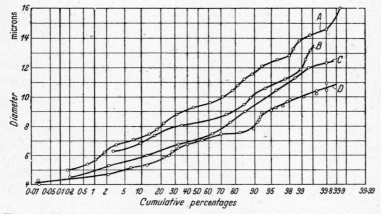

Figure 22 Nuclear diameter in the normal mouse liver plotted as in Figure 20 from the data of (A) VOSS[201]; (B) JACOBJ[196]; (C) HEIBERG[200]; and (D) MÜLLER[202]. No well marked modes can be recognized.

SCHERSCHULSKAJA[203]). Furthermore, no discontinuities in nuclear size were found by LEWIS (W. H.)[204] in either mouse fibroblasts in tissue cultures, or in a rat sarcoma.

However, it is still possible for the growth of the interphase nucleus to be rhythmic as JACOBJ suggested, even if his own indirect evidence for a periodic increase in size may be insufficient. WERMEL and PORTUGALOW[205] studied this question directly by taking time-lapse films of living cells in tissue cultures, and measured individual nuclei at intervals over periods of several hours. Their published curves for nuclear volume plotted against time show an irregular periodicity, with a rapid increase in size every fifty minutes or so (Figure 23). WERMEL and PORTUGALOW concluded that these periodic increases in volume were much smaller than twofold. They assumed that these nuclei in their cultures were spherical; this is certainly untrue for flattened cells in the outgrowth of a tissue culture. It would be of value to repeat the work of these authors although the significance of such rhythmic changes might still remain obscure.

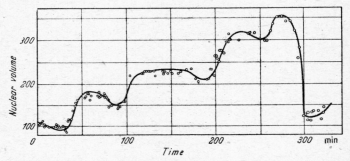

Figure 23 Change in volume of the nucleus of a chick cell in tissue culture with time. The nucleus finally divided by amitosis. From WERMEL and PORTUGALOW.[205] Time in minutes; volume in arbitrary units.

SCHREIBER[206] in a review of investigations in the field of 'caryometric analysis' has discussed the possible events in the life of the nucleus which could correspond with the increase in volume which JACOBJ refers to as 'innere Teilung'. This process could involve the duplication of either the individual chromosomes or of chromatic material at a lower order of size within the chromosomes. Where the increase in size of a nucleus at each step is less than twofold, SCHREIBER suggests that this may be due to the doubling of its maternal and paternal chromatin on separate and possibly alternate occasions. A less unplausible suggestion is that of HERTWIG (G.)[207] who claims that it is nuclear surface rather than nuclear volume which doubles at each step; here the increase in volume would be proportional to the square root of 2. This is understandable if the interphase chromonemata are usually distributed over the inner surface of the nuclear membrane as seems true in some nuclei (p 30).

If discontinuous changes in size of nuclei do occur, the question arises whether any corresponding visible events within the nucleus are recognizable. Various modifications of mitosis are known in which the ploidy of nuclei is changed (p 149). However, there is one example where ploidy increases independently of any mitotic process. In the ileum of the larval mosquito (BERGER[208]), the nuclei grow in size, and the chromosomes reduplicate without any visible changes within the nuclei, which remain in the resting phase throughout.

One example from a vertebrate tissue where, by a modified form of mitosis, the degree of heteroploidy and nuclear size is doubled has been described by BEAMS and KING[199] in their work on the regenerating liver of the rat. In this animal two-thirds of the whole organ may be removed experimentally, and the normal size will be regained within a month. Extremely frequent mitoses are seen in the liver tissue within a few days after the operation, and marked variation in size of the interphase nuclei is then seen. Large polyploid nuclei are formed by mitoses of binucleate cells (p 149), in which the chromosomes from both nuclei join a common metaphase plate. Two polyploid daughter nuclei are then formed in telophase. If the cell divides, two mono-nucleate tetraploid daughter cells result; if not, the cell still remains binucleate, but now the nuclei are tetraploid. By the repetition of such mitoses octoploid nuclei will result. BEAMS and KING studied the distribution of nuclear size in mononucleate and binucleate cells in both regenerating liver and in the normal pieces removed at the time of operation. In the normal liver, as we have already discussed, this distribution is bimodal (Figure 21) while it becomes markedly poly-modal in the regenerating tissue. In the normal development of the liver, tetraploid nuclei are presumably formed in the same way; the commoner of the two modes of normal nuclear size is the large one, which must correspond with the tetraploid grade. SULKIN[209] is of opinion that only 10 per cent of normal liver nuclei in the rat corres-pond in volume to the diploid mode. In a careful study of the cytology of this material BIESELE[210] finds that chromosome counts at metaphase in both the normal and the regenerating organ indicate a proportion of diploid nuclei of somewhere between one-half and two-thirds; four to five per cent of octoploid nuclei are present in both.

Variations in chromosomal size

A further factor which affects the size of a nucleus is variation in the size of the chromosomes themselves. Again, most of what is known on this topic refers to the Diptera, particularly to the giant chromosomes of the larval tissues. According to HERTWIG (G.)[211], the salivary gland nucleus in *Drosophila melanogaster* increases in volume by at least 264 times during larval development. Similar chromosomes are present in other larval organs as BALBIANI[212] mentions in his original description of the salivary nucleus in *Chironomus*. BOGOJAWLENSKY[213] finds that in the development of the *Anopheles* larva, giant chromosomes are not seen in any tissue until the fourth of a series of nuclear size classes has been attained. PAINTER and REINDORP[214] find that the nurse cells of the *Drosophila* ovary undergo a discontinuous increase in size by means of successive cycles of endomitosis (Figure 59).

The only investigations on the relationship between chromosomal and nuclear size in vertebrate tissues are those of BIESELE *et alii*. Their

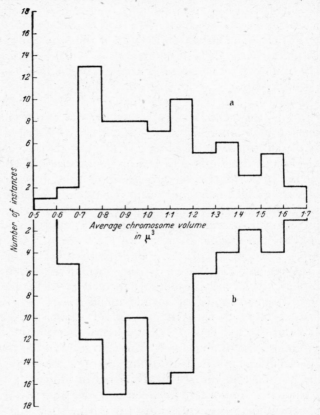

Figure 24 Histograms showing distribution of chromosomal volumes in nuclei of the rat liver (a) normal, and (b) during regeneration. Plotted from data given by BIESELE.[210]

results suggest a clear distinction between growth in a normal tissue such as the regenerating liver (BIESELE[210]) and in some tumours, for whereas the same distribution of chromosomal size is found in both diploid and polyploid cells of the normal and the regenerating liver (Figure 24), chromosomes of double the usual size were found in tumours of a goldfish (BIESELE[215]), of the mouse (BIESELE *et alii*[216]), and in a human mammary carcinoma (BIESELE and POYNER[217]). In the latter, chromosomes of both twice and four times the normal volume were found in metaphase figures all of which were approximately diploid. The nuclei of these tumours are therefore polytene and not polyploid. Three modes of interphase nuclear volume correspond with the three sizes of mitotic chromosomes.

It must be admitted that the doubts expressed above concerning the accuracy of volumes computed from measurements in microscopical preparations of the order of tens of microns apply with still greater force when one dimension of the object is a fraction of a micron. BIESELE is aware of the possibility of error in his methods, and at least it can be said that his *camera lucida* drawings demonstrate that the chromosomes of tumours can be larger than those of normal cells. Nothing is yet known for certain of the internal structure of such polytene chromosomes.

It is not only in the malignant cell, however, that chromosomes can vary in size. It has long been known that both intermitotic nuclei and chromosomes decrease in size as the segmentation of the egg is in progress. During the first few cleavages, the total volume of all the nuclei may either increase at each cleavage by some factor less than 2, or remain constant as in the mouse, according to HERTWIG (G.).[218] In Echinoderms, both intermitotic nuclei and chromosomes decrease in size during development, although in the literature of this subject divergent views are expressed on the precise course of these diminutions in volume (ERDMANN[219]; GODLEWSKI[220]).

HERTWIG (G.) refers to the chromosomes of the fertilized mouse egg as 'polymers' which are progressively halved at each cleavage, without increase in their substance between divisions. On the other hand ALFERT[221] finds that the range of relative DNA content of the nuclei of the mouse egg during early cleavage stages is similar to that of the primary oocyte. Again, we have yet no evidence of the internal structure of these chromosomes, which even at their largest are not readily amenable to microscopical investigation. BIESELE[222] has compared the volume of the chromosomes in the liver of the newborn and the full grown rat, and finds that there is a twofold increase in their volume during adult life. It would be of great interest to extend such studies backwards into foetal life, and to compare the size of the chromosomes and of the interphase nuclei with their content of nucleic acids in absolute terms.

ISOLATION OF CHROMATIN THREADS FROM RESTING NUCLEI

The development of fractionation methods for the isolation of cell constituents in an almost undamaged condition has been one of the most striking advances in experimental cytology. These procedures have been applied both to the cytoplasm and to whole nuclei, methods for the isolation of which have long been known (p 1). The final achievement of these techniques seemed to be the subdivision of the nucleus itself from which it has been claimed that veritable chromosomes can be prepared in bulk. This further step, however, involves more than the separation of bodies already present in the cell, for the initial material is the interphase nucleus. A claim that the end-product consists of isolated chromosomes must therefore be examined with some care.

The first accounts of nuclear fractionation were given by CLAUDE[223] and by CLAUDE and POTTER.[224] The material used by these authors is the spleen of leucaemic mice, which is completely infiltrated by lymphocytes, mainly haemocytoblasts. The tissue is first frozen and then ground with sand at 5° C. and the chromatin threads afterwards are separated by differential centrifugation. The final product consists of Feulgen-positive threads, either single or paired 0·5–1·0μ in diameter. As to the nature of these threads, the authors' view may be quoted: 'Their typical arrangement in pairs with similarities in width and beading suggest that these threads may correspond to the chromosome strands as they occur in the nucleus during the resting stage.' It is clear from the authors' illustration that the interphase leucaemic nuclei are very markedly of the 'thread type', as SERRA[225] terms such nuclei with much residual chromatin. However, CLAUDE and POTTER state further that, 'similar material has been obtained from normal tissues, for example guinea pig or rat liver'.

The claims of MIRSKY *et alii* are more outspoken. Their material is isolated by means of the Waring blender from fish and bird erythrocytes and from mammalian tissues (POLLISTER and MIRSKY[226]); and again we may quote the description of the microscopical appearance of threads prepared by this method (MIRSKY and RIS[227], p 4):

> They vary greatly in size and organization. Usually their doubleness can be clearly seen. They show a specific pattern with trabants, heterochromatic and euchromatic sections. Like chromosomes they can be uncoiled by certain agents, KCN for example. These characteristics by themselves are strong evidence for the chromosome nature of these threads. Final proof, however, lies in the repeated occurrence of the same type of chromosome.

Such a remarkable claim we must attempt to discuss. In the first place, as MIRSKY and RIS[227] point out, their threads differ in form from those of CLAUDE and POTTER, for they are shorter and more coiled than those of the latter authors. The nitrogen and phosphorus content of both types of threads are, however, very similar (MIRSKY and RIS[227]).

If these threads are really chromosomes, they have been formed from an interphase nucleus, which, subjected to violent mechanical stresses, must swiftly have undergone a process corresponding to the comparatively slow evolution of natural prophase. The obvious method of finding whether this is so, is to examine samples of the material at intervals while it is being prepared. Such observations have been made subsequently by LAMB[228] [229] who has repeated the various methods of disintegrating isolated nuclei. He has concluded that the first effect of them all is to draw out the whole nucleus into elongated bodies, which later break up into the smaller threads. These cannot thus be regarded as morphologically equivalent to chromosomes. Nor was LAMB able to confirm the double nature of these threads by electron micrography.

Thus the conclusion seems unavoidable that isolated chromosomes have not yet been artificially prepared from resting nuclei.

REFERENCES

Nucleus of chick and mammalian cells in living tissue cultures

[1] VANDERLYN, L., *Science*, 104 (1946), 514
[2] CHAMBERS, R., and FELL, H. B., *Proc. Roy. Soc. Lond.*, B, 109 (1931), 380

Chromosomes and the deoxynucleoproteins

[3] WHITE, M. J. D., *Animal Cytology and Evolution*, Cambridge, 1945
[4] GRAY, J., *Brit. J. exp. Biol.*, 5 (1927), 102
[5] LEWIS, W. H., and LEWIS, M. R., *General Cytology*, Ed by C. V. Cowdrey, Chicago, 1924
[6] STRANGEWAYS, T. S. P., and CANTI, R. G., *Quart. J. micro. Sci.*, 71 (1927), 1
[7] FLEMMING, W., *Zellsubstanz, Kern, and Zelltheilung*, Leipzig, 1882
[8] LEWIS, M. R., *Johns Hopk. Hosp. Bull.*, 34 (1923), 373
[9] FELL, H. B., and HUGHES, A. F., *Quart. J. micr. Soc.*, 90 (1949), 355
[10] TELLYESNICZKY, K., *Arch. Mikr. Anat.*, 66 (1905), 367
[11] SHINKE, N., *Cytologia*, Fujii Jub., 1 (1939), 449
[12] WIGGANS, R. G., *Amer. J. Bot.*, 8 (1921), 30
[13] WEBER, F., *Protoplasma*, 2 (1927), 305
[14] SERRA, J. A., *Symp. quant. Biol.*, 12 (1947), 192
[15] SHIWAGO, P., *Biol. Zbl.*, 46 (1926), 679
[16] RICHARDS, A., *Biol. Bull.*, 63 (1917), 113
[17] KATER, J. McA., *Z. Zellforsch*, 5 (1927), 263
[18] —, *ibid*, 6 (1928), 587
[19] LEWIS, W. H., *Anat. Rec.*, 97 (1947), 433
[20] RIS, H., and MIRSKY, A. E., *J. gen. Physiol.*, 33 (1949), 125
[21] ARNESEN, K., GOLDSMITH, Y., DULANEY, A. D., *Cancer Res.*, 9 (1949), 609
[22] LUDFORD, R. J., SMILES, J., and WELCH, F. V., *J. roy. micr. Soc.*, 68 (1948), 1
[23] —, and SMILES, J., *ibid*, 70 (1950), 186
[24] RIS, H., and MIRSKY, A. E., *J. gen. Physiol.*, 33 (1949), 489
[25] BROWN, G. L., CALLAN, H. G., and LEAF, G., *Nature, Lond.*, 165 (1950), 600
[26] VENDRELY, R., and VENDRELY, C., *Experentia*, 4 (1948), 434
[27] DAVIDSON, J. N., and McINDOE, W. M., *Biochem. J.*, 45 (1949), Proc. XVI
[28] DOUNCE, A. L., TISHKOFF, G. H., BARNETT, S. R., and FREER, R. M., *J. gen. Physiol.*, 33 (1950), 629
[29] BOIVIN, A., VENDRELY, R., and VENDRELY, C., *C. R. Acad. Sci.*, Paris, 226 (1948), 1061
[30] MIRSKY, A. E., and RIS, H., *Nature, Lond.*, 163 (1949), 666
[30a] —, —, *J. gen. Physiol.*, 34 (1951), 451
[31] ZITTLE, C. A., and O'DELL, R. A., *J. biol. Chem.*, 140 (1941), 899

[32] KURNICK, N. B., *Exp. Cell Res.*, 1 (1950), 151
[33] SCHRADER, F., and LEUCHTENBERGER, C., *Proc. Nat. Acad. Sci.*, 35 (1949), 464
[34] SCHMIDT, G., HECHT, L., and THANNHAUSER, S. J., *J. gen. Physiol.*, 31 (1948), 203
[35] VENDRELY, R., and VENDRELY, C., *C.R. Soc. Biol.*, 143 (1949), 1386
[35a] LISON, L., and PASTEELS, J., *Arch. Biol.*, 62 (1951), 1
[36] POLLISTER, A. W., and RIS, H., *Symp. quant. Biol.*, 12 (1947), 147
[37] LEUCHTENBERGER, C., *Chromosoma*, 3 (1950), 449
[38] DI STEFANO, H. S., *ibid*, 3 (1948), 282
[39] PASTEELS, J., and LISON, L., *Nature, Lond.*, 167 (1951), 948
[40] RIS, H., and MIRSKY, A. E., *J. gen. Physiol.*, 33 (1949), 125
[41] SWIFT, H. H., *Physiol. Zool.*, 23 (1950), 169
[42] KURNICK, N. B., *J. gen. Physiol.*, 33 (1950), 243
[43] —, and MIRSKY, A. E., *ibid*, 33 (1950), 265
[44] POLLISTER, A. W., and LEUCHTENBERGER, C., *Proc. Nat. Acad. Sci.*, 35 (1949), 111
[45] SCHNEIDER, W. C., and HOGEBOOM, G. H., *Cancer Research*, 11 (1951), 1
[46] OGUR, M., ERICKSON, R. O., ROSEN, G. U., SAX, K. B., HOLDEN, C., *Exp. Cell Res.*, 2 (1951), 73
[47] PRICE, J. M., and LAIRD, A. K., *Cancer Res.*, 10 (1950), 650
[48] BRACHET, J., *Arch. Biol.*, 44 (1933), 519
[49] VILLEE, C., LOWENS, M., GORDON, M., LEONARD, E., and RICH, A., *J. Cell Comp. Physiol.*, 33 (1949), 93
[50] MAZIA, D., *Growth* Suppl. 13 (1949), 5
[51] ALFERT, M., *J. Cell Comp. Physiol*, 36 (1950), 381
[52] DAVIDSON, J. N., and LESLIE, I., *Nature, Lond.*, 165 (1950), 49

Nucleoli

[53] LUDFORD, R. J., *J. roy. micr. Soc.* (1922), 113
[54] BRACHET, J., *Arch. Biol.*, 53 (1942), 207
[55] FONTANA, F., *Traité sur le venin de la vipere* Florence, 1781
[56] BAKER, J., *Quart. J. Micr. Sci.*, 90 (1949), 87
[57] MONTGOMERY, T. H., *J. Morphol.*, 15 (1899), 265
[58] WALKER, C. D. and TOZER, F. M., *Quart. J. exp. Physiol.*, 2 (1909), 187
[59] GATES, R. R., *Cytologia* Fujii. Jub. Vol. (1939), 977
[60] —, *Bot. Rev.*, 8 (1942), 337
[61] OGATA, M., *Arch. Anat. Physiol.* (Physiol. Abt.) (1883), 405
[62] WERMEL, E., *Z. Zellforsch*, 5 (1927), 400
[63] BAUER, H., *ibid*, 18 (1933), 254
[64] DAVIDSON, J. N., *Symp. quant. Biol.*, 12 (1947), 50
[65] — and WAYMOUTH, C., *J. Physiol.*, 105 (1946), 191
[66] GERSCH, I. and BODIAN, D., *J. Cell Comp. Physiol.*, 21 (1943), 253
[67] DAVIDSON, J. N., LESLIE, I., and WHITE, J. C., *J. Path. Bact.*, 60 (1948), 1
[68] WILSON, E. B., *The Cell in Development and Heredity*, 3rd Ed., New York, 1925
[69] CASPERSSON, T., *Naturwiss.*, 29 (1941), 33
[70] HYDÉN, H., *Acta physiol Scand.*, 6 (1943), Suppl. 17
[71] HOGBEN, L., *Proc. roy. Soc.* B., 91 (1920), 305
[72] SCHREINER, K. E., *Arch. Mikr. Anat.*, 89 (1916), 79
[73] BRADFIELD, J. R. G., *Exp. Cell. Res.* Suppl., 1 (1949), 338
[74] BALBIANI, E. G., *C.R. Soc. Biol.*, Sect. 4, 1 (1864), 64
[75] BÖHM, A., *Arch. f. mikr. anat.*, 32 (1888), 613
[76] LEWIS, W. H., *Amer. J. Anat.*, 30 (1922), 39
[77] LUDFORD, R. J., *Proc. roy. Soc.* B., 98 (1925), 457
[78] STRANGEWAYS, T. S. P., *ibid*, 94 (1923), 137
[79] LEWIS, W. H., *Cancer. Res.*, 3 (1943), 531
[80] LASNITZKI, I. and WILKINSON, J. H., *Brit. J. Cancer*, 2 (1948), 369
[81] ZOLLINGER, H. U., *Mikroskopie*, 3 (1948), 1
[82] HUGHES, A. F., *Exp. Cell Res. (In press)*, (1951)
[83] HYGÉN, G., *Berg. Mus. Arb. Naturvid.* (1941), 1
[84] EHRENBURG, L., *Hereditas*, 32 (1946), 407

[85] DURYEE, W. R., *Ann. N.Y. Acad. Sci.*, 50 (1950), 920
[86] BUNGENBERG DE JONG, H. G. and KRUYT, H. R., *Proc. Ned. Akad. Wetensch. Amster.*, 32 (1929), 849
[87] DERVICHIAN, D. G., *Research*, 2 (1949), 210
[88] GERSCH, M., *Z. Zellforsch.*, 30 (1940), 483
[89] DARLINGTON, C. D., *Recent Advances in Cytology* 2nd ed., Lond. 1937
[90] DEARING, W. H., *J. Morphol.*, 56 (1934), 157
[91] KAUFMANN, B. P., *Z. Zellforsch.*, 28 (1938), 1
[92] CHEN, T. T., *Proc. Nat. Acad. Sci.*, 22 (1936), 602
[93] FANKHAUSER, G. and HUMPHREY, R. R., *ibid*, 29 (1943), 344
[94] BEATTY, R. A., *Nature, Lond.*, 163 (1949), 644
[95] KAWAGUCHI, E., *Cytologia*, 9 (1938), 88
[96] SCHULTZ, J. and LAWRENCE, P., *J. Hered.*, 40 (1949), 31
[97] ANDREASSI, G., *Ric. Morfol.*, 19 (1942), 141
[98] BIESELE, J. J., *Cancer Res.*, 4 (1944), 232
[99] —, *ibid*, 4 (1944), 737
[100] LEWIS, W. H., *Bull. Johns Hopk. Hosp.*, 66 (1940), 60
[101] FELL, H. B. and HUGHES, A. F., *Quart. J. micr. Sci.*, 90 (1949), 355
[102] BIESELE, J. J., POYNER, H. and PAINTER, T. S., *Univ. Texas Publ.* 4243 (1942)

Heteropycnosis

[103] HENKING, H., *Z. wiss Zool.*, 51 (1891), 685
[104] McCLUNG, C. E., *Biol. Bull.*, 3 (1902), 43
[105] MONTGOMERY, T. H., *ibid*, 6 (1904), 137
[106] GUTHERZ, S., *Arch. mikr. Anat.*, 69 (1907), 491
[107] HEITZ, E., *Jb. wiss. Bot.*, 69 (1928), 762
[108] BACCARINI, J., *Nuovo Giorn. Bot. Ital.*, N.S., 15 (1908), 189
[109] ROSEN, F., *Beitr. Biol. Pflanzen.*, 5 (1892), 443
[110] WHITE, M. J. D., *J. Genet.*, 40 (1940), 67
[110a] — *Proc. Roy. Soc.* B, 124 (1937) 183
[111] DARLINGTON, C. D. and LA COUR, L. F., *J. Genet.*, 40 (1940), 185
[112] CALLAN, H. G., *Proc. roy. Soc.* B., 130 (1942), 324
[113] SAEZ, F. A., ROJAS, P. and DE ROBERTIS, E., *Z. Zellforsch.*, 24 (1936), 727
[114] SCHULTZ, H., *Symp. quant. Biol.*, 12 (1947), 179
[114a] PAINTER, T. S., *J. Hered.*, 25 (1934) 465
[115] LOVELESS, A. and REVELL, S., *Nature Lond.*, 164 (1949), 938
[116] CASPERSSON, T., *Naturwiss.*, 29 (1941), 33
[117] HYDÉN, H., *Acta physiol. Scand.*, 6 (1943), Suppl. 17
[118] CASPERSSON, T. and SCHULTZ, J., *Nature, Lond.*, 142 (1938), 294
[119] SCHULTZ, J., CASPERSSON, T. and AQUILONIUS, L., *Proc. Nat. Acad. Sci.*, 26 (1940), 515
[120] RESENDE, F., *Planta*, 29 (1939), 306
[121] HEITZ, E., *ibid*, 12 (1931), 775
[122] BAKER, J. R. and CALLAN, H. G., *Nature, Lond.*, 166 (1950), 227

Proteins of the nucleus

[123] MIESCHER, F., *Ber. dtscher. chem. Ges.*, 7 (1874), 376
[124] KOSSEL, A., *Z. physiol. chem.*, 8 (1884), 511
[125] SERRA, J. A., *Naturwiss.*, 32 (1944), 46
[126] —, *Symp. quant. Biol.*, 12 (1947), 192
[127] STEDMAN, E. and STEDMAN, E., *Nature, Lond.*, 166 (1950), 780
[128] — —, *ibid*, 152 (1943), 267
[129] MIRSKY, A. E. and POLLISTER, A. W., *J. gen. Physiol.*, 30 (1946), 117
[130] — and RIS, H., *J. gen. Physiol.*, 31 (1947), 1 and 7
[131] BROWN, G. L., CALLAN, H. G. and LEAF, G., *Nature, Lond.*, 165 (1950), 601
[132] POLLISTER, A. W. and LEUCHTENBERGER, C., *Proc. Nat. Acad. Sci.*, 35 (1949), 66

[133] DOUNCE, A. L., *J. biol. Chem.*, 147 (1943), 685
[134] RICHTER, D. and HULTIN, R. P., *Abstr. Biochem. Congr. Camb.*, 1949
[135] DOUNCE, A. L., *Ann. N.Y. Acad. Sci.*, 50 (1950), 982
[136] GOMORI, G., *Proc. Soc. exp. Biol. Med.*, 42 (1939), 23
[137] —, *Arch. Path.*, 32 (1941), 189
[138] DANIELLI, J. F., *J. exp. Biol.*, 22 (1946), 110
[139] JACOBY, F. and MARTIN, B. F., *Nature, Lond.*, 163 (1949), 875
[140] WOLF, A., KABAT, E. A. and NEWMAN, W., *Amer. J. Path.*, 19 (1943), 423
[141] WILLMER, E. N., *J. exp. Biol.*, 19 (1942), 11
[142] CHÈVREMONT, M. and FIRKET, H., *Arch. Biol.*, 60 (1949), 441
[143] DANIELLI, J. F. and CATCHESIDE, D. G., *Nature, Lond.*, 156 (1945), 294
[144] KRUGELIS, E. J., *Genetics*, 30 (1945), 12
[145] —, *Biol. Bull.*, 90 (1946), 220
[146] —, *J. Cell. Comp. Physiol.*, 19 (1942), 376
[147] MOOG, F., *Biol. Rev.*, 21 (1946), 41
[148] CLOETENS, R., *Enzymologia*, 6 (1941), 46
[149] HEATH, J. C., *Nature, Lond.*, 164 (1949), 1055
[150] DOUNCE, A. L. and BEYER, G. T., *J. biol. Chem.*, 174 (1948), 859
[151] —, TISHKOFF, G. H., BARNETT, S. R. and FREER, R. M., *J. gen. Physiol.*, 33 (1950), 629

Lipoids of the nucleus

[152] STONEBERG, C. A., *J. biol. Chem.*, 129 (1939), 189
[153] BAVAUM, G. P., NASH, C. W., JENNINGS, E., NYGAARD, O. and VERMUND, H., *Arch. Biochem.*, 25 (1950), 376
[154] WILLIAMS, H. H., KAUCHER, H. M., RICHARDS, A. J., MAYER, E. Z. and SHARPLES, G. R., *J. biol. Chem.*, 160 (1945), 227
[155] COHEN, I., *Biol. Bull.*, 97 (1949), 236
[156] LISON, L., *Histochimie animal*, Paris, 1936
[157] GATES, R. R., *Biol. Bull.*, 81 (1941), 298
[158] SHINKE, N. and SHIGENAGA, M., *Cytologia*, 4 (1933), 189
[159] MENSINKAI, S. W., *Ann. Bot.*, 3 (1939), 763
[160] CLAUDE, A., *Adv. Prot. Chem.*, 5 (1949), 423

Nuclear membrane

[161] PISCHINGER, A., *Z. Zellforsch.*, 26 (1937), 249
[162] BUNGENBERG DE JONG, H. G., *La coacervation et son importance en biologie*, Paris, 1936
[163] CHAMBERS, R. and FELL, M. B., *Proc. roy. Soc. B.*, 109 (1931), 380
[164] DAHLGREN, U., *Publ. Carn. Inst. Wash.*, 212 (1915), 213
[165] CHURNEY, and KLEIN, H. M., *Biol. Bull.*, 72 (1937), 384
[166] —, *Cytology, Genetics, Evolution* (Univ. Pennsylvania Bicent. Conf.), Philadelphia, 1942
[167] SCOTT, G. H., *Bull. d'Histol. appliq.*, 7 (1930), 251
[168] BUREAU, V., *Arch. int. Physiol.*, 39 (1934), 311
[169] LUYET, B. J. and ERNST, R. A., *Proc. Soc. exp. Biol. Med.*, 31 (1934), 1225
[170] BAUD, C. A., *Exp. Cell Res.*, Suppl., 1 (1949), 47
[171] CALLAN, H. G., *ibid*, Suppl., 1 (1949), 48
[172] — and TOMLIN, S. G., *Proc. roy. Soc. B.*, 137 (1950), 367
[173] ABELSON, P. H. and DURYEE, W. R., *Anat. Rec.*, 101 (1948), 653
[174] HAMBURGER, H. J., *Osmotischer Druck und Ionenlehre in den medicinischen Wissenschaften* Bd 3, Wiesbaden, 1904
[175] BECK, L. V. and SHAPIRO, H., *Proc. Soc. exp. Biol. Med.*, 34 (1936), 170
[175a] CHAMBERS, R., and POLLACK, H., *J. Gen. Physiol.*, 10 (1927), 739
[176] ZOLLINGER, H. U., *Mikroskopie*, 3 (1948), 1
[177] MONNÉ, L., *Proc. Soc. exp. Biol. Med.*, 32 (1935), 1197

Size of interphase nucleus and of the chromosomes

[178] HERTWIG, R., *Biol. Zbl.*, 23 (1903), 49 and 108
[179] WILSON, E. B., *The cell in development and heredity*, 3rd ed., New York, 1925
[180] BOVERI, TH., *Jena. Z. Naturw*, 39 (1905), 445
[181] HERTWIG, O. and HERTWIG, R., *ibid*, 20 (1887), 120
[182] HARVEY, E. B., *Biol. Bull.*, 62 (1932), 155
[183] FANKHAUSER, G., *Quart. Rev. Biol.*, 20 (1945), 20
[184] HERTWIG, G. and HERTWIG, P., *Arch. mikr. anat.*, 94 (1920), 34
[185] FANKHAUSER, G. and HUMPHREY, R. R., *Proc. Nat. Acad. Sci.*, 29 (1943), 344
[186] ARTOM, C., *Arch. Zellforsch.*, 9 (1912), 87
[187] —, *R. C. Accad. Lincei.*, 32 (1923), 505
[188] —, *C. R. Soc. Biol.*, 99 (1928), 29
[189] BARIGOZZI, C., *Proc. 7th Int. Cong. Genet. J. Genet. Suppl.*, 1941, 57
[190] WHITE, M. J. D., *Animal Cytology and Evolution*, Cambridge, 1945
[191] BOWEN, R. H., *Proc. Amer. Acad. Arts Sci.*, 57 (1922), 388
[192] SCHRADER, F., *Chromosoma*, 3 (1947), 22
[192a] —, LEUCHTENBERGER, C., *Exp. Cell. Res.*, 1 (1950), 421
[193] BEATTY, R. A. and FISCHBERG, M., *Nature, Lond.*, 166 (1950), 238
[194] CONKLIN, E. G., *J. exp. Zool.*, 12 (1912), 1
[195] FELL, H. B. and HUGHES, A. F., *Quart. J. micr. Sci.*, 90 (1949), 355
[196] JACOBJ, W., *Arch. EntwMech.*, 106 (1925), 124
[197] —, *Z. mikr. anat. Forsch.* 38 (1935), 161
[198] HARDING, J. P., *J. Mar. Biol. Ass.*, 28 (1948), 141
[199] BEAMS, H. W. and KING, R. L., *Anat. Rec.*, 83 (1942), 281
[200] HEIBERG, K. A., *Anat. Anz.*, 31 (1907), 306
[201] VOSS, H., *Z. Zellforsch.*, 7 (1928), 187
[202] MÜLLER, H. G., *Z. mikr. anat. Forsch*, 41 (1937), 249
[203] WERMEL, E. M. and SCHERSCHULSKAJA, L. W., *Z. Zellforsch*, 20 (1934), 54
[204] LEWIS, W. H., *Anat. Rec.*, 100 (1948), 247
[205] WERMEL, E. M. and PORTUGALOW, W. W., *Z. Zellforsch*, 22 (1935), 185
[206] SCHREIBER, G., *Biol. Bull.*, 97 (1949), 187
[207] HERTWIG, G., *Anat. Anz.*, 87 (1938), 65
[208] BERGER, C. A., *Amer. Nat.*, 71 (1937), 187
[209] SULKIN, N. M., *Anat. Rec.*, 84 (1942), 503
[210] BIESELE, J. J., *Cancer Res.*, 4 (1944), 232
[211] HERTWIG, G., *Z. indukt. Abstamm.-u. Vererb Lehr.*, 70 (1935), 496
[212] BALBIANI, E. G., *Zool. Anz.*, 4 (1881), 637
[213] BOGOJAWLENSKY, K. S., *Z. Zellforsch.*, 22 (1934), 47
[214] PAINTER, T. S. and REINDORP, E. C., *Chromosoma*, 1 (1939), 276
[215] BIESELE, J. J., *Cancer Res.*, 3 (1943), 411
[216] —, POYNER, H. and PAINTER, T. S., *Univ. Texas Publ.* 4243 (1942)
[217] — —, *Cancer Res.*, 3 (1943), 779
[218] HERTWIG, G., *Z. mikr. anat. Forsch.*, 45 (1939), 37
[219] ERDMANN, R., *Arch. Zellforsch.*, 2 (1908), 76
[220] GODLEWSKI, E., *Arch. Entw.Mech.*, 26 (1908), 278
[221] ALFERT, M., *J. Cell Comp. Physiol.*, 36 (1950), 381
[222] BIESELE, J. J., *J. Gerontol.*, 1 (1946), 433

Isolation of chromatin threads from resting nuclei

[223] CLAUDE, A., *Trans N.Y. Acad. Sci.*, 4 (1942), 79
[224] — and POTTER, T. S., *J. exp. Med.*, 77 (1943), 345
[225] SERRA, J. A., *Symp. quart. Biol.*, 12 (1947), 192
[226] POLLISTER, A. W. and MIRSKY, A. E., *Genetics*, 28 (1943), 86
[227] MIRSKY, A. E. and RIS, H., *J. gen. Physiol.*, 31 (1947), 1, 7
[228] LAMB, W. G. P., *Nature, Lond.*, 164 (1949), 109
[229] —, *Exp. Cell Res.*, 1 (1950), 571

4

CELLS IN DIVISION

PROPHASE AND TELOPHASE IN THE LIVING NUCLEUS

In the succeeding pages, observations on the nuclear cycle in a number of living cells in mitosis will be described. The use of living material for such studies has a history of some interest. In 1879 three papers were published on the course of division in the living cells; FLEMMING[1] and SCHLEICHER[2] observed cells of larval Amphibia, and independently published their results in the same volume of one journal; while STRASBURGER[3] described a method of observing the living cells of the staminal hairs of *Tradescantia*; and a series of drawings of these cells in division appeared in the following year in a new edition of his *Zellbildung und Zelltheilung*.[4] These studies clearly established that the normal method of nuclear multiplication both in plants and animals consists of a series of complex events in which two new nuclei are formed from one. FLEMMING's description was the most detailed; he showed that the later stages of the process are the reverse of the early ones. The decisive effect of these discoveries is well illustrated by a remark of NORDENSKIOLD's[5] in comparing the first and third editions of STRASBURGER's book:

> Even in the first edition (1875), Strasburger makes the nucleus of the egg-cell in the plants he investigated dissolve upon fertilization and its mass disperse into the plasm of the cell; in the latter are then formed a number of concretions, which give rise to fresh nuclei. In the third edition, on the other hand, it is asserted that examples of independent cell formation can no longer be cited from the vegetable kingdom; fresh nuclei invariably arise through the division of older ones.

In the following decades, studies on living material played a decreasing part in the growth of further knowledge of the cell. Advances in microscopical technique, both in methods of staining and in the optics of the instrument were relevant only to the study of fixed preparations. Furthermore, the discovery of SUTTON[6] that in the reduction division of the germ cells there were events which corresponded to MENDEL's segregation and free assortment of the hereditary characters led to researches on cellular anatomy which demanded the utmost resolution of which the microscope was capable; this development necessarily enhanced the tendency of cytologists to work exclusively with stained material. There were still occasional researches on living cells, but they did not directly relate to the dominant concern with the microscopy of inheritance.

However, interest in the study of the living cell revived, notably in the nineteen-twenties when workers such as STRANGEWAYS and BĚLAŘ showed that living preparations could still yield fresh information about the behaviour of cells in division. BĚLAŘ's study of the classical staminal hair cell of *Tradescantia* (BĚLAŘ[7]) led to a series of further investigations on the same material by the Japanese school of cytologists, for with such refractile cells, the bright-field microscope is adequate, as BĚLAŘ's superb photomicrographs clearly demonstrate (Plate V). In the study of the extremely thin cells in the outgrowth of living tissue cultures, its limitations in contrast and resolution of unstained objects are more severe, though by no means prohibitive, as is clearly shown by the researches of the LEWISES (e.g. LEWIS (W. H.)[8 9]).

It is now well known that thanks to the phase-contrast principle of ZERNICKE these particular difficulties in microscopy are largely overcome, and that the resolution of thin transparent objects can be equal to, or even superior to that of stained preparations (ZERNICKE,[10] TAYLOR,[11] RICHARDS,[12] HUGHES[13]). Phase-contrast microscopy can be very appropriately combined with serial photographic recording on cinematograph film. Cells in division were first followed by serial photography as far back as 1913 by COMANDON and JOLLY; in the nineteen-twenties, CANTI[14] began his well known series of films on tissue cultures. The first phase-contrast film was made in the early nineteen-forties by MICHEL[15] on the meiotic divisions of an Orthopteran spermatocyte. MICHEL's demonstration of the possibilities of phase microscopy has led to a remarkable impetus in the study of the living preparations of biological material. Studies on mitosis in tissue cultures, both under normal and experimental conditions have been subsequently made by HUGHES[16 17] and on malignant cells by GEY.

The limiting factors in the wider investigation of further types of living cell in division are both optical and biological. Some cells seem to be so nearly optically homogeneous that isotropic retardation methods such as phase contrast are inapplicable. For the rest, in which structural details can be seen in life, suitable methods of cultivation are needed to permit observations of healthy cells over a sufficient period of time. By some means, a thin and preferably single layer of cells must be prepared under conditions in which their normal activity will be fully maintained. The tissue culture method is almost ideal for material which can be grown in this way, provided that a rapid rate of cell division can be maintained in the cultures; at present, this applies only to a number of vertebrate tissues. The use of liquid paraffin for mounting living material is surprisingly successful for *Tradescantia* staminal hairs, and probably would be for other plant tissues. According to TELEZÝNSKI[18] oxygen dissolves more readily in paraffin than in water. It was used by MICHEL for the spermatocytes of *Psophus*, but seems less effective for those of other Orthoptera. Further exploration of possible methods for the cultivation of rapidly growing tissues might well prove to be rewarding; a technique generally applicable to the Insecta would be of great value. A general account of the earlier studies on mitosis in living cells of both animals and plants is given by MARTENS.[19] BECKER[20] has reviewed the later work on plant material.

Mitosis in the living plant cell

Probably no cells have been so extensively studied in the living state as those of the staminal hairs of *Tradescantia*. BROWN's[21] vivid description of protoplasmic streaming and of the texture of the nucleus should be familiar to every student of cell biology. The course of mitosis in these cells has been described by SCHAEDE,[22] BĚLAŘ[7] (Plate V), TELEZYŃSKI[18] and by KUWADA and NAKAMURA[24] amongst others, though as mentioned above, the earliest descriptions go back to STRASBURGER.[4] BĚLAŘ mounted the staminal hairs in hanging drops of 1–3 per cent solutions of cane sugar; but later authors used liquid paraffin as a mounting medium. So successful is this method, that KUWADA and NAKAMURA found that cells in their preparations would remain healthy with no trace of abnormality for as long as seven days.

The interphase nucleus, in addition to the nucleoli, is uniformly filled with what appear to be fine granules, which are really the gyres of the irregularly disposed coiled chromonemata (KUWADA and NAKAMURA[24]). In early prophase the appearance of the nucleus is quite distinct, for the chromonemata become regularly arranged as a series of parallel spirals. Around each spiral is the matrix of the chromosome. There are no spaces between the chromosomes in early prophase; BĚLAŘ states that they are so closely packed that their cross-section is polygonal and that the nucleoli are indented. During prophase, the chromosomes pass through an optimal point at which their spiral condition is most clearly evident. This stage of 'spiral prophase' is equally recognizable in fixed material, and according to NEBEL[25] two pairs of chromonemata can then be seen within each chromosome. As the spiral condition of the chromosomes becomes less clear in the living stage, they shrink to some extent, and spaces appear between them. According to KUWADA and NAKAMURA[24] the chromonemata are then swollen and the refractive index of the whole chromosome has increased. An interpretation of the arrangement and structure of the chromosome spirals at each stage is given by KUWADA.[26]

The spaces between the chromosomes becomes most evident at opposite ends of the nucleus; these are known as 'pole caps' and here the orientation of the spindle must originate.* At one of them, all the centromeres

* The development of the spindle in cells of plant meristems has been studied by ROBYNS. In *Hyacinthus*, two unequal 'calottes polaires' are formed in prophase within the nuclear membrane. The orientation of the chromosomes is at first transverse to the axis of the nucleus.

are grouped round the 'pole field', with the arms of the chromosomes hanging parallel downwards. This arrangement corresponds to that of the chromosomes during the late anaphase of the previous division, and demonstrates the morphological continuity of the chromosomes between one division and the next.* This must mean that the chromosomes remain immobile during this whole period, although there seems to be some disarrangement of the chromonemata.

The duration of prophase is four hours or more. There is no abrupt transition to metaphase; the pole caps enlarge, the nuclear membrane disappears and the chromosomes contract still further. BĚLAŘ was not able to follow the dissolution of the nucleoli. At 20° C. the interval between late prophase and late anaphase is about one and a half hours. The changes undergone by the chromosomes in telophase are apparently the reverse of those seen in prophase; for gradually their spiral condition becomes clearly evident, and is later obscured once again as the nucleus assumes the interphase condition. The chromosomes shrink as they approach their 'spiral telophase' stage; afterwards the chromonemata loosen out and approach each other. Their parallel arrangement may persist for the first hour or more of interphase, and the nucleoli do not reappear until after the wall has been formed between the daughter cells.

Mitosis in living cells in other plant tissues was studied by MARTENS.[19] His technique was to cut thin free-hand sections of developing organs and to mount them in isotonic saccharose ('Beaucoup de prudence et de promptitude sont nécessaires'); observation of a single preparation was limited to a maximum of 75 minutes. MARTENS compared the appearance of the living cell at each stage of division with that of the same cell on fixation, but he did not make parallel observations with stained preparations. The material which MARTENS used for these studies was the developing stigma of the grass *Arrhenatherum* and the embryo of the orchid *Listera* (the Twayblade), in both of which the nuclei differ in several respects from those of *Tradescantia*. In interphase, their structure is reticular, and does not greatly alter in appearance during early prophase. The meshes of the network are gradually resolved into spiral threads which become the chromosomes; for a long time they are linked by delicate filaments. In mid-prophase, the volume of the nucleus increases; both the nucleoli and the anastomoses between the chromosomes then stand out more clearly, while the spirals of the chromosomes become gradually less visible.

In *Arrhenatherum*, there are comparatively swift changes at the end of prophase. The cross-filaments between the chromosomes disappear, and within twelve minutes or less, they begin to move into a parallel

* RABL[27] first drew attention to such residual orientations of prophase in Amphibian cells in 1885.

arrangement, which at first lies transversely across the cell; then slowly this orientation shifts to become parallel with the main axis. This change is apparently a re-orientation of the chromosomes and is not a simple rotation of the whole nucleus. At this stage the nuclear membrane disappears. In the telophase of *Arrhenatherum*, the chromosomes maintain their individuality for some time after cytokinesis; the spaces between them widen, as the area occupied by the whole daughter group increases. Then anastomoses between the chromosomes appear once more ten to fifteen minutes after anaphase movement has ceased; they increase in number as the daughter nucleus continues to enlarge. These changes influence the form of the chromosomes; their general orientation is maintained, but they become less regular and more sinuous in their course. At the same time, they become thinner as their charge of chromatin is gradually lost.

The interphase nucleus of *Tradescantia* is not reticular in structure, nor, to judge from BĚLAŘ's photographs, does the daughter nucleus increase much in size during telophase, though it has been shown by SHIGENAGA[28] that the absorption of water plays an essential role in nuclear reconstruction, for the whole process can be inhibited by hypertonic sucrose. Telophase is resumed if the cell is then transferred to a hypotonic medium. A further difference between the course of cell division in *Tradescantia* and in *Arrhenatherum* is that the arrangement of the chromosomes remains almost unchanged in the former during the whole mitotic cycle, while in the latter they orientate rapidly at the end of prophase, and disperse again to some extent in telophase. Again this difference may be related to the apparently greater absorption of water in the telophase nucleus of *Arrhenatherum*. It would be of interest to see whether evidence from other material could warrant generalizations of this kind. This subject is further discussed later in this chapter (p 80).

A plant which offers considerable scope for the study of living cells in division is the Alga *Chara* (the Stonewort), PEKAREK[29] [30] has described the development of rhizoids from nodes of the plant cultivated *in vitro*, and the course of mitosis in the terminal cell of which the nucleus may be as much as 50μ in length. The nucleolus and nuclear membrane disappear early in prophase, but the chromosomes are not recognizable until metaphase. Nuclear reconstruction begins as soon as the anaphase movement is completed, but the development of the nucleoli and the growth of the daughter nucleus occupies several hours. The antheridial filaments of *Chara* are composed of much smaller cells, which all undergo mitosis simultaneously (KARLING[31]), the course of which in life has yet to be described.

In general, it seems that cells undergoing meiosis are more intolerant of experimental conditions than are those in somatic mitosis, though the greater duration of reduction divisions may be partly responsible for these differences. The living pollen mother cell has been studied by several workers, though the complete meiotic cycle has yet to be followed in a single preparation of isolated cells. GREGORY[32] attempted to cultivate excised anthers of several species in a nutrient solution; and found that the early phases of meiosis never progressed in his material, but that in *Lilium* anthers, pollen mother cells at diplotene would continue the cycle to the formation of quartettes. STERN[33] found that those of *Trillium* cultivated in sucrose lost their cell walls and fused together. In *Tradescantia*, meiosis proceeded comparatively rapidly, and SHIMAKURA[34] was able to observe and photograph the remaining stages in pollen mother cells mounted at metaphase during the subsequent eight hours or so. Successful cultivation of excised whole anthers has recently been achieved by TAYLOR.[35]

The haploid mitosis within the pollen tube has not yet been followed in the living state, although the necessary technique for the artificial germination of the pollen grain is available (DARLINGTON and LA COUR[36]).

Protozoa—In BĚLAŘ's[37] great monograph on the Protozoan nucleus his Table I lists investigations on living Protozoa in mitosis from which it can be seen that several such studies date from the nineteenth century. Of these, the most complete was that of HERTWIG,[38] who in 1884 followed nuclear division in *Actinosphaerium*. Before turning his attention to the Metazoan cell in division, BĚLAŘ himself studied the mitosis of several Protozoa in both living and fixed individuals and published papers on *Chilomastix* and *Bodo* (BĚLAŘ[39]) and on *Actinophrys* (BĚLAŘ[40]). In the latter paper the drawings of the living nucleus during mitosis are particularly fine.

Among the Amoebidae, little is seen of the nucleus during fission in either *Amoeba proteus* (CHALKLEY and DANIEL;[41] DAWSON *et alii*[42]) or *A. dubia* (DAWSON *et alii*[43]), but COMANDON and DE FONBRUNE[44] have found that in a large *Acanthamoeba* the nuclear detail is exquisitely visible throughout fission. Their paper contains no illustrations, however, and is limited to a description of the admirable film which they have made of mitosis in this organism. These authors have generously provided a series of still photographs from their film for reproduction in this book and these are to be found in Plate VI.

The resting nucleus of *Acanthamoeba* is circular, with a diameter of 10μ; a central nucleolus occupies two-thirds of the volume of the whole nucleus. Close to the nuclear membrane on one side is a centrosomal body from which a number of definite rays originate, in such a manner that COMANDON and DE FONBRUNE describe it as a 'figure en arraignée'. A full hour before mitosis is due to begin, an individual which will divide can be recognized because there is now a 'figure en arraignée' at either end of the nucleus, which has become elliptical. As prophase

75

begins, numerous fine granulations appear within the nucleus, and one minute later the nucleolus disappears; the early occurrence of this event is noteworthy. The intranuclear granulations increase in volume, and migrate to the centre of the nucleus, where they form the chromosomes which become arranged in a regular equatorial plate. The nuclear membrane, as judged from the living *Acanthamoeba* disappears during metaphase.

In telophase, the chromosomes are closely packed against the centrosphere. They become less and less visible; they appear to take up water, and are then lost to sight. Although the observations of these authors on the daughter nuclei are restricted to this single statement, they also describe contemporary events of great interest within the cytoplasm some of which will be mentioned later (p 133).

Grasshopper embryonic neuroblasts—CARLSON and his colleagues have developed a method for the study of the dividing neuroblasts of the embryo of the grasshopper, *Chortophaga vividifasciata*, which is dissected out of the egg membrane and mounted as a hanging drop preparation in a suitable medium, with the ventral side uppermost (CARLSON;[45] CARLSON and HOLLAENDER[46]). These neuroblasts have several features of great interest; at 38° C. they divide about every four hours, and prophase occupies a full half of the whole mitotic cycle. Cell division is unequal, and of the two daughter cells, one is a neuroblast, the other a ganglion cell. The interphase nucleus is ring-shaped (Figure 25).

So far, the only descriptions given of mitosis in this material have been incidental to the experimental studies of these authors; a full and illustrated description of the normal cycle would be of great value. The interphase nucleus contains two nucleoli and is filled elsewhere with highly refractile granules. In early prophase, chromatin threads make their appearance which at first are recognizable only with difficulty; the granules then disappear, and the threads become more distinct. At mid-prophase, the chromatin threads are 'thick enough to be traceable from one part of the nucleus to another by careful focussing'. Late prophase is 'initiated as the chromatin threads become sufficiently short and well spaced that about seven can be counted near the nuclear membrane in one quarter of its circumference in mid-optical section'. As soon as the course of the chromosomes can be traced within the nucleus, they are found to be orientated round the nuclear core at the polar side of the cell. At the end of prophase the nucleoli and the nuclear membrane disappear.

The duration of telophase at 38° C. is 57 minutes. Early in this period the chromosomes lose their definite outlines; in mid-telophase the nuclear membrane is formed, and the two nucleoli appear and gradually increase in size. At first they are spherical in form, but later their outline becomes uneven and 'finally they have the appearance of two irregular masses not sharply set off from the surrounding karyolymph'.

Interphase lasts no longer than 27 minutes. In cells with so short a resting period it should readily be possible to determine whether the polarity of chromosomes in prophase is a relic of their previous telophase orientation.

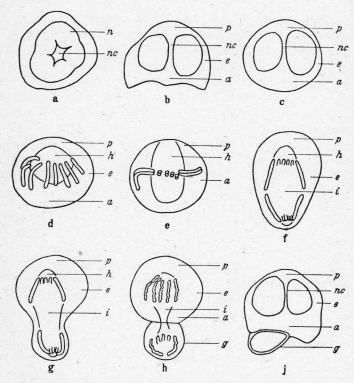

Figure 25 Diagrams of an embryonic neuroblast of *Chortophaga viridifasciata* during mitosis. **a** polar and **b** side view in interphase or prophase **c** prophase, just before breakdown of nuclear membrane, cell rounding up **d** Prometaphase **e** metaphase **f** mid-anaphase **g** late anaphase **h** early telophase **j** late telophase, the cells have lost their spherical form. (*a* and *p*) polar (*e*) equatorial cytoplasm. (*nc*) cytoplasm of nuclear core. (*g*) ganglion cell. (*h*) half spindle. (*i*) interzonal region. (*n*) nucleus. From CARLSON[45] (*By courtesy, Biol. Bull.*).

Vertebrate cells in culture: Amphibia — The original description of JOLLY's[47] method for obtaining dividing erythroblasts free in the blood of the newt was published in 1901. The first paper with COMANDON[48] on the cinematography of such cells in hanging-drop preparations appeared in 1913, but a description of early prophase, based on their final film is not found until the 1934 paper (COMANDON *et alii*[49]). In their short account of early prophase in the newt erythroblast, these authors speak of the great size of the nucleus, which then nearly fills the cell. It is relatively opaque. Slow movements occur in the cytoplasm, and the nucleus rotates, in one instance through a complete turn in six minutes. Some time after this rotation has ceased, the nuclear membrane suddenly disappears. The longitudinal split in the chromosomes is then apparent.

HUGHES and PRESTON[50] described the mitosis of a newt liver fibroblast in tissue culture (Plate VII). Their observations began at a stage when the nucleoli had already disappeared, and the nucleus was filled with granules of comparatively low contrast relative to the nuclear sap. These lay along the developing chromosome threads; gradually the granules seemed to fuse together as more material was deposited on them, and about five minutes after observation had begun, chromosomes of regular form stood out in clear contrast to their surroundings, and in some their split condition could already be seen. So far, the changes were not accompanied by movement within the nucleus, but from this point the chromosomes began to move, and within three minutes were radially orientated round a clear central space, which was occupied by the developing spindle. There was no definite moment of dissolution of the nuclear membrane. The chromosomes soon began to move to a fresh orientation with the metaphase plate at right angles to the plane of the preparation, and the cell then assumed a more rounded form. The chromosomes contracted in length as they reached the spindle poles, and lost their uniform outlines as they bunched together. Anastomoses between them then were formed. These are clearly seen both in the living fibroblasts and erythrocytes, and also in fixed tissues of the larva of *Ambystoma* (DEARING[51]). These cross-filaments are so regularly arranged, that in the erythrocyte COMANDON *et alii*[49] speak of 'la disposition caracteristique en damier que prend le resaux chromatique'. To judge from DEARING's drawings this condition persists in a very fine reticular structure of the interphase nucleus. In the succeeding prophase, these fine filaments are gradually resolved.

Chick and mammalian cells (Plate VIII)—The structure of the interphase nucleus of the mouse has already been described (p. 30). In between the nucleoli and the large heterochromatic granules, the nucleus is evenly filled with the chromonemata (Plate II(4)). In Feulgen preparations of very early prophase these threads are seen to have contracted slightly, leaving empty spaces in between them, the large heterochromatic aggregates have broken down into smaller units, each of which appears to form part of an individual chromosome. This stage can be recognized by phase-contrast in the living nucleus, for the background of the nucleus is then faintly granular. Where one is fortunate enough to follow with the time-lapse camera a cell into prophase, it can be seen that the nucleoli have already begun to change in form when this stage has been reached. Their movement, together with that of the whole nucleus, may continue throughout prophase. The developing chromosomes gradually acquire their slowly increasing contrast which we see both in the living state and in Feulgen preparations. This phase lasts for half an hour or perhaps more, for the process is usually already under way when observation begins. The phase-contrast microscope with its extreme shallowness of focus reveals the fact that the chromosome threads are closely applied to the inner surface of the nuclear membrane; when one focuses into the interior of the nucleus, nucleoli and chromocentres alone come into view.

Here also, the whole nucleus often revolves during prophase, and the nuclear outline may repeatedly change. The end of prophase comes with remarkable suddenness. The nuclear membrane contracts and vanishes; the nucleoli breaks up equally abruptly, and the chromosomes begin to move freely in the cell. Often the chromosomes congregate at either end of the nucleus round the poles of the developing spindle, and thus momentarily give a spurious appearance of anaphase (Plate XII (16b)). It seems that the dissolution of the nuclear membrane and of the nucleoli begins at the same instant. As the nuclear membrane contracts, so do the chromosome threads which line its inner surface. Sometimes the developing poles of the spindle then momentarily indent the shrinking membrane at opposite ends of a diameter (Plate XI (14b)). The spindle quickly joins across the line between the two poles, and sometimes the chromosomes can then be seen moving towards it.

In Feulgen preparations the split in the chromosomes can be seen in mid-prophase, behind the apparently terminal heterochromatic granules. In the living cells, the chromosomes are not seen to be double until they approach metaphase.

In cells of the chick, the general course of prophase is similar. JACOBSON and WEBB[52] have shown that as the nucleoli disappear, the chromosomes then first become able to take up basic dyes, as for instance methylene blue in the May-Grunwald-Giemsa stain. This suggests that the ribonucleoproteins of the nucleoli are rapidly trans-ⅼerred to the chromosomes at the end of prophase. This change precedes the final dissolution of the nucleoli, remains of which can sometimes be seen among the chromosomes in metaphase. Very early in anaphase, the basophilic material begins to leave the chromosomes (Plate XII (17)).

In the mouse, reconstruction of the daughter nuclei from late anaphase onwards proceeds in the following manner. At first the daughter chromosomes are closely packed together in apparent fusion; then the whole mass begins to swell, and as its texture becomes looser, fine

79

threads may be seen within it, much smaller in diameter than the anaphase chromosomes (Plates IX, X(13)). The swelling of individual chromosomes may occasionally be seen in those separated by chance from the main daughter group. At the interface between the cytoplasm and the outer chromosomal vesicles, the nuclear membrane is formed and expands in area, and the daughter nucleus continues to enlarge. The structure of the nucleus at this stage is reticular, and the main chromosome threads which are still Feulgen-positive, may be seen to be double. Nucleoli seem to form wherever there are dense groups of chromonemata and their relationship to individual chromosomes seems here to be obscure from the first (p 42).

At this stage, some thirty minutes after the beginning of anaphase, the general structure of the nucleus consists of a coarse meshwork of thick chromosome threads linking up the nucleoli. Gradually, these threads differentiate into heterochromatic granules and fine chromonemata, and the nucleoli undergo repeated re-arrangements in form and position. The nucleus is still rapidly enlarging, and some three hours after the beginning of anaphase is about two-thirds the size of the mother nucleus in prophase. In full interphase, the structure of the nucleus can no longer be called reticular. Occasional threads can still be seen in the living state, but well-fixed material shows that the whole nucleus is then uniformly filled with fine chromonemata. ALFERT[53] finds that there is no decrease in the relative DNA content of embryonic mouse nuclei from telophase to full interphase. At this time the apparent decrease in the intensity of Feulgen reaction as judged subjectively must be due to dispersal of DNA throughout an increasing nuclear area.*

In the foregoing descriptions of the nuclear changes in mitosis, the swelling of the young daughter nuclei in telophase has been ascribed to the absorption of water. Another explanation of telophase swelling is given by CASPERSSON,[54] mainly with reference to Grasshopper spermatocytes. He claims that the chromosomes in telophase swell by the accumulation of protein within them. 'During the course of the swelling the chromosomes gradually fill the spaces between them, and the rounded cell results.' In prophase the process is reversed and the major part of the nuclear proteins disappears from the nucleus. The marked volume changes of mammalian cells during mitosis are shown by the data of BIESELE et alii[55] here reproduced as Figure 26.

Here clearly is a point of some importance which needs to be decided; it should not be impossible to distinguish between increase of protein and of water in the nuclei during telophase. The X-ray method of ENGSTRÖM[56] for measuring the mass of cell constituents

---

* LISON and PASTEELS[23] maintain that the early post-telophase growth of the nucleus is the period when DNA is synthesized in embryonic and adult rat tissues, in chick cultures, and in Echinoderm larvae.

could probably be used for this purpose. It is unlikely that movement of water is never involved in nuclear reconstruction, for SHIGENAGA[28] has directly observed the inhibition of the process when water was withdrawn from a staminal hair cell of *Tradescantia* by adding a hypertonic medium. It does not seem that an exactly comparable experiment on animal cells in mitosis has ever been done, although several authors have shown that the course of cell division can be gravely disturbed by hypertony. In grasshopper spermatocytes, the spindle is much more sensitive to such treatment than are the chromosomes (BĚLAŘ[57]).

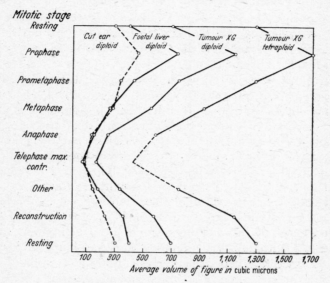

Figure 26 Volume of nuclei and mitotic figures in various mouse tissues. From BIESELE *et alii* (*By courtesy, University of Texas Publications*).[55]

AISENBERG[58] examined the dividing cells in the web of a frog's foot which was immersed in Ringer Solutions of varying osmotic pressure and made counts of each phase of mitosis therein. It does not appear from his figures that the proportion of telophases was increased in hypertonic media. There is no indication in GRAY's[59] careful study of cleavage of the sea-urchin egg in sea water to which various amounts of sodium chloride had been added, that nuclear reconstruction was specially sensitive to this treatment. However, it is possible that in animal cells, the effect of variations in the osmotic pressure of the external medium is not transmitted to the nucleus because of changes in the water content of the cytoplasm at that time, for its behaviour often suggests that water movements are then in progress. In *Acanthamoeba* for instance, COMANDON and DE FONBRUNE[44] have observed that 'un semis de tres fines vésicules' appear in the cytoplasm at telophase; these run together and form the contractile vacuoles of the daughter individuals, which at once begin their pulsations.

TIME SCALE OF THE MITOTIC CYCLE

The methods by which the duration of mitosis may be measured are of several kinds. Clearly the most direct is to use living cells in preparations where they are optically accessible, and to time the events which occur either by continuous observation, or through the medium of photographic recording. The earliest example of direct measurement of the duration of a phase of cell division dates from 1848, when MITSCHERLICH[60] observed that cytokinesis in *Conferva glomerata* (*Cladophora* sp.) took four to five hours to be completed. Other methods are used when it is not possible to observe the living nucleus, because the cells either are not sufficiently transparent or cannot yet be effectively isolated under physiological conditions. If a number of similar cells can be induced to enter mitosis all at the same time, then batches can be fixed at known intervals, and their stages of division can be investigated subsequently by staining methods. This is the method applied to egg cells which can be fertilized experimentally. Some may be caused to resume their development at will. Thus, for example, FAURÉ-FREMIET[61] found that fertilized *Ascaris* eggs remain at the stage with unfused male and female pronuclei until exposed to atmospheric oxygen.

In a tissue where cells are dividing at random, or in an unpredictable manner, indirect and statistical methods of estimation must be used. If it can be assumed that cells are entering mitosis at an approximately even and constant rate, then in a sample of cells fixed at the same instant, the percentages of each stage of mitosis are proportional to the time occupied by each phase of division. If the duration of either of the separate phases can be estimated by another method, then these relative figures may readily be converted into absolute intervals of time. An example of the use of this method is provided by WRIGHT's[62] study of cell division in chick tissue cultures.

Recently, GRAY and SCHOLES[63] have estimated both the mitotic time and the intermitotic period of dividing cells in the bean root by an elegant method which also involves the rate of elongation of cells which do not again divide, beyond the meristem. Only one of each pair of meristematic daughter cells differentiates in this way and so cells enter division and the subsequent period of elongation at the same rate. This quantity can be calculated; and it is equal to the number of dividing cells in the meristem divided by the average time occupied by mitosis. These authors have also computed the percentages of the meristematic cells in three phases of division and in Table III their figures have been converted to the respective proportions of the total duration of mitosis.*

If cells in a tissue do not enter mitosis at a regular and even rate, then proportionate counting of stages cannot be used to estimate their relative duration, unless it can be assumed that the irregularities can be averaged out by taking a large number of samples. If, however, cells

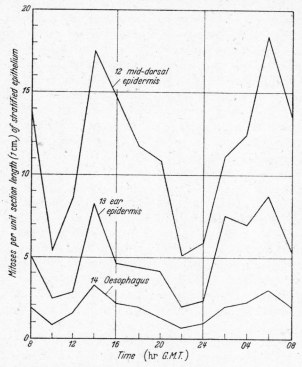

Figure 27 Daily variation in the number of mitoses in three stratified epithelia of the mouse. From BULLOUGH[68] (*By courtesy, Proc. roy. Soc. B*).

enter division in 'waves' which follow a relatively quiescent period, then the time occupied by mitosis can be approximately estimated by following the progress of such a peak through a series of samples of tissue taken at successive intervals. It will first be detected as an increase in the number of prophases; this increase will subsequently be transferred to later stages of mitosis, and finally when the high telophase count begins to subside, it can be surmised that those cells which first entered mitosis in increased numbers have now finished their division. An involved statistical analysis was made of mitosis in the root

* BROWN[63a] has made similar observations on the roots of *Pisum* seedlings; he estimates the rate of production of cells in the meristem by a more direct method.

tip of the onion by LAUGHLIN[64] along these lines, in which the duration of each phase of mitosis is expressed in minutes to two places of decimals, though perhaps of doubtful significance. In animals, mitotic rhythms are being discovered (COOPER and SCHIFF;[65] COOPER and FRANKLIN;[66] BLUMENFELD;[67] BULLOUGH;[68] MÖLLERBERG[69]) (Figure 27) though these are usually not traceable with sufficient clarity for the purpose of mitotic timing.

In the course of a series of researches on factors which affect mitotic activity in the mouse, BULLOUGH[70] has observed that the injection of carbohydrate stimulates epidermal mitosis and has been able to use the consequent wave of cell division to estimate the time occupied by these cells in mitosis. To his results we shall again refer.

The accuracy of all methods of measuring mitotic periods is limited by the difficulty of choosing recognizable events to serve as boundaries between interphase and mitosis, and between each of the several phases of the division process. There is only one sharply defined moment during mitosis, namely the beginning of anaphase; in film records this can be recognized within the limits of a minute. Other events in mitosis demarcate phases sufficiently clearly in some cells, but these criteria may break down when we compare mitosis in different species. For example, the disappearance of the nucleoli which marks the end of prophase in a chick or mammalian cell either passes unnoticed in plant cells with larger chromosomes or may occur at the very beginning of prophase in a Protozoan such as *Acanthamoeba*. The earliest signs of prophase are usually difficult to recognize.

Comparisons of the data in each column of the table of mitotic phases (Table III) must be made with these difficulties in mind. It is clear, however, that the range of recorded times for each phase is much beyond possible observational errors. An important consideration is the effect of temperature which, as several authors have shown, can vary the length of the mitotic period by a factor of several times within the physiological range. To this subject we shall return in discussing the attempts which have been made to analyse the mitotic process by means of temperature co-efficients.

In so far as any conclusions may be drawn from the data in Table III, it would appear that the range of mitotic times is less among vertebrate cells than in plants or Protozoa. The shortest duration of mitosis so far known would seem to be that of the embryo of *Drosophila melanogaster*, which according to HUETTNER[82] is no more than 10 minutes at 23° C., though no further details are given by this author. Lengthy mitotic times are generally due to extended prophase or telophase; the apparent variety in the length of telophase in flowering plants is notable. It seems that the duration of mitosis in different organisms varies with the size of the mitotic figure. That of *Drosophila* is very small, while that of *Tradescantia* or an Amphibian is comparatively large. It would be interesting to know whether nuclei in one species with different degrees of heteroploidy divide at approximately

TABLE III. TABLE OF MITOTIC TIMES IN MINUTES

	Prophase	Metaphase	Anaphase	Telophase	Total
PROTOZOA					
Acanthamoeba (COMMANDON and DE FONBRUNE[71])	4·35	4·8	10·4 (to end of cleavage)		19·5
Euglypha sp. (BÉLAŘ[72a]) (mean of 40 observations)	47*	18	14	100	≈ 180
Actinophrys sol (BÉLAŘ[72b])	14	3·6	6	30	53
Acanthocystis aculeata (STERN[73])	9	4	5	23	41
PLANTS					
(1) Direct measurements:					
Sphacelaria fusca (Brown alga, 17°C.) (ZIMMERMANN[74])	10	7	4	9	30
Arrhenatherum (a grass, 19°C.) (MARTENS[75])	36–45	7–10	15–20	20–35	78–110
Tradescantia (staminal hairs, 20°C.) (BÉLAŘ,[7] BARBER[76])	181	14	15	130	340
(2) Indirect measurements:					
Allium cepa (root tip, 20°C.) (LAUGHLIN[64])	71	6·5	2·4	3·8	83
Vicia faba (root tip, 19°C.) (GRAY and SCHOLES[63])	90	31	34	34	155
Pisum sp. (root tip, 20° C.) (BROWN,[63a])	78	14·4	4·2	13·2	110
METAZOA (POST-SEGMENTATION STAGES)					
Chortophaga (embryonic neuroblasts) (CARLSON and HOLLAENDER[77])	102	13	9	57	181
Triton (erythroblasts, 20°C.) (JOLLY[78] interpreted by WASSERMANN[79])	35	20–25	35	90	180
Liver fibroblast, 26°C (HUGHES and PRESTON[81a])	>18	17–38	14–26	28†	≈ 170
Gallus (HUGHES and FELL[80]) (HUGHES[81])	19–25	4–7	3·5–6	7·5–14	34–52
Mus (spleen cells in culture)	20–35	6–15	8–14	9–26	43–90
Ear epithelium (BULLOUGH[70])					120–180

* Including transition to metaphase.
† End of cleavage to appearance of nucleoli.

the same speed. In the mouse, the data of FELL and HUGHES[83] do not suggest any differences between nuclei of different sizes in this respect.

An extreme instance of the prolongation of the mitotic period is found among the Opalinid ciliates which, according to METCALF,[84] are unique among organisms for in many their nuclei are not customarily found in a reticulate condition, but rather come to 'rest' in some other phase of the mitotic cycle, which varies with the species. The remarkable flagellate *Holomastigotoides*, however, provides another example of this, for the resting period here is in late prophase (CLEVELAND[85]). It is common for meiotic divisions to be interrupted at one point or another in the maturation cycle; thus the egg of the Annelid *Chaetopterus* is laid at the stage of the first metaphase, and remains in this condition until fertilization.

Some comment is required on the difference between the mitotic period of mouse cells in culture and in the epithelium of the intact ear of the same animal. This divergence may be due to the fact that the temperature of the ear lobe is below 37°C. This view is supported by an inspection of BULLOUGH's figures for the proportions of each stage of mitosis in the ear epithelium (BULLOUGH[68]). The proportion of metaphases is very high and generally is more than half the total. It might be expected that metaphase would be prolonged at a temperature below the optimum. BUSCHKE *et alii*[86] are of the opinion that the duration of mitosis in the corneal epithelium of the rat is 'slightly over one hour'; they derive this result from a study of the rate at which cells in metaphase accumulate when the cornea is treated with colchicine.

Effects of temperature

The marked effect of temperature on the rate of the mitotic process has attracted the attention of a number of workers. As with most biological processes, there is an optimal temperature at which mitosis proceeds most rapidly, above and below which the rate is decreased (Figure 28). Thus DE WILDEMAN,[87] as early as 1891, observed that in *Spirogyra*, cell division took place in 45 minutes at 12°C. but occupied several hours at both lower and higher temperatures. It would be desirable to see whether this very sharp fall in the speed of mitosis on either side of the optimum could be confirmed. It is well known that the relationships between temperature and the rates of several biological processes have been studied as a possible means of analysing the nature of the 'master reactions' which govern or limit the visible events in cells and tissues. Such data are frequently expressed as the co-efficient Q_{10}, which is the ratio of the speed of a process at one temperature to the corresponding velocity at a temperature 10°C. higher. A general account of this field of research is given in Chapter 31 of HEILBRUNN's text-book.[88] In the inorganic world 'many chemical reactions have Q_{10} values between

2 and 4, while a physical process such as diffusion or viscous flow is apt to have a temperature coefficient in the neighbourhood of 1·2 to 1·3' (HÖBER[89]). It may be doubted if the study of temperature coefficients has proved to be of much value in biology generally, and no definite contribution of this kind to the study of mitosis has yet been made. Since the rate of mitotic process rises to an optimum with increase of temperature and then subsequently declines, calculated Q_{10} values vary greatly according to the point on the whole temperature velocity curve to which they relate. The best known paper in this field is that of

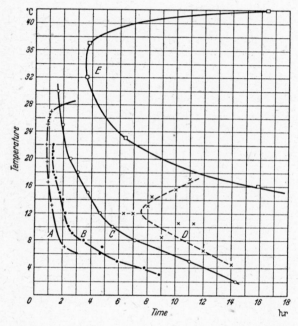

Figure 28 The duration of mitosis as a function of temperature. **A** 1st maturation division of egg of *Sabellaria*. From FAURÉ-FREMIET[619]. **B**. Fertilization to 1st cleavage in *Strongylocentrotus purpuratus*. From LOEB[679]. **C**. Mitosis in erythroblasts of *Triton*. From JOLLY.[78] **D**. In *Spirogyra*. From DE WILDEMAN.[87] **E**. From fusion of pronuclei to 1st cleavage in *Ascaris*. From FAURE-FREMIET.[61]

EPHRUSSI,[90] who found that both in the Echinoderm *Paracentrotus* and in the Nematode *Ascaris* the Q_{10} values for each stage of mitosis were at a minimum in metaphase. However, this result was obtained by comparing his own observations for *Paracentrotus* at a comparatively high temperature with those of FAURÉ-FREMIET[61] for *Ascaris* at a relatively low one. EPHRUSSI's work on *Paracentrotus* was repeated by FRY[91] on *Arbacia* over a similar temperature range with dissimilar results. Two authors, LAUGHLIN[64] and BARBER[76] have estimated Q_{10} values for mitotic phases in the cells of flowering plants and the inspection of their results does not suggest any common features. BARBER's paper reviews most of the previous work in this field, and in it he calculates values from the data of BUCCIANTE[92] on the duration of metaphase and anaphase of chick cells in tissue culture. Both in *Tradescantia* and *Gallus* these values range from 1·0 to over 8·0. It is not possible to draw any conclusions concerning the underlying nature of the events in cell division from such data.

Intermitotic period

We now pass to the consideration of that portion of the whole mitotic cycle which is complementary to the phase of division, the intermitotic period. This also can be measured both directly and indirectly,

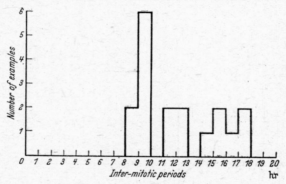

Figure 29 Histogram of 17 intermitotic periods observed in the growth of a single culture of the mouse spleen. From FELL and HUGHES[83] (*By courtesy, Quart. J. micr. Soc.*).

though it is usually of such a length that either the duration of survival of isolated tissues or the patience of the observer waiting in the hope that a particular cell will divide may prove inadequate.* Probably the shortest intermitotic period which has been followed directly is that of the *Chortophaga* neuroblast (CARLSON and HOLLAENDER[77]) which is only 27 minutes, just over a quarter of the duration of prophase in these cells. In tissue cultures of chick or mammalian cells growing under optimal conditions, the intermitotic period is of the order of twelve hours though there are wide variations in individual instances. FELL and HUGHES[83] found that of seventeen intermitotic periods measured in a film record of the growth of one mouse spleen culture, the range was between eight and eighteen hours (Figure 29). Longer intervals may have been overlooked in the analysis of this record.

* In a notebook of STRANGEWAYS is the entry: '15th Feb. 1921, Cell watched 49 hrs.— did not divide.'

In the early cleavages of fertilized eggs, there may be no period of interphase between successive cycles of nuclear division, as in *Echinus* (*Psammechinus*) *miliaris* (GRAY[93]) where the duration of mitosis remains constant at approximately 33 minutes for at least the first six cleavages, despite the successive halving in size of the blastomeres. Micromeres and macromeres cleave at the same rate. In the frog *Rana pipiens* (RUGH[94]) cleavages 2–4 follow each other at about hourly intervals; the duration of mitosis in these yolky blastomeres is less than in their fibroblastic descendants. Cleavages in the rabbit egg last for 9–10 minutes (PINCUS[95]) and follow each other at intervals of 8–9 hours (LEWIS and GREGORY[96]), most of which the blastomere nuclei must spend in interphase.

Within a tissue the relative proportions of cells in mitosis and in interphase can be used as a basis for the estimation of the intermitotic period, provided that some estimate of the duration of mitosis is available. However, the fact that two interphase cells result from one cell in normal mitosis complicates the calculations. In the grasshopper neuroblast this is not so, for, of the two daughter cells, one becomes a ganglion cell, and the other a neuroblast; hence the intermitotic period will be directly proportional to the number of neuroblasts in interphase. An equation relating the intermitotic period to the proportion of cells in mitosis in a tissue was derived by OLIVO and SLAVITCH.[97] Their formula however is not correct, for it involves the addition of the time of mitosis to log 2, the result of which will clearly depend upon the unit of time employed. CRICK in 1948 recalculated this equation, and he is kind enough to allow his formula to be quoted here. It is as follows:

$$\frac{\text{Time of mitosis}}{\text{Total time of mitosis and interphase}} \times \log_e 2 = \log_e \frac{1 + 2R}{1 + R}$$

where R is the fraction of cells in mitosis.

If the intermitotic period is relatively long and R is thus small, then the right-hand side of the equation approximates to R, and hence:

$$\frac{\text{Time of mitosis}}{\text{Total time of cycle}} \approx 1 \cdot 44 \, R$$

The relationship between the mitotic index and the duration of interphase is plotted in Figure 30 for three possible values of the mitotic period. As an example, this formula may be applied to the measurements of SCHULTZ[98] of the mitotic index in the chick embryo between 20 and 70 hours of incubation in which the range of percentage values was found to be between 5 and 1. The upper limit of this range corresponds to the shortest intermitotic periods which have been observed in

G

tissue cultures. The calculations of LAUGHLIN[64] on the intermitotic period in the onion root meristem, which are derived by different reasoning, suggest values of this interval between 194 and 33 minutes over a temperature range of 10–30°C. In the bean root, GRAY and SCHOLES[63] find that the average intermitotic period in the most rapidly

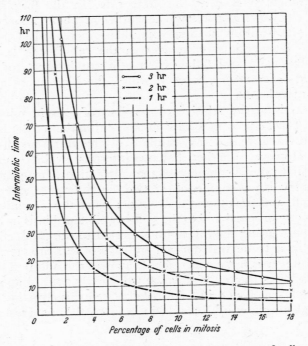

Figure 30 The relationship between the percentage of cells seen in division in a tissue and the average intermitotic period, plotted for three values of the duration of mitosis.

dividing part of the meristem is 16·8 hours (1,000 minutes). At 19–20°C. the proportion of cells in division in the onion meristem is about three times that in the bean.

Mitotic rhythms

The CRICK formula assumes that the rate of entry of cells into mitosis is uniform. It does not apply if there is any tendency towards synchronous nuclear division, such as is found in the meiosis of flowering plants where the post-diplotene stages in all pollen mother cells proceed in step during the course of a morning. Mitotic divisions in post-embryonic stages of animals and plants do not keep pace in this manner, although as we have already described, LAUGHLIN[64] found that the waves of entry of cells into mitosis in the onion root were sufficiently clear-cut to serve as a means of measuring the duration of the mitotic cycle. More usually, mitotic rhythms are less marked and take the form of an increased proportion of cells in division at particular periods of the day. These periodicities have been described both in animals and in plants (TISCHLER[99]). FRIESNER[100] studied the growth of the roots of several flowering plants in darkness and at constant temperatures, and thus eliminated the normal diurnal changes in environmental conditions. Rhythmic variations in the number of mitoses in the root-tip were still detectable, and a period of enhanced cell division alternated with one in which enlargement of cells was more prominent. The times at which these maxima and minima were found to occur were not related to the hour of the day, but only to the time at which germination had been begun, and were thus governed by factors intrinsic to the growth of the plant. No evidence of mitotic rhythms in root meristems were found by WINTER[101] in *Gladiolus*, by GRAY and SCHOLES[63] in *Vicia*, or by BROWN[63a] in *Pisum*. The latter author states that the 'exclusion of light [is] an important condition for the elimination of mitotic periodicity.'

The mitotic rhythms in animal tissues seem to be related to environmental conditions. BULLOUGH has clearly demonstrated that in the ear epithelium of male laboratory mice, cell division is at a maximum when the animals are at rest, and at a minimum when they are awake and active; the mitotic peaks observed by BULLOUGH are thus related to the daily routine in the animal house of his laboratory.* Further researches by this author have suggested that glucose is transferred from the blood to the tissues while the animal is at rest, and that the extent of mitotic activity in the ear epithelium is related to the concentration on the available blood sugar (p 187). It is possible that a diurnal mitotic rhythm in the eight-day-old human epidermis may be governed by the same factors, according to the results which COOPER and SCHIFF[65] obtained by counting mitosis in the excised prepuce removed at different periods during the twenty-four hours. Considerably more mitoses were found in the foreskin of a child when it had been circumcised at night.

STRUCTURE OF CHROMOSOMES

AT metaphase, the general shape of most large chromatids in plants or animals is that of cylindrical threads divided into equal or unequal limbs by a constriction at the site of the attachment to the spindle. Several names for this have been used; DARLINGTON's[102] term 'centromere' is now usual in this country, while 'kinetochore' (SHARP[103]) is often used by American cytologists. Instances of terminal centromeres

* In the bone marrow of the mouse, MILLETTI[101a] has recently found a mitotic peak at 4 a.m., and a minimum at mid-day.

are known; the clearest of which has recently been described by CLEVELAND[104] in the very large chromosomes of flagellates parasitic in termites, where an elastic thread 5–10μ long connects chromosome and centromere (Figure 31). In Coccids there is no localized point of spindle attachment (HUGHES-SCHRADER and RIS[105]); this diffuse condition is characteristic of the Hemiptera in general.

The chromosomes are surrounded by a sheath of material of different composition, which in some instances appears to contain lipoproteins (HIRSCHLER;[106] SERRA[107]). Probably the sister chromatids are thereby

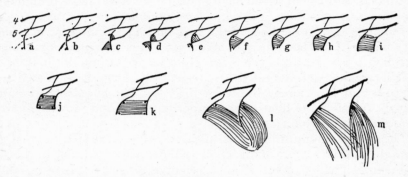

a-h *late telophase*, after cytoplasmic division. a centromeres of both chromosomes attached to existing centriole which is linked to the 4th flagellar band. A new centriole is growing out from the 5th band; b astral rays from new and old centrioles about to join and form central spindle of new achromatic figure; c central spindle formed; d-h centrioles move to parallel positions as achromatic figure develops and spindle becomes more rigid; d lower right centromere has shifted its connection from old to new centriole. i-j *Prophase.* Centromeres duplicated and one from each group moves. k-m growth and function of achromatic figure; k metaphase; l anaphase; m early telophase, before cytoplasmic division.

Figure 31 The achromatic figure of *Holomastigotoides tusitala*, and its connection with the spiral flagellar bands. From CLEVELAND[104] (*By courtesy, Trans. Amer. Phil. Soc.*).

kept together before anaphase (METZ[108]); SCHRADER[109 110] has found that interzonal connections in early anaphase are an extension of this chromosome sheath.

Suitably stained preparations of large chromosomes show coiled filaments within, the chromonemata, set in an apparently homogenous material, the matrix, the appearance of which around the chromosome thread is sometimes the first event within the nucleus in early prophase. Probably the composition of the matrix is variable (KAUFMAN[111]). Some authors look upon most of the Feulgen-positive material deposited on the chromosomes during prophase as belonging to the matrix; SERRA[107] speaks of this as the 'peripheric nucleo-proteins'. In the salivary chromosomes of the *Drosophila* larva, there is evidence of a difference between the proteins of the chromonemata and of the matrix (p 103). It is believed by KUWADA[112] that in *Tradescantia* changes in the state of hydration of the matrix during the chromosome cycle play a part in the arrangement of the spirals of the chromonemata.

There is increasing evidence of chromosomes at all stages of nuclear division containing at least two chromonemata. This subject is reviewed by KAUFMAN.[111] The crucial stage is that of the daughter chromosomes at anaphase; in *Tradescantia* and *Trillium* the anaphase chromosomes in somatic metaphases are four-stranded (NEBEL and RUTTLE[113]). In animal material, a double-stranded condition of the somatic chromosomes had been described in a number of Orthoptera (MICKEY[114]) (Figure 32); in the giant ganglion cells of the embryo of *Drosophila*

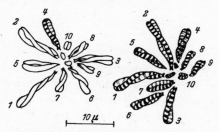

Figure 32 The two daughter haploid groups of chromosomes during anaphase in the second maturation division of the male germ cells of *Romalea microptera*. The x-chromosome (4) is seen in both. Each monad is comprised of two twisted chromatids: the internal spirals are drawn in only part of the figure x1500. From MICKEY[114] (*By courtesy, American Naturalist*).

(KAUFMAN[115]); and in one vertebrate, namely the amphibian *Ambystoma*, by CREIGHTON.[116] In spleen cells of the mouse in tissue culture (FELL and HUGHES[117]) phase-contrast photomicrographs have revealed that the stage of apparent coalescence of the daughter chromosomes in anaphase is succeeded by one in which the whole mass loosens to reveal fine threads much smaller in diameter than the metaphase chromosomes (PLATES IX and X (13)). The bearing of the evidence of multiple nature of chromosomes on the question of the period of their duplication in relation to mitosis is summarized by MANTON:[118]

If a chromosome is at all times multiple, 'splitting' in any literal sense may never occur at all. The multiplication of unit strands viewed as a chemical problem may, but need not, involve fission of the small sub-microscopic threads. Chromosome bipartition, on the other hand, may possibly only entail the spatial separation of bundles of strands each of which has long had an individual existence.

The alternative view is that the chromosome splits at a definite point in the division cycle. DARLINGTON[119] maintains that this is before the prophase of mitosis, but the meiotic prophase is believed to begin precociously in advance of this. Evidence bearing on the mitotic aspect of this theory is derived from the comparative effects of X-rays on cells at various times before prophase (Lea[120]). A break in an unsplit chromosome will result in similar effects in both chromatids, while unequal breakages will denote that the chromatids were already separate at the time of irradiation. It is found that the proportion of the former gradually decreases as mitosis approaches. The question at issue is really one of the order of size of the chromosomal units at the time when they part into two groups. The verdict of Lea[120] on this question is that 'In view of the smooth rather than discontinuous change from the stage at which isochromatid breaks are much less frequent than chromatid breaks, it is evident that the X-ray method cannot give conclusive evidence of a chromosome being unsplit'.

Spirals

Wherever the individual chromonemata within a chromosome are separately distinct, they are seen to be spirally coiled. Often special technical methods, such as 'pretreatment' before fixation, are needed to reveal the spirals, but they are visible in some living pollen mother cells, and in such were first described by Baranetsky.[121] The phase microscope clearly reveals the structure of the metaphase chromosomes in the living pollen mother cells of *Tradescantia* (Ruch[122]). The whole subject has recently been admirably reviewed by Manton.[123] She has suggested that spirals result from a multiple stranded condition of the chromosomes (Manton[124]).

When a chromosome is made up of a number of closely apposed spiral chromonemata an extremely complex appearance results, in which the individual spirals lie near the limits of microscopical resolution. It is therefore not surprising that observers disagree whether a further minor coil exists within the major spiral. Nebel[125] has attempted to analyse the structure of intact chromosomes by comparing them with macroscopic models made of glass spirals. Such a comparison, however, neglects the effects of diffraction, which may well play some part in the make-up of the magnified image of so complex an object.

Much attention has been given to the question whether there are regularities in the directions of the spirals of the chromonemata, and most observers now agree that left- and right-handed spirals occur equally at random. White[126] has shown that in a group of grasshopper spermatogonia derived from a single mother cell, the number of right- and left-handed chromosomes is approximately equal. Manton and Smiles[127] have shown in their superb ultraviolet photomicrographs of the chromosomes of the fern *Osmunda* that the two chromonemata of a prophase chromosome may actually be coiled in opposite directions.

It is only in a small minority of animal cells that spiral structure is clearly seen, as for instance in the Orthopteran chromosomes described by WHITE[126] and MICKEY,[114] and in Ambystoma by CREIGHTON.[116] Among Protozoa with a small number of large chromosomes, their spiral structure is exceptionally clear, as for instance in *Collozoum* (PÄTAU[128])) and such flagellates as *Holomastigotoides* (CLEVELAND[104 129]) (Figure 33). CLEVELAND's recent paper is one of the most remarkable papers on nuclear cytology ever to be published. This organism and the related Protozoa offer unique advantages for the study of nuclear cytology which this author is exploiting to the full.

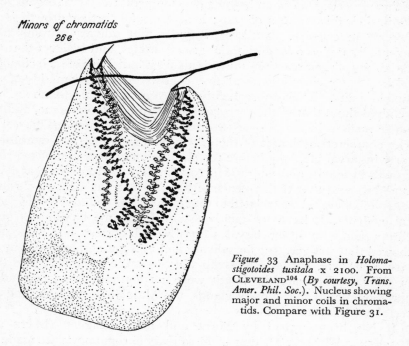

Figure 33 Anaphase in *Holomastigotoides tusitala* x 2100. From CLEVELAND[104] (*By courtesy, Trans. Amer. Phil. Soc.*). Nucleus showing major and minor coils in chromatids. Compare with Figure 31.

Their number of chromosomes is either two or three and they can be recognized individually throughout their life cycle.

Chromosomes in prophase, at stages before contraction has begun, often show a banded structure, in which there are irregularities in density and calibre along the course of the chromonemata; these denser segments are known as chromomeres. It is debated whether these chromomeres are in reality coiled regions of a uniform chromonema which elsewhere is nearly uncoiled; this point of view is maintained by RIS[130] who denies that chromonemata are ever seen in a fully uncoiled condition. RIS quotes a number of instances where structures described as chromomeres have later been found to be coils in chromonemata, and maintains that this is true of the leptotene chromosomes of the Orthopteran spermatocytes, which have previously been regarded as a clear example of chromomeric structure. This question has further been extensively discussed in relation both to the giant chromosomes of the Diptera, and the 'lamp-brush' chromosomes of the vertebrate oocyte.

Salivary chromosomes

The nuclei of the salivary glands of larval Diptera are an extreme instance of a general mode of growth during this stage of cells and tissues of these insects. During embryonic development, the larval organs soon attain their full number of cells; henceforth all further growth is by increase in cell-size. PAINTER[131] suggests that salivary chromosomes repeatedly undergo 'endomitotic' growth cycles, and believes that the variability of their reactions towards alkalis is indicative of such changes. Each salivary chromosome at first consists of the chromatids of the diploid pairs. They subsequently increase in length to about one hundred times that of the corresponding normal chromosome, and the whole nucleus increases over two hundredfold in volume (Figure 15). The characteristic bands of the salivary chromosomes are established early in larval life, long before the chromosomes have completed their growth in length and width (HINTON[132]). It is well known that PAINTER[133] showed that the sequence of the bands in the salivary chromosomes of *Drosophila* was related to that of the genes deduced from genetical evidence. It has been tacitly assumed that the banding of giant chromosomes in other larval tissues would correspond; BERGER[134] showed that this was true for salivary and mid-gut chromosomes in the larvae of *Sciara*, but later KOSSWIG and SHENGÜN[135] demonstrated that in *Chironomus* larvae, the bands were not constant in corresponding chromosomes of the salivary glands, the Malpighian tubules, and the rectal epithelium.

It has been argued by METZ and his colleagues (METZ and LAWRENCE,[136] METZ[137]) that if the salivary chromosomes are made up of chromonemata, then the unitary threads must be much larger than those of normal nuclei, which would be sub-microscopic in diameter if stretched to the length of the salivary chromosomes. The longitudinal striations which are seen in extended salivary chromosomes on this view cannot separate normal chromonemata. METZ believes that the basic structure of the salivary chromosomes is an alveolar one; on the other hand RIS and CROUSE[138] argue that they are composed of spiral chromonemata, and that the bands are formed at particular cross-sections of the chromosomes where the coils of all the chromonemata are disposed at right angles to the long axis of the whole structure. KOSSWIG and SHENGÜN[135] suggest that the variety of banding in the same chromosome in various tissues of *Chironomus* is due to differences in the coiling of the constituent chromonemata. Experimental investigations do not, however, support this view, for if the bands consisted purely of coils in a spiral thread at microscopical orders of size they should be obliterated by stretching the whole chromosome, in the way which is described by CHAMBERS[139] for an early prophase chromosome of a spermatocyte of *Dissosteira*. However, neither chromomeres nor bands disappear when salivary chromosomes are stretched, either if pulled out in making smear preparations (HINTON[132]) or when the isolated chromosome is stretched by micromanipulation (BUCK[140]). Most of the elongation occurs in the interband regions (Plate XVI).

The technique of the isolation of salivary chromosomes was further improved by D'ANGELO.[141] The main difficulty is that their physical properties are altered by contact with torn cytoplasm; BUCK found it necessary first to treat the whole salivary glands with osmic vapour for a day before dissection, but D'ANGELO was able to avoid such pretreatment, and found that the chromosomes retained their natural condition in a suitable mixture of sodium and potassium chlorides with a phosphate buffer. Their elasticity is so great that they return to their normal length even after a tenfold extension; this requires that at some level of sub-microscopical dimensions their structure must be made up of folded or coiled units. D'ANGELO was able to pull off fine fibrils from the chromosomes in which the bands were represented by nodular swellings at intervals. These fibrils were highly extensible and returned to their original state on relaxation; D'ANGELO does not mention whether the nodular swellings persisted when the fibrils were stretched, but it may perhaps be assumed that they did.

Further evidence of the fine structure of salivary gland chromosomes has been provided by electron micrography (PALAY and CLAUDE;[142] PEASE and BAKER;[143] SCHULTZ et alii[144]). All of these authors agree that the bands of salivary chromosomes are made up of chromomeres denser than the intervening chromonemata. PEASE and BAKER[143] describe cigar- or leaf-shaped bodies, within the bands, 0.15μ or less in length, comparable with virus or bacteriophage particles and which, they suggest, it is reasonable to regard as the genes themselves. However, although judgement on this point may be suspended, it may be agreed that most of the evidence on the structure of salivary chromosomes suggests that the bands are made up of granules arranged transversely and that the interband regions consist of filaments, though it is still obscure what morphological status is to be assigned to the latter. They are very clearly demonstrated in the replica micrographs of PALAY and CLAUDE.

Studies on chromosomes with the polarizing microscope have been reviewed by PICKEN[145] and by FREY-WYSSLING.[146] The birefringence of fibres of nucleic acids is negative, while that of fibrous proteins is positive; the appearance in polarized light of a structure composed of

97

both of these will vary according to the proportions and also to the degree of orientation of each component. CASPERSSON[147] has found that the nucleic acids in the bands of the larval salivary chromosomes of *Drosophila* are not highly orientated, although sufficiently orientated to produce an overall negative birefringence (SCHMIDT[148]). In the interband regions which consist mainly of protein, the orientation increases on stretching to give a positive birefringence (SCHMITT[149]).

Such studies should be extended to the 'lamp-brush' chromosomes of the vertebrate oocyte, which in virtue of their looser structure might

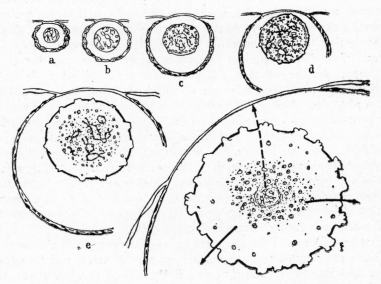

Figure 34 Diagram of nuclear growth stages during the later development of frog eggs. From DURYEE.[152] a & b Stages 1 and 2: Egg < 0·2 mm. in diameter. Chromosomes barely visible in life. c Stage 3: Egg 0·2–0·5 mm. in diameter. Large irregular nucleoli just beneath nuclear membrane. Chromosomes forming lateral loops. d Stage 4: Eggs 0·5–0·75 mm. in diameter. Chromosomes reach maximum length. e Stage 5: Eggs 0·75–0·85 mm. in diameter. Sac-like protrusions from nuclear membrane. f Stage 6: Eggs 1·8 mm. in diameter. Chromosomes and nucleus much contracted. Central 'cloud' of nucleoli. Heavy arrows indicate mixing of nuclear material in cytoplasm after germinal vesicle membrane breaks down. Dotted arrow indicates migration of central chromosomal mass towards the animal pole, where 1st polar body maturation spindle will form. (*By courtesy, Ann. N.Y. Acad. Sci.*)

prove to be more readily accessible to optical investigation. Discussion about the nature of these chromosomes closely parallels that concerning the salivary chromosomes. They are regarded as polytene by PAINTER[150]; RIS[130] considers that they are wholly composed of coiled chromonemata, while DODSON[151] and DURYEE[152] regard them as chromomeric.

Lamp-brush' chromosomes

In the Amphibian oocyte, the development of the 'lamp-brush' chromosomes begins some time before the deposition of yolk, while the nucleus is already in the diplotene stage of meiosis, in which it remains for the whole of the period of their development (Figure 34). Each chromosome pair then consists of the four normal chromatids with their chiasmata. They begin to elongate and finally attain a length greater even than that of the salivary chromosomes; at the same time

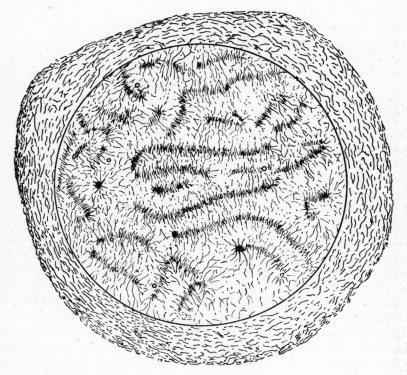

Figure 35 Flemming's drawing of the oocyte nucleus of *Ambystoma tigrinum* in which the chromosomes are in the lamp-brush stage. From FLEMMING.[154]

bristle-like lateral branches develop. Thus they assume the appearance which reminded RÜCKERT[153] of a lamp-brush, a name which may help a future historian of science to relate the progress of cytology with that of the technology of domestic illumination. In FLEMMING's *Zellsubstanz, Kern, und Zelltheilung*[154] is a drawing of a section through the oocyte nucleus of the Axolotl, in which the chromosomes are at this stage of development (Figure 35). As the bristles grow, they stain less readily and apparently develop into loops, though in electron micrographs the bristles do not appear thus, but as fern-like branches (CLARK *et alii*[155]). At the same time, nucleoli begin to form at particular loci on the chromosomes, and this process continues until a surrounding 'cloud' of small nucleoli has developed; the chromosome loops are then shed into the nuclear sap. The whole complex of chromosomes and nucleoli later contracts away from the nuclear membrane; the chromosomes then shorten and resume their normal diplotene condition.

It is clear that the lamp-brush cycle is a remarkable example of rapid ribonucleoprotein production, related to the deposition of yolk. The morphological question concerning them is whether the loop-like bristles are to be regarded as pulled out gyres of a coiled chromonema; the answer to this seems to be in the negative, for DODSON[151] has shown that axis and branches differ in chemical composition, for the fully developed loop is Feulgen negative, while the main axis is Feulgen positive. Moreover DURYEE[152] found that the chromosomes could be greatly stretched by micromanipulation, without ever undoing their lateral loops.

Thus, with regard to these two large and specialized types of chromosome, most of the evidence is against the view that the structural unit is a spirally coiled chromonema; on the other hand, in the larger normal mitotic chromosomes their spiral structure is often beyond doubt, though in many somatic chromosomes the most that can be said about their internal structure is that in prophase they consist of apparently chromomeric filaments. When contracted in metaphase, such chromosomes give the appearance of short cylinders of uniform density. It is usually assumed that their contraction is always due to 'spiralization' which proceeds *pari passu* with the concentration upon them of nucleoproteins (KOLLER[156]). Definite proof of this has not yet been provided. At present, perhaps the most plausible point of view intermediate between the two extremes is the following. Due to the great length of the salivary and oocyte chromosomes they are composed of uncoiled chromonemata, along which are solid aggregates of chromatic material, the chromomeres. Chromosomes of normal length in general have a spiral structure, and may vary in structure along their length both in the arrangement of their coiling, and also in density of deposited material. RUCH[157] claims that the minor spiral of the *Tradescantia* chromosomes at meiotic metaphase is resolved by means of the phase microscope into a series of chromomeres. On the other hand, CLEVELAND[104] can clearly see the minor spirals in the living flagellate *Holomastigotoides* by this means.

The researches of OURA[158] and of KUWADA *et alii*[154] on the effect of treating chromosomes with dilute alkalis has shown that some contracted plant chromosomes can be partly unravelled to exhibit a clear spiral structure. SHIGENAGA[160] has used neutral sodium chloride for the same purpose. Both of these agents are solvents for DNA.

Further investigation of small metaphase chromosomes by means of the electron microscope is greatly desirable, especially in combination with alkaline treatment. Most of the papers on this subject are as yet on a preliminary scale (ELVERS;[161] BUCHHOLZ[162]). The electron micrograph of a human pachytene chromosome published by SCHULTZ et alii[144] suggests a chromomeric structure. In a recent study of this kind by ROZSA and WYCKOFF,[163] onion root meristems were sectioned sufficiently thinly to show nuclear structure. Neutral fixation in formalin gave the best results, but showed detail in neither the spindle nor the chromosomes, which to quote these authors 'do not present a definite fine structure at any order of magnitude visible in the electron microscope'. HOVANITZ[164] isolated 'chromosomes' from chick erythrocytes by the method of POLLISTER and MIRSKY,[165] and found a suggestion of spiral arrangement in electron micrographs of this material; similar threads prepared from mammalian nuclei by MIRSKY[166] are clearly coiled, but since those prepared by a different method by CLAUDE and POTTER[167] consist of straight fibres, it is probable that the revolving blades of the Waring blender are the source of these particular spirals.

COMPOSITION OF CHROMOSOMES

We come now to the important subject of the changes in chemical composition of the chromosomes during the mitotic cycle. So far, those researches which bear on this problem have all used cytochemical methods; it would be desirable to employ bulk methods by the analysis of batches of simultaneously fertilized eggs, but the sea-urchin egg, the most accessible material for such an investigation, has a very low content of DNA in proportion to its ribonucleoproteins (SCHMIDT et alii,[168]) and nuclear changes over the period of the cleavage cycle would probably not be revealed with sufficient accuracy.

Nucleic acids

We shall first consider the question of the nucleic acids during cell division. Inspection of Feulgen preparations of tissues in which mitoses are frequent suggests that a nucleus in division contains very much more Feulgen-positive material than one in interphase; quantitative measurements, however, do not confirm this. The apparent difference between a daughter group of chromosomes in anaphase and an interphase nucleus is in part due to the effect of the dispersal of material in the latter through a wider area; the importance of this factor cannot be assessed by subjective impressions alone.*

The first measurements which relate to the changes in composition

---

* LEUCHTENBERGER[169] has shown that by measurements on pycnotic nuclei, their intense reaction towards the Feulgen reagent does not apparently indicate any increase in the amount of DNA therein.

of the chromosomes during cell division are due to CASPERSSON.[170] By means of ultraviolet microspectrophotometry, he was able to calculate the total nucleic acid content of the nuclei of the spermatocytes of the grasshopper *Gomphocerus* between the leptotene and diplotene stages. Some increase during early leptotene was found, but thereafter the amount of nucleic acid present remained approximately constant. This point was not confirmed by the later work of RIS,[171] whose extinction measurements at 2,537Å on spermatocyte nuclei of *Chortophaga* indicated a considerable increase in total nucleic acids between the leptotene and pachytene stages; in onion root-tip nuclei such estimations between prophase and metaphase showed a similar increase of approximately twofold. In interphase and prophase, the total nucleic acid content of the onion nucleus appeared to be the same. RIS made other measurements at appropriate wavelengths on material stained by several cytochemical methods. In Feulgen preparation of onion roots,

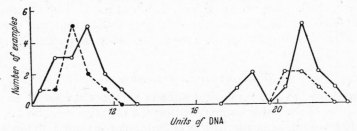

Figure 36 Distribution of DNA content in arbitrary units of nuclei of larval *Ambystoma*. Solid lines: interphase nuclei of liver of two size classes. Dotted lines: pronephric nuclei in telophase (left), and in prophase (right). From SWIFT[172] (*By courtesy, Physiol. Zool.*).

dividing cells showed an increase in DNA content both on entering prophase and also between this period and metaphase. In similar measurements on embryonic mammalian and larval amphibian tissues, SWIFT[172] finds that the range of relative DNA content in interphase nuclei is approximately twofold, and that the values for all nuclei in prophase are at the upper end of this range (Figure 36). His conclusion is that the DNA which will be required for the next division is synthesized during interphase, and once the cell has entered mitosis, there is no further increase in Feulgen-positive material.* Thus SWIFT and RIS, using different material, do not agree on this last point. The degree of accuracy of these microcolorimetric measurements is uncertain. RIS's figures show only a very approximate halving of the total DNA content of the

* This conclusion is confirmed by similar measurements made by ALFERT[173] on cleavage stages in the mouse. By using bulk methods of analysis, OGUR *et alii*[174] have shown that the DNA content of the microspores of *Lilium* increases linearly in the interphase between meiosis and the succeeding mitosis. In microphotometric measurements, again on Feulgen-stained material, LISON and PASTEELS[174a] have found that DNA is rapidly synthesized in or after telophase ('des l'apparition de la membrane nucléaire'), both in embryonic and adult rat tissues, in chick cultures, and in the eggs and larvae of *Paracentrotus lividus*.

chromosomes when the daughter groups separate in anaphase; in general, there is some doubt whether the values obtained are independent of the degree of concentration of the Feulgen-positive material within the nucleus, for in corresponding measurements on interphase nuclei Ris and Mirsky[175] lay some stress on the fact that reproducible results depend on the even dispersion of DNA throughout the nucleus by means of hypertonic sucrose.

Evidence from a different type of investigation supports the conclusion that DNA is synthesized in resting cells which will later undergo mitosis. Howard and Pelc[176] have shown that when seeds of *Vicia faba* are germinated in culture solutions containing P^{32}, the isotope is incorporated into meristematic nuclei during interphase, probably in the form of DNA (Plate IV). The work of these authors clearly shows the possibilities of their autoradiographic technique in this field.

The relative proportions of DNA and RNA in the chromosomes during the division cycle appears to be approximately constant in Ris's microcolorimetric measurements on onion root nuclei and grasshopper spermatocytes stained by the Unna technique. Jacobson and Webb,[177] however, have shown that in chick cells in tissue culture, the chromosomes first become methylene blue-positive at the time when the nucleolus breaks up at the end of prophase; this suggests that its ribonucleoproteins are then rapidly transferred to the chromosomes. The loss of RNA from the daughter chromosomes in early anaphase is equally rapid, for they leave behind them a track of methylene-blue-staining material in the interzonal region of the spindle. Such observations could be readily extended to other material, and these authors have confirmed by digestion experiments the accuracy of their localization of RNA.

Proteins

The proteins of the chromosomes during the division cycle must now be discussed. In earlier pages (12, 47), it has been mentioned that two types are associated with nucleic acids, namely basic proteins of comparatively low molecular weight, the protamines and histones; and secondly, larger and non-basic proteins containing appreciable amounts of tryptophane. Mazia's[178] evidence on the proteolytic digestion of chromosomes suggests that histones are associated with the chromonemata and non-basic proteins with the matrix. Chromosomes shrink when treated with pepsin, which according to Mazia does not attack histones, while trypsin digests them completely. This shrinkage is seen most clearly in an isolated and stretched salivary chromosome, and mainly affects the interband regions. In a later paper, Mazia[179] has shown that the fibrous nature of the proteins of chromosomes modifies their behaviour towards enzymes. In particular, they are resistant to preparations of cathepsin which digest dissolved proteins and nucleo-proteins. DALY *et alii*[179a] find that isolated histones are readily attacked by pepsin. CASPERSSON[180] suggested that the proteins associated with metaphase chromosomes are mainly of the histone type and that during telophase their heterochromatic regions synthesize histones, while the euchromatin produces non-basic protein. Thus a protein cycle during mitosis is postulated in which the amount of histones keeps parallel with that of the Feulgen-positive material. The young nucleus in telophase is believed to produce relatively large quantities of protein, to which, CASPERSSON maintains, the swelling of the chromosomes and the nucleus at that time is due. He considers that much of this protein disappears during prophase (p 80). CASPERSSON's recent admission has already been quoted (p 12) that in metaphase chromosomes, the character and amount of the proteins cannot be determined by ultra-violet microspectrometry alone.

RIS[171] maintains that the relative proportions of histone and non-basic protein remain the same from interphase to prophase in the cells of the onion root-tip, and from pre-leptotene to pachytene in the spermatocytes of the grasshopper. His method was an indirect one, based on the Millon reaction for tyrosine, which is present in both histones and non-basic proteins. Chromosomes were first shown to be Millon-positive by HEINE.[181] RIS applied the reaction in the presence first of trichloroacetic acid which does not dissolve histones, and then of sulphuric acid in which basic proteins are soluble (MIRSKY and POLLISTER[182]). Microphotometric readings on the chromosomes were made in each case.

It is clear that much remains to be learnt about the changes in the chromosomal proteins during mitosis. We may expect that different types of cell will be found to vary in this respect; the differences be-tween the histones of intermitotic nuclei which are being disclosed by the work of the STEDMANS[183] may well apply also to dividing cells.

Inorganic chemistry

We turn now to the inorganic chemistry of the chromosomes, a subject which in J. H. NEWMAN's phrase, has 'a vagueness of an equally intense kind'. Nearly all the evidence in this field comes from studies in which the technique of micro-incineration has been used. This technique and its applications have been described by HORNING[184] in a well-known review. After micro-incineration of a section or a smear, the residual ash of the cells remains sufficiently undisturbed for the whole structure of the tissue to be recognizable under the microscope with suitable illumination. The method is extremely sensitive; the quantities of the substances involved lie beyond the limit of micro-chemical tests. Unfortunately, at present the method suffers from grave disadvantages. There are no adequate methods for testing the chemical composition of the ash, and furthermore it is probable that artefacts result from the movement of inorganic salts within the cell during chemical fixation.

The first observations on cells in division which were made by means of micro-incineration methods are due to SCOTT,[185] [186] who described how the whole ash of the cell during mitosis seems to be concentrated in the chromosomes both in mouse spermatogonia and in epithelial cells of the frog skin. In the interphase nucleus, nuclear membrane nucleoli and residual chromatin all leave their recognizable traces of ash. In SCOTT's preparations, it appeared that inorganic material was gradually concentrated in the developing chromosomes during prophase. A similar concentration of cellular ash in nuclei and chromosomes was observed by FUNAOKA and OGATA[187] in ova and cells of the oviduct of *Ascaris*, and in pollen mother cells of the bean. BARIGOZZI[188] micro-incinerated salivary gland chromosomes and found that their Feulgen-positive bands have a high content of ash. However, a warning against generalizing too readily from these results is to be found in the work of LUCAS[189] on the ash of Opalinids, for he found no residue whatever in the chromosomes of these Protozoa although they too are Feulgen-positive.

It was assumed by SCOTT that the ash of the nucleus and the chromosomes consisted mainly of calcium and magnesium. Two Polish workers (KRUSZYNSKI;[190] [191] BAGINSKI[192]) endeavoured to apply chemical tests to ashed preparations under the microscope by adding suitable reagents with micropipettes held in a Chambers micromanipulator. Thus the presence of calcium in the ash was shown by the formation of characteristic crystals of gypsum when sulphuric acid and alcohol were added. SCOTT and PACKER[193] confirmed the presence of calcium and magnesium in the ash of the cell by a technique which combines micro-incineration with electron microscopy. A tissue section is mounted on the cathode of a special instrument, and is there ashed *in situ*. When heated further, the ash of the material emits electrons which are imaged on a fluorescent screen. It is claimed by these authors that the emission from the ash is mainly due to atoms of calcium and magnesium. In electron micrographs of smooth muscle-fibres made in this way, SCOTT[194] has shown that the nuclei are prominent.

Other evidence, however, indicates that the ash of nuclei and chromosomes is not entirely composed of salts of calcium and magnesium. UBER and GOODSPEED[195] consider that the ash of chromosomes in pollen mother cells is mainly due to phosphates from the nucleic acids, the phosphorus content of which is high; for instance GULLAND[196] states that there is 9·3 per cent phosphorus in dried DNA from calf thymus. ENGSTRÖM[197] has shown that both the ash and the adenylic acids are concentrated in the isotropic segments of insect striped muscle, though a still greater part of the phosphate there present is due to phosphagen, and is thus unrelated to nucleotides. However, in a previous paper (ENGSTRÖM[198]) this author showed that a range of other tissues, the ash after micro-incineration is concentrated in regions where, ultraviolet absorption was high.

It is probable that in general both divalent cations and phosphate contribute to the ash of the nuclei and chromosomes. WILLIAMSON and GULICK[198] have analysed mammalian nuclei prepared by the anhydrous method of BEHRENS and find therein 2·5 per cent phosphorus, 1·35 per cent calcium, and 0·08 per cent magnesium.* These authors calculated the percentage of nucleic acids to which this phosphorus content would correspond, and concluded that at the pH of the living nucleus, the nucleic acids were combined with the maximum possible amount of calcium. If this is so, any further concentration of calcium in the nucleus during mitosis would necessitate the synthesis of more nucleic acids.

The elasticity of both lamp-brush chromosomes (DURYEE[199]) and those of the salivary glands of *Chironomus* (D'ANGELO[200]) is markedly reduced by calcium ions. If, therefore, such effects of this ion are shared by all chromosomes in general, and if their elastic properties have any relevance to the changes in form which they undergo during mitosis, a concentration of calcium round the chromosomes might play a part in their contraction at metaphase.

Further progress in this field demands the use of a method by which both calcium and phosphorus can be recognized with certainty in the same material on a cytochemical scale. Development of the X-ray absorption histospectroscopy of ENGSTRÖM[201] at present offers the best hope of such progress.

THE CENTRAL BODY

As early as the mid-nineteenth century, several authors, among which DERBÈS[202] may be mentioned, described the astral rays in various eggs well before their significance as part of the division mechanism of the cell was realized. A quarter of a century later, when the general form of the achromatic figure in the animal cell with its asters and spindle was understood, attention was directed to the nature of the focal point at each pole. VAN BENEDEN[203] was among the first to describe this 'corpuscule polaire' which he had observed in the cells of organisms no less obscure than the Mesozoan Dicyemid parasites of Cephalopods. Later came the concept of the central body as a permanent organ of the cell which remains when the rest of the achromatic figure has

---

* JUNGNER[198a] has recently found appreciable quantities of magnesium in DNA and nucleohistone isolated from the calf thymus, and in RNA prepared from yeast.

disappeared after mitosis is completed. This was mainly derived from studies in the eighteen-eighties on fertilization and cleavage in *Ascaris*. In the description of the cleavage cycle in *Ascaris* given by VAN BENEDEN and NEYT,[204] they showed that in anaphase the 'corpuscule polaire' has already divided within the 'sphere attractive', which itself follows suit in early interphase. Both division centres are then ready for the next mitosis (Figure 37).* The modern usage of centriole and centrosome was established by BOVERI[205] in 1901, though as WILSON[206] points out, the latter term has since been used in several senses.

The observation that in some instances the centriole was a permanent cell organ persisting from one cell generation to the next led to the

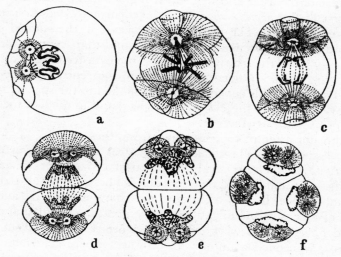

Figure 37 Stages in the first cleavage of the egg of *Ascaris megalocephala* to show division of the central body. **a** ♂ and ♀ pronuclei not yet fused; only one pronucleus is shown. **c** The centrioles divide during anaphase. **d** & **e** The centrospheres divide after cleavage is completed. **f** Interphase following second cleavage. From VAN BENEDEN and NEYT[204].

hypothesis that an aster could only develop round a centriole derived by division from the original centriole of the fertilized egg. On BOVERI's theory of fertilization, this was contributed by the sperm. Not all cytologists have been able to agree that the granule at the astral centre is a permanent cell organ, which alone can evoke a radial arrangement of the surrounding cytoplasm. Within both unfertilized and fertilized eggs, adventitious monasters with centrioles can be

---

* LEWIS[204a] has followed the division of the centrosome and the migration of the daughter centres over the nuclear membrane in a living egg of a monkey before the prophase of the first cleavage.

produced by a variety of experimental treatments, though neither GRAY[207] nor WILSON[206] in reviewing this work is convinced that the possibility has been wholly excluded that material from nucleus or centrosome may have contributed to the accessory asters.

Some have doubted whether the centriole is more than a fixation artefact. In FISCHER's[208] monograph on the action of fixatives and stains on biological material, their effect on the achromatic figure is one of the main subjects of inquiry. The author reviews previous descriptions of the centriole, and concludes: 'Alle diese Beschreibungen reichen nicht aus, um durch die Gestalt granulationen zu unterscheiden oder von etwaigen Fallungsartefacten'. About 30 years later, FRY re-examined this question by studying the effect of various fixatives on the appearance of the aster and its central region, mainly in marine eggs; in the first of this series, cytasters induced in activated *Echinarachnius* eggs were examined. The texture of the asters in the stained sections varies with the fixative used, and it was found that 'central bodies are present only when the fixative coagulates the cytaster in such a manner that rays are distinctly fixed and extend to the centre'. In succeeding papers (FRY[209 210]) this conclusion was extended to the sperm aster and first cleavage figure of the *Echinarachnius* egg, and to the first metaphase spindle of *Chaetopterus* (FRY[211]).

FRY did not attempt to generalize from these results, and in the last paper suggests a classification of central bodies as seen in fixed preparations in which his 'focal staining artefacts' are but one category, clearly distinguishable from true centrioles. These are 'stable structures, which unlike focal bodies, maintain their characteristic size and shape in spite of extensive modifications in the coarseness and shape of the rays and fibers'. FRY's work evoked a vigorous reaction from several cytologists, who cited a number of instances where centrioles can be traced as permanent cell organs. Some of the classical examples were re-investigated. POLLISTER[212] maintained that in the amphibian leuco-cyte, the centriole was not a coagulated focal point, because in inter-phase it is a double structure eccentrically placed inside a single aster; a similar argument had been used by BOVERI[205] in answer to FISCHER. HUETTNER[213] was able to trace the continuity of the centrioles during the cleavage of the egg of *Drosophila melanogaster*, and in a further paper, HUETTNER and RABINOWITZ[214] describe central bodies in the pole cells of the living egg and their movement round the surface of the nucleus in prophase.

Other authors have also identified centrioles in living cells. Those of the hypermastigote flagellates which have been described by CLEVE-LAND[215 216] are 1–3μ in width, and up to 80μ in length; from them the origin of the achromatic figure and of all other extranuclear organelles has been clearly traced. JOHNSON[217] has followed them through the cycle

of spermatogenesis in *Oenacanthus* and other members of the Orthopteran family Gryllidae, both in living and fixed material; in the spermatogonia they are short rods and become V-shaped during the

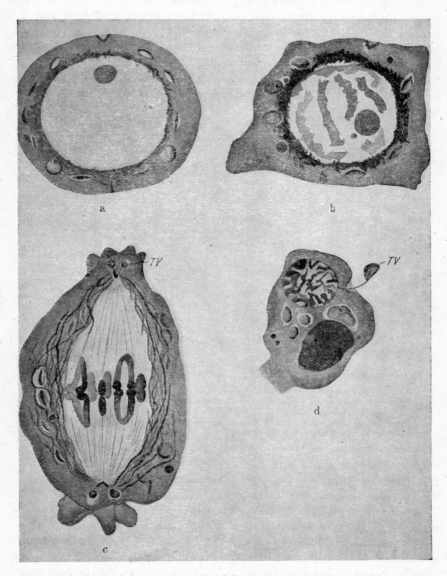

Figure 38 Stages in the spermatogenesis of *Oenocanthus* to show the centrioles. x 3200.
a Living spermatocyte of *Oe. quadipunctatus* and b Fixed spermatocyte of *Oe. nigricornis* at
pachytene. The V-shaped centrioles are seen at opposite poles of the nucleus. c Metaphase of meiosis I, and d Early spermatid, *Oe. nigricornis*. The axial thread connects
centriole and terminal vesicle. From JOHNSON[217] (*By courtesy, Z. wiss. Zool.*).

meiotic stages. From them develop the axial filaments of the future sperm tails (Figure 38).

Since the centrioles of the spermatocyte generally become the blepharoplasts of the sperm tails, the presence of these granules in the spermatogonia may be related only to their future function, and not necessarily to the achromatic figure in the preceding cell divisions. However, in *Ascaris megalocephala*, the sperm has neither tail nor axial filament, yet centrioles are found in the developing sperm cells, similar to those of the fertilized egg. This fact has been confirmed by STUR-DIVANT.[218] A converse relationship is found in the cryptogamic plants, which have motile male gametes, the flagellae of which are provided

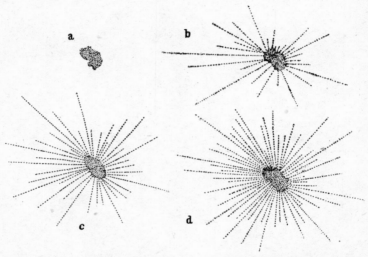

Figure 39 Progress of the formation of an aster-like figure when 1 per cent osmic acid is added to a section of elder-pith impregnated with protein (2 per cent 'Deuteroalbumose') x 600. a Remains of nucleus of elder-pith cell before addition of OsO_4. b, c, d 4 mins, 14 mins and 60 mins respectively after addition of OsO_4. From FISCHER.[208]

with blepharoplasts. These are derived from centrosomes, which in *Equisetum*, for instance (SHARP[219]), appear in the haploid generation for the first time in the early mitoses of the spermatogenous tissue. There is evidence that in many plants these bodies come from inside the nucleus. This subject is reviewed by YUASA.[220]

It is abundantly clear that orientating centres within the cell are not all of one kind, nor do they all originate similarly. The non-astral spindle of plants is alone sufficient to demonstrate this fact. A more fundamental question than the morphological status of the centriole is the nature of the orientating process which it induces in the surrounding cytoplasm. This subject is discussed by SWANN in a succeeding section.

We are better able to realize the nature of this problem now that it is understood that the unit of structure in the living aster and spindle is not the microscopically visible ray, but the sub-microscopic micelle; though the shift of the inquiry to a lower order of magnitude reveals how formidable are the difficulties in the way of investigation. There is some evidence that nucleic acids may be found at the centre of orientation; this is suggested by the basophily of the centriole, and also by some of the model experiments of FISCHER.[208] He impregnated pieces of elder pith with protein solutions which were then fixed and sectioned. 'Astral figures' were common within the coagulated protein of these preparations, and frequently the remains of the nucleus of the pith cell was seen at their centres (*Figure* 39). The fact that in the development of the spindle, the centromere also serves as an orientating centre is in accordance with this hypothesis. YUASA[220] [221] [222] finds that although the centrosome of many cryptogamic plants is derived from the nucleus, it is Feulgen-negative; he considers it to be of the same nature as the nucleolus. If it is generally true that under appropriate circumstances a granule of ribonucleoprotein can orientate the surrounding cytoplasm, this would possibly explain why accessory cytasters can be so readily induced in the sea-urchin egg. It seems, however, that a nuclear component is also involved, for as FRY[223] says 'if eggs are immature, neither sperms nor artificial agents produce asters, since they do not arise before the germinal vesicle has released nuclear substances into the cytoplasm'.

CHROMOSOMES AND THE ACHROMATIC FIGURE

Close study of time-lapse films of chick and mammalian cells in mitosis shows that towards the end of prophase two changes happen at the same time: at opposite ends of the nucleus the asters appear, and then the chromosomes begin to move. The further sequence of events varies in detail; either within the still intact nuclear membrane the paired chromatids congregate opposite each aster (Plate XII (16)), or, if the membrane is at once broken down, the spindle is completed and the chromosomes are then drawn towards the whole achromatic figure (FELL and HUGHES[224]) (Plate XI (14)).

Cells in meiotic division provide other and better known examples of the orientation of chromosomes towards asters, which are all the more remarkable because the influence, of whatever kind it is, must be exerted across an intact nuclear membrane. In the bouquet stage of meiotic prophase the ends of the chromosomes at zygotene or pachytene are bunched together opposite the centrosome (Figure 40); but this is not invariably seen, and is commoner in animals than in plants. The chromosomes in the bouquet usually consist of thin loops with their polarized ends densely contracted, which are thus heteropycnotic. SCHRADER[225] has shown that among the Pentatomidae (the Shield-bugs) a bouquet stage is found only in those species which have heterochromatin.

Some workers (SMITH[226]) see in this polarization merely the residual orientation of the previous telophase, the persistence of which in the interphase nucleus was first described by RABL.[227] HUGHES-SCHRADER,[228] however, has been able to prove that in some Mantids (the 'praying insects') this explanation of the bouquet polarization

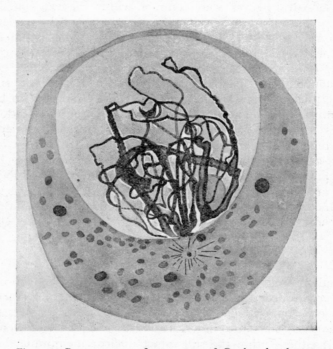

Figure 40 Bouquet stage of an oöcyte of *Dendrocoelum lacteum* x 2933, from GELEI[228a] (*By courtesy. Arch. Zellsforsch*). Polarization related to the position of the central body.

cannot apply. Polarization is seen twice in the meiosis of the spermato-cytes; first in leptotene, opposite the yet undivided centrosome. This stage is succeeded by one in which the chromosomes lose their arrange-ment and the division centre is then no longer seen. Later, in mid-pachytene, two centrosomes reappear in their final positions at opposite poles of the nucleus, towards which the ends of the chromosomes are again pointed. Again, in the spermatocytes of the earwig *Anisolabis*, SCHRADER[229] has followed the division of the centrosomes and their gradual movement apart, during which he finds that each division centre is closely followed by a group of chromosomes on the inner side of the nuclear membrane (Figure 41).

These examples, among others, clearly show that the effects of the achromatic figure on the chromosomes may be seen before metaphase is reached. Nor does the congression of the chromosomes to the metaphase plate always follow a simple course; a remarkable instance of

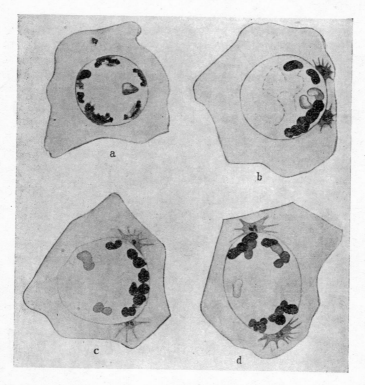

Figure 41 Spermatocytes of *Anisolabis maritima*, showing movement of centrioles and chromosomes during diakinesis. a Early stage. Double centriole in cytoplasm. Autosomes at the periphery. b-d They follow the movement of the centrioles. The sex chromosomes on left in c and d are not affected. From SCHRADER[229] (*By courtesy, J. Morph.*).

an apparently premature movement of the chromosomes on the spindle has been described by HUGHES-SCHRADER,[228] again in the spermatocytes of Mantids, and also in the related Phasmids (the stick insects[230]). The second bouquet polarization comes to an end when the nuclear membrane disappears; the spindle is then very rapidly formed, and the orientation of the ends of the chromosomes is exchanged for one in which the centromeres of each bivalent separate, each towards one pole of the spindle, just as in anaphase (Figure 42). The ends of the sister chromatids, however, remain in contact; and this 'pre-metaphase stretch' is still well in advance of metaphase, for there is yet no congression. The chromosomes are then by no means fully nucleinated and are drawn out to an almost fantastic extent. This stage is brought to

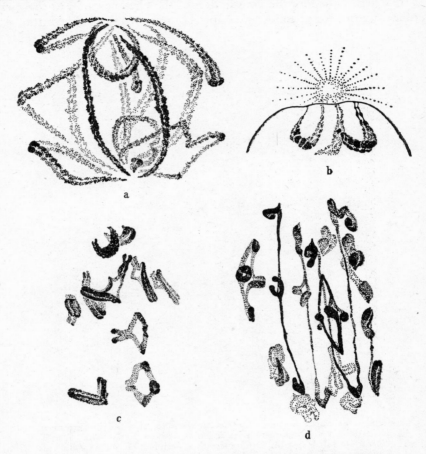

Figure 42 Stages of spermatogenesis in *Stagmomantis carolina* x 2700. From HUGHES-SCHRADER[228] (*By courtesy, Biol. Bull.*). a and b The second polarization of the bivalents. In b terminal chromomeres are applied to the nuclear membrane under the central body. c Early stage of premetaphase stretch. The nuclear membrane has gone. Upper bivalents are still polarized, others are opening as their centromeres orient to the poles. d Mid-stage of premetaphase stretch.

an end by contraction of the chromosomes, during which their centromeres again approach each other; at the same time, each bivalent comes into the normal equatorial position of metaphase and the whole spindle then shortens.

These remarkable observations present us with the question whether such pre-metaphase movements are of the same nature as those in anaphase, but clearly this cannot be answered unless we can form some idea of the nature of the forces by which chromosomes are then moved. Broadly we may distinguish between two kinds of hypotheses of chromosomal movement, namely field theories which postulate attractions and repulsions of some kind between chromosomes and spindle poles, usually electrostatic in nature, and those theories which hold that the chromosomes are directly moved by the spindle. It is still true of all such field theories that they rest almost wholly on inference from chromosome movements; some authors speak of forces within the cell without specifying of what nature they may be, but this practice has no

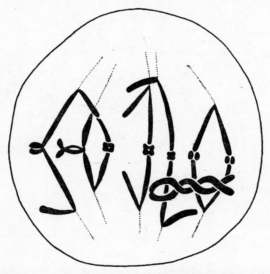

Figure 43 Pollen mother cell of *Tradescantia* after thermal shock. One bivalent is not attached to the spindle, and does not show the normal 'repulsion' of the centromeres. From SWANSON[231] (*By courtesy, American Naturalist*).

more than linguistic convenience to recommend it. There is abundant evidence that the spindle is directly involved in anaphase movement, and that unattached chromosomes (SWANSON[231]) (Figure 43) or fragments of chromosomes (WHITE[232]) do not behave normally during anaphase.

The chromosomes may be moved by the spindle in two ways, either by shortening of the half spindles between chromosomes and poles, or by interzonal expansion between the daughter chromatids, as in the 'Stemmkorper' theory of BĚLAŘ.[233] Either contraction of spindle fibres, or growth of a negative tactoid (BERNAL[234]) may bring about the former movement. It is probable that polar contraction and interzonal lengthening of the spindle both occur in anaphase, though not in the same proportions in different cells (RIS[235]). HUGHES and SWANN[236] have shown that in the chick fibroblast, the early rapid part of anaphase movement is associated with polar contraction (Figure 44). Arguments for the 'traction fibre' theory of anaphase movement have been summarized by CORNMAN;[237] the question is discussed further in the

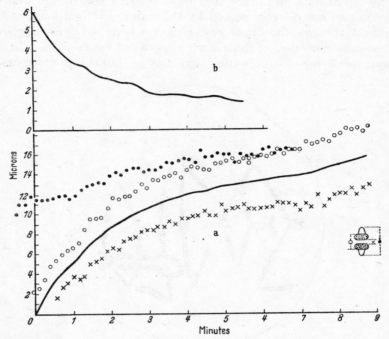

Figure 44 Movement of spindle poles and chromosomes in anaphase of chick osteoblast in culture. **a** Dimensions plotted from alternate phase-contrast and polarized light photographs as indicated. In **b** the length of one set of chromosome fibres (from chromosomes to pole) is plotted. From HUGHES and SWANN[236]
(*By courtesy, J. exp. Biol.*).

following section, in which SWANN considers the nature and behaviour of the spindle.

The contraction of spindle fibres during anaphase, however, raises the question of why it is that the chromosomes move and the spindle poles do not then approach (p 127). It is necessary to conclude that a number of factors must then cooperate, such as the differential rigidity of various regions of the cell. No simple theory of the spindle will account for anaphase separation, nor, *a fortiori*, for the behaviour of the chromosomes in metaphase as well. During metaphase the chromosomes move from random positions into the 'equatorial plate'. The spindle is already present before these movements begin, and is already able to exert tractive effort on the chromosomes, as is shown by the remarkable phenomenon of the 'pre-metaphase stretch' in Mantids. It is difficult to explain the phenomena of metaphase without postulating a state of balance between opposing forces, though in the succeeding section (p 126) SWANN suggests that it may be misleading to apply our usual macroscopic conceptions of elastic tensions to the mitotic spindle. It appears that these equilibria act both along and transversely across (ÖSTERGREN[238]) the spindle. The random metaphase movements of the chromosomes in chick and mammalian cells at metaphase (LEWIS;[239] HUGHES and SWANN[236]) are presumably an expression of this longitudinal balance, though these probably do not occur in all cells. The equilibrium position of chromosomes on the spindle at metaphase is not always median; ÖSTERGREN[240] has found that in two triploid organisms (*Anthroxanthum*, a grass, and the Urodele *Triton*), at meiotic metaphase the trivalents are disposed nearer that pole of the

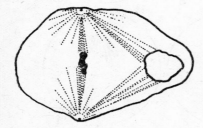

Figure 45 Expulsion of clumped autosomes from spindle in spermatocyte in harlequin lobe of testis of *Mecistorhinus melanoleucus* during metaphase I. (sex chromosomes in black) x 1500. From SCHRADER[242] (*By courtesy, Chromosoma*).

spindle towards which they present two centromeres (p 125). These transverse equilibria are expressed in several ways; there is a tendency for bodies to be extruded from the spindle; it is thus kept free of cytoplasmic granules, and the arms of long chromosomes are usually outside it. Factors intrinsic to the chromosomes modify this centrifugal tendency. Autosomes and sex chromosomes do not behave in the same way, especially if they differ in the timing of their cycles of nucleination. Sometimes, as in the Mantid *Humbertiella* (HUGHES-SCHRADER[241]) it is the X-chromosome which is expelled, while in the 'harlequin lobe' of the testes of some Pentatomids (SCHRADER[242]) the clumped autosomes are displaced, in *Mecistorhinus* to such a degree that the cell outline is distorted (Figure 45). An extreme instance of the differential behaviour of chromosomes on the spindle is provided by the monocentric first division of the spermatocytes of the fungus-fly *Sciara*, where paternal chromosomes move outwards at anaphase and maternal ones inwards (METZ[243 244]) (Figure 46). These examples of aberrant chromosomal behaviour are not exhaustive. There are always individual instances which cannot be fitted into any attempted general theory of chromosome movement. It is possible to pile on subsidiary theories, though perhaps with decreasing plausibility, and in defiance of the principle of OCCAM's razor. When the spindle is present, direct traction by spindle elements is, in the writer's opinion, the most likely explanation of chromosome movement. However, it must be admitted that in the instances with which this section began, where the nuclear membrane is still intact, it is improbable that this can apply. The fact may be of some significance that the orientations and movements of the chromosomes both in prophase and in later stages are profoundly influenced

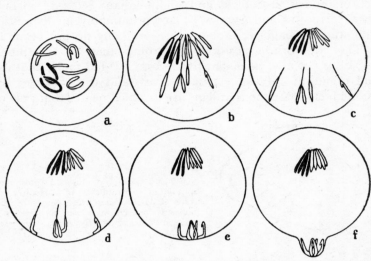

Figure 46 Diagram illustrating chromosome movements in the monocentric first spermatocyte mitosis in *Sciara coprophila* a Prophase showing lack of synaptic association of homologues. b Beginning of separation of two groups. The large 'limited chromosomes' which contain only few genes (represented in black) both go toward the pole; the others separate so that the paternal member of each pair of homologues goes away from the pole, and the maternal member toward it. c and d Later stages in the movement of the four paternal chromosomes away from the pole. Note their inverted orientation, with spindle fibre attachment hindmost. e and f The four chromosomes eventually converge at a point opposite the single pole and are extruded in a polar-body-like process which becomes separated from the spermatocyte. This later degenerates. From METZ[244] (*By courtesy, Cytologia*).

by their degree of nucleination. A close study of the movements of heteropycnotic chromosomes in suitable living nuclei might prove of some importance.

There is some evidence that the chromatin within the intact nuclear membrane can be moved under the influence of electrical forces. Both McCLENDON[245] and HARDY[246] have shown that this can be effected in the onion root by the application of a direct current and that the nuclear contents migrate towards the anode.* The rough sketches which illustrate

---

* The fact that nuclear membrane and chromatin are on the opposite sides of their respective isoelectric points has been mentioned above, on p 52.

the second of these papers are sufficient to show an arrangement within the interphase nucleus strikingly similar to the bouquet stage of meiosis. Both authors agree that at stages of mitosis after prophase, the chromosomes do not readily migrate cataphoretically. McCLENDON used a stronger current than did HARDY, and found that the spindle and chromosomes could be moved as a unit, but that the relative displacement of the chromosomes in anaphase was unaffected.

One of the subsidiary objections that have been urged to the theory that the chromosomes move in anaphase under electrical forces is that on simple inverse square repulsion, it is unlikely that charges of sufficient magnitude to account for the observed rate of movement could be maintained in a conducting medium. This argument does not necessarily apply to the orientations of the chromosomes in interphase or in the early stages of mitosis. HARRIS[247] discovered a polarity in the oocyte of *Echinus esculentus* which affected the rate of fall of the nucleolus through the nuclear sap; the velocity in opposite directions showed a constant difference. He calculated that to account for this polarity, a potential difference of 1·5 mv would be enough, which could be maintained by an expenditure of energy roughly equivalent to 2 per cent of that of the whole metabolism of the cell.

It would be desirable to extend the electrical experiments of McCLENDON and HARDY to meiotic nuclei which were directly observed in life, to see whether potential differences can affect either the migration of the centrosomes, or their apparent influence on the chromosomes within the nucleus.

THE SPINDLE

Structure of the spindle

The living spindle is a clear, apparently structureless body usually visible only because it is outlined by the granules and inclusions of the cytoplasm. Nevertheless, it is not structureless. It is birefringent; small particles in it show unidirectional Brownian movement; on dehydration it shrinks more in width than in length, and on fixation it becomes fibrous in appearance (BĚLAŘ[248]). There is not the least doubt that it consists of elongate particles arranged lengthwise, and the argument that the fibrous appearance is an artefact because it only appears after fixation, need not be taken seriously. It is certainly an artefact, but as DARLINGTON[249] has pointed out, so is everything in a fixed cell. Spindle fibres are not produced solely by fixatives, but by their action on an elaborate structure of orientated protein molecules. The problem is to decide what sort of orientated structure existed before fixation.

The fact that the living spindle looks structureless in ordinary light, shows, of course, that it does not contain microscopic fibres of high density. The ordinary microscope, however, is not very sensitive to differences in refractive index, but even the phase-contrast microscope seldom shows fibres or striations in the living spindle. According to OETTLÉ[250] the phase microscope is capable of detecting refractive index differences in small objects, of as little as 0·004, so that it should be possible to distinguish fibres differing in degree of hydration by as little as 2 per cent from their surroundings. If there are fibres in the living spindle, therefore, either they must be as hydrated as the protoplasm round them or they must be sub-microscopic in size.

Examined in polarized light, sea-urchin and chick spindles show no sign of discrete fibres (Plate XIII (19, 20)) (SCHMIDT;[251] [252] HUGHES and SWANN;[253] SWANN[254] [255]). In both these examples, however, the chromosomes are numerous, so that spindle fibres might be

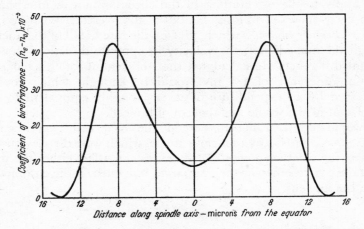

Figure 47 Coefficient of birefringence along the axis of the mitotic spindle of a living egg of *Psammechinus miliaris*.

expected to be many and small. In the *Chaetopterus* egg on the other hand, the chromosomes are fewer. Here INOUÉ[256] has found, amidst the general birefringence of the spindle, strands of stronger birefringence, some of them apparently running from the centrioles to the chromosomes (Plate XIII (21)).

SWANN[254] has measured retardation curves for the living spindles and asters of sea-urchin eggs, and calculated from them the coefficient of birefringence at different points within the mitotic figure. In both spindles and asters, he found a low coefficient of birefringence in the centrosome, which rose to a maximum at about 5μ from the centre, and then fell rapidly to a minimum at the equator of the spindle and at the periphery of the asters (Figure 47). This rapid fall from the maximum at 5μ must be due either to a decrease in the proportion of orientated material within the spindle and asters, or, if this proportion remains

THE PLATES

Numbers *1, 2, 3, 5, 11, 12, 14, 15, 20* and *23–27* of these Plates are enlargements from frames of 16 mm time-lapse films of living cells in tissue culture. The phase microscope was used for all of these except No. 20 which is taken by polarized light. Such 'stills' give only a partial idea of the changes which are revealed by the film itself. The cultures of the spleen of the mouse and rabbit were prepared by Dr H. B. FELL; those of chick tissues were made by Mr L. J. KING or Miss J. RAWLINSON.

Abbreviations in keys

C Central body or aster. *CF* Cleavage furrow. *Ch* Chromosomes, or groups of chromosomes. *G* Granule. *H* Heteropycnotic chromocentres. *M* Mitochondria. *N* Nucleoli. *NM* Nuclear membrane. *S* Spindle. *PK* Pole cap. *V* Vacuoles. *Z* Cell plate.

A reel of 16 mm film including these sequences is being prepared and will be deposited in the Film Library of the Royal Microscopical Society (B.M.A. House, Tavistock Square, London, W.C.1.). Copies may be purchased from Science Films Ltd., Bromley, Kent.

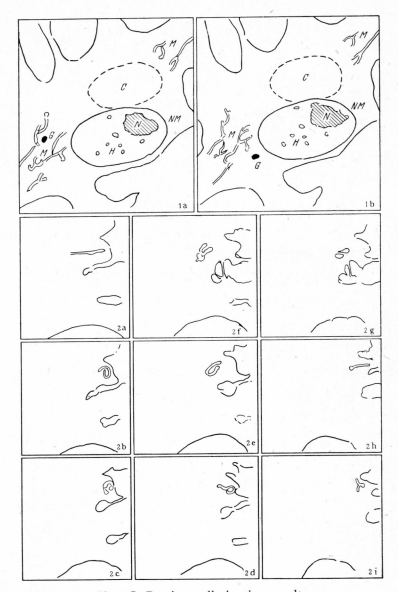

Plate I. Resting cells in tissue cultures

No. 1. (*a*) Chick osteoblast × 2000 (reduction 7/10.) Within the nuclear membrane is the large nucleolus and the heteropycnotic chromocentres. Above the nucleus is a diffuse centrosphere, beyond which are lipoid granules and mitochondria. (*b*) The same cell 28 seconds later than (*a*). Notice the migration of the granule (**G**) independently of the surrounding inclusions.

(*Continued on opposite page.*)

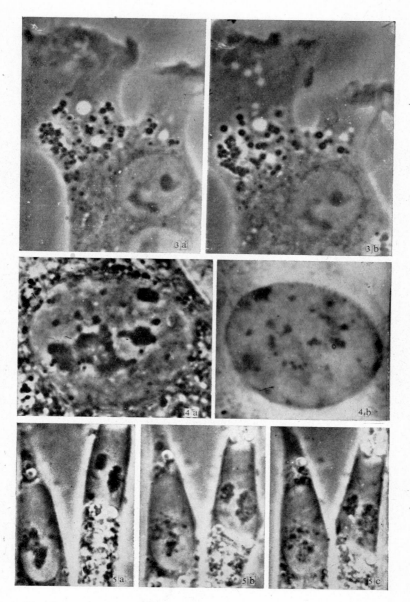

No. 4 Interphase nucleus of mouse spleen cell in culture (*a*) living (*b*) fixed and Feulgen-stained. In (*b*) the chromocentres are prominent; those which are not obscured by the nucleoli in (*a*) are seen in the same position in both. × 2400 (reduction 3/4).

No. 5 (*a*) Two interphase cells in culture of chick osteoblasts to illustrate the effect of 12·5 millimolar adenosine on the nucleoli. × 2000 (reduction 3/4). (*b*) 14 minutes after (*a*), (*c*) 37 minutes after (*a*). (Some effect on the nucneoli is seen at much greater dilutions.)

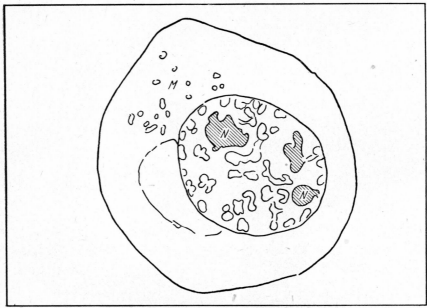

Plate III

No. **6** Phase contrast photomicrograph of tumour cell in prophase of mouse sarcoma 'Rb' by Ludford and Smiles (*J. roy. micr. Soc.* 70 (1950) 186) reproduced by kind permission. × 1250 (reduction 3/4). To the left of the nucleus is a central body which the authors describe as a 'juxta-nuclear accumulation of granular material and associated canalicular system'.   (*Continued on opposite page.*)

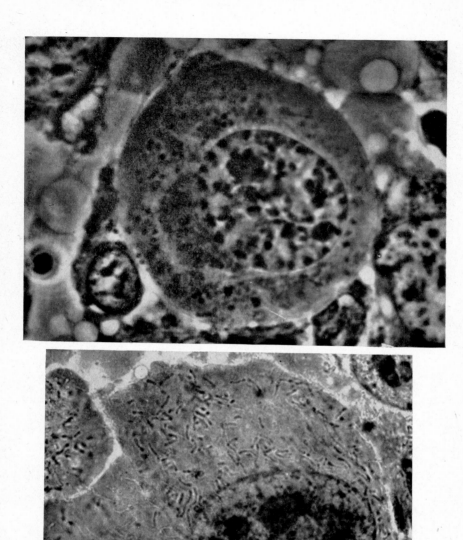

No. 7 Ultraviolet photomicrograph of similar tumour cell in interphase, at 2750°A, by courtesy of the same authors. × 3300 (reduction 3/4). Notice the presence in the nucleus of absorbing material other than the nucleoli, apparently similar to the heterochromatic granules of embryonic mouse cells. (*By courtesy*, *J. Roy. Micr. Soc.*)

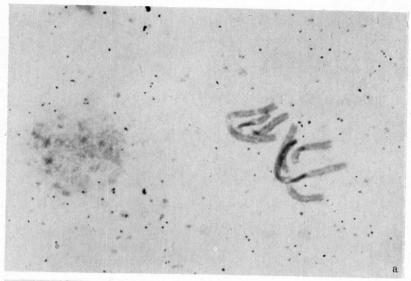

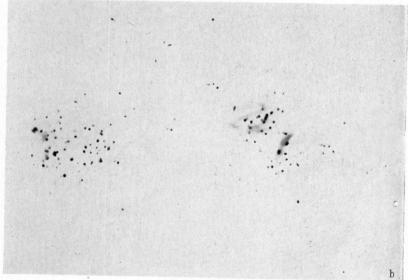

Plate IV

No. 8 Squash of tip of bean root which had been grown in medium containing P^{32}, prepared by Dr J. R. PELC, and reproduced with his kind permission. × 2000 (reduction 7/10). (*a*) Intermitotic nucleus (left) and metaphase chromosomes (right) Feulgen staining. (*b*) Autoradiograph of same field, focused at level of silver grains, which reveal the presence of P^{32}. The isotope had been incorporated in both nuclei, probably in the form of nucleoproteins.

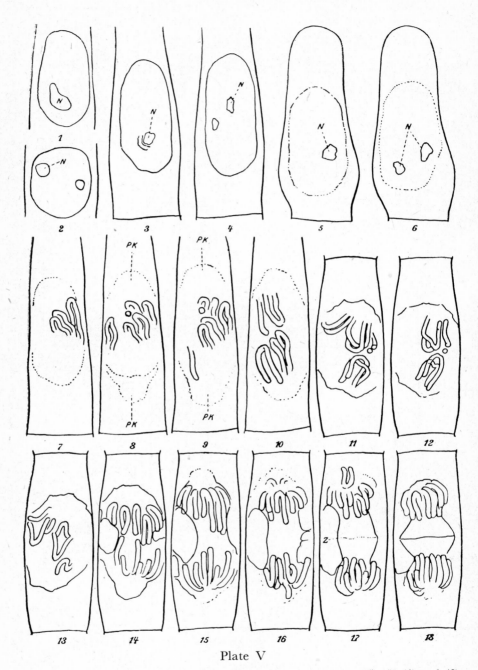

Plate V

No. 9 Living staminal hair cells of *Tradescantia virginica*. × 900. From Bělař[7] (*1*) and (*2*) In interphase. (*3*) and (*4*) One cell in early prophase; (*4*) 35 minutes later than (*3*). (*5*) and (*6*) One cell in later prophase. Nucleoli still present. (*6*) is 60 minutes later than (*5*). (*7*)–(*10*) One cell in metakinesis (stage of formation of metaphase plate). (*8*) is 28 minutes,

(*Continued on opposite page.*)

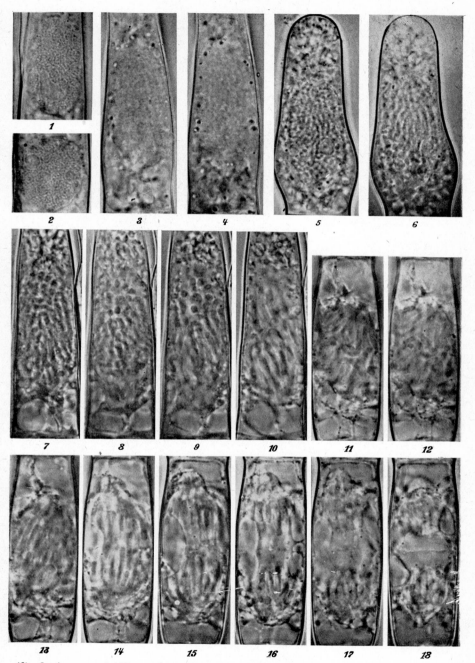

(9) 36 minutes, and (10) 74 minutes later than (7). (11)–(18) One cell in anaphase to telophase; (11) soon after anaphase begins; (12) 2 minutes, (13) 4 minutes, (14) 10 minutes, (15) 15 minutes, (16) 20 minutes, (17) 23 minutes, and (18) 27 minutes after (11). (16) Telophase. Equatorial swelling of the 'Stemmkorper'. (17) Cell plate appears. (18) Shortening and thickening of the phragmoplast. In BĚLAŘ's original paper, the series is continued till 124 minutes after (11), by which time the daughter nuclei are in interphase. (By courtesy, Z. Zellsforsch.)

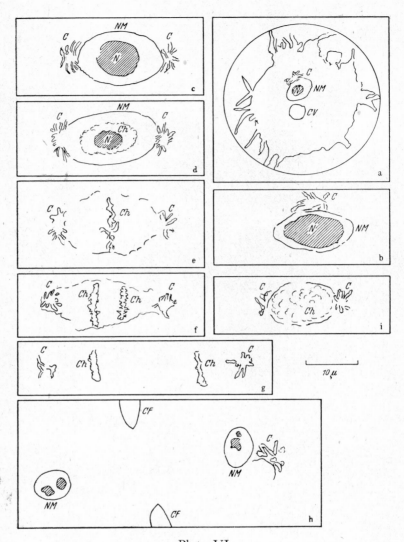

Plate VI

No. 10 Mitosis in living *Acanthamoeba*. Stills reproduced by kind permission from the film of Drs COMANDON and DE FONBRUNE. Magnification of all except (*a*) × 2000 (reduction 7/10). (*a*) 'Vegetative' individual, low power. (*b*) Interphase nucleus of similar individual. In both *a* and *b* a single astral body is seen above the nucleus. The nucleolus occupies most

(*Continued on opposite page.*)

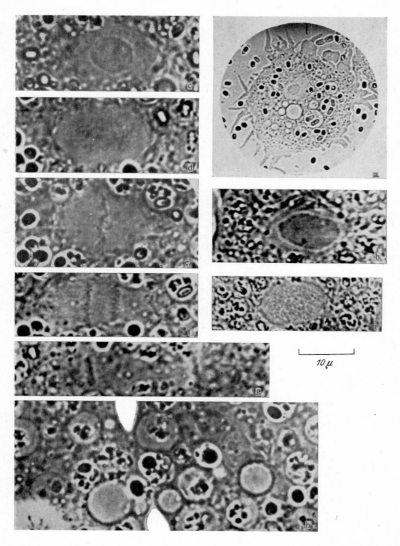

of the nuclear volume. (c)–(h) show the mitotic figure of one individual at intervals during cell division. (c) Early prophase. Asters at each pole of the nucleus. Fine chromosomal granules are seen around the nucleolus. (d) Prophase nucleolus nearly gone. Chromosomes more evident. (e) Metaphase. (f) Early anaphase. (g) Late anaphase (h) Cleavage in process. The daughter nuclei have already been reconstructed. (i) Shows a stage from another nucleus in mitosis intermediate between d and e.

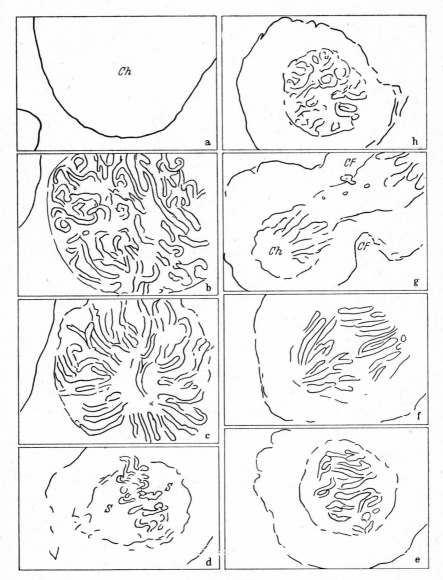

Plate VII

No. 11 Mitosis in a fibroblast of *Triton* in tissue culture × 1200 (reduction 6/7). Culture by Miss M. M'E. Preston. (*a*) Early prophase. The nucleoli have already disappeared. (*b*) 5½ minutes after (*a*). The chromosomes are now distinct; in some the split is recognizable. (*c*) 8½ minutes after (*a*). (*Continued on opposite page.*)

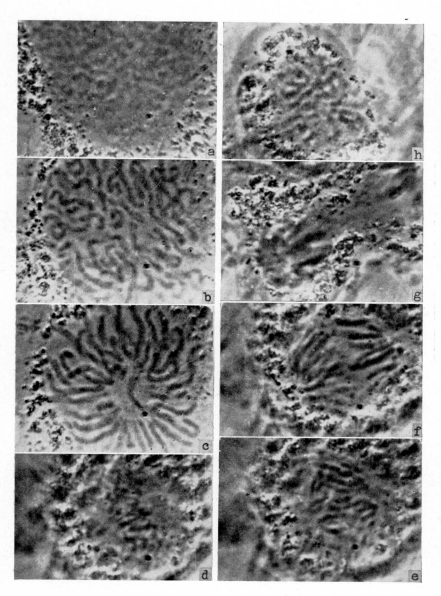

The chromosomes are now orientated round a central space, in which is the developing spindle. (*d*) Late metaphase, 43 minutes after (*a*). The spindle has turned through a right-angle, and its axis is now parallel with the plane of the field. (*e*) Early anaphase. $44\frac{1}{2}$ minutes after (*a*). The arms of the chromosomes trail behind their centromeres. (*f*) 48 minutes after (*a*). (*g*) 61 minutes after (*a*). Cleavage in progress. (*h*) Telophase. 76 minutes after (*a*). One daughter nucleus in reconstruction. The chromosomes are linked by cross-filaments.

Plate VIII

No. 12 Mitosis in a spleen cell of the rabbit in culture. × 2000 (unreduced). (*a*) Prophase. Nucleoli still present. (*b*) 2 minutes after (*a*). Nucleoli disappearing. (*c*) 8½ minutes after (*a*).

(Continued on opposite page.)

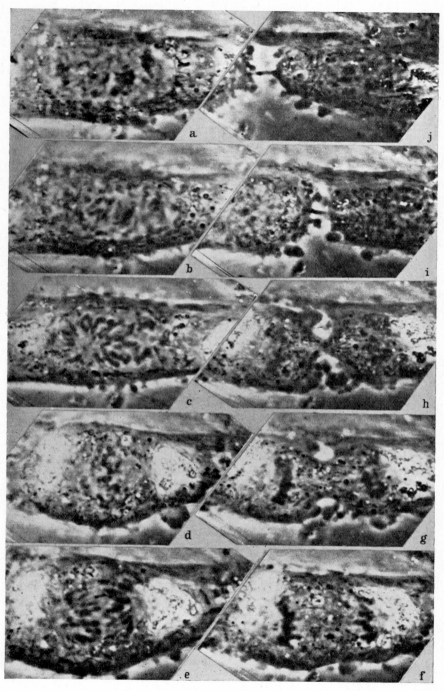

Chromosomes orientated round central bodies. (*d*) Late metaphase. 26 minutes after (*a*).
(*e*) Early anaphase. $29\frac{1}{2}$ minutes after (*a*). (*f*) 31 minutes after (*a*). (*g*) 35 minutes after (*a*).
In cleavage. (*h*) 37 minutes after (*a*). (*i*) Telophase. 47 minutes after (*a*). Daughter nuclei in
reconstruction. (*j*) One daughter cell 54 minutes after (*a*).

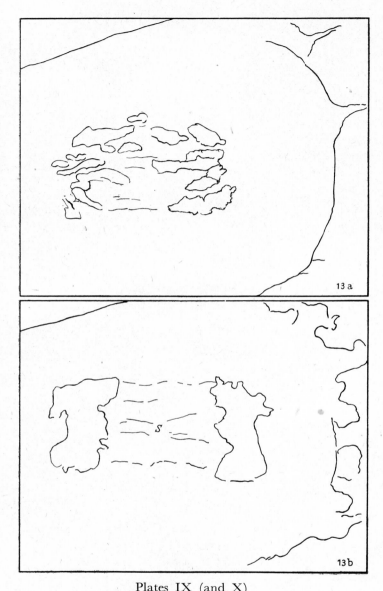

Plates IX (and X)

No. 13 Anaphase and telophase in a spleen cell of the mouse in culture. × 5500 (reduction 5/6). (*a*) 2 minutes after anaphase began. The chromosomes are still distinct. (*b*) 5 minutes later than (*a*). Stage of apparent fusion of the chromosomes. (*c*) 7 minutes later than (*a*). The daughter group is expanding, and now reveals a mass of fine chromonemata.

(*Continued on opposite page.*)

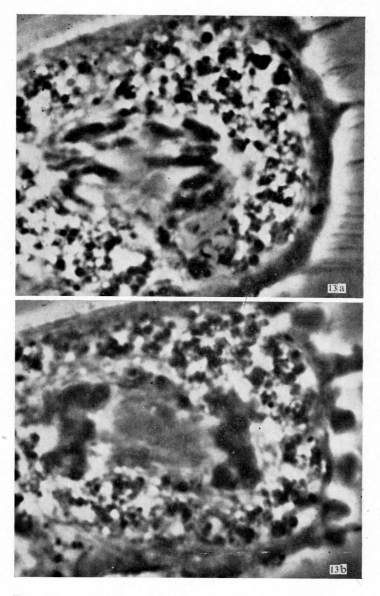

The spindle is constricted, as mitochondria and granules are pressed against it. This precedes the appearance of the cleavage furrow. 'Bubbling' at the polar surface of the cell. (d) Telophase. 22 minutes later than (a). Cleavage nearly complete and the nuclear membrane has formed. The nucleus has a reticular structure, with masses of chromatin and developing nucleoli connected by chromonemata.

Plate X

(See legend to Plate IX)

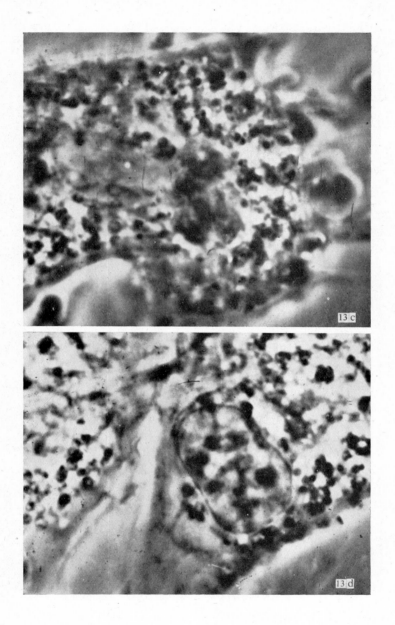

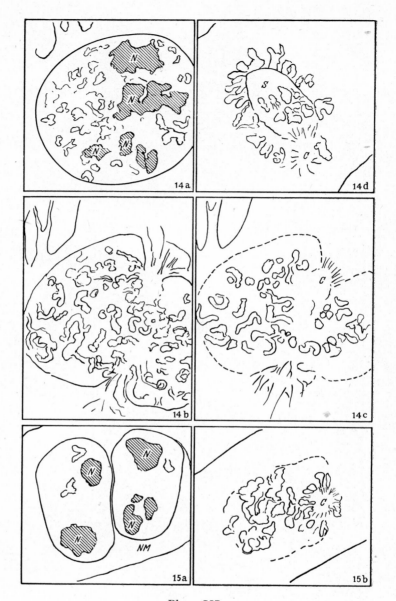

Plate XI

No. 14 Prophase and metaphase of a mouse spleen cell in culture.
× 2000 (reduction 7/9). (*a*) Nucleoli are still present. (*b*) 5·9 minutes
later than (*a*). The developing poles of the spindle have deeply
indented the nuclear membrane. (*c*) 7·8 minutes later than (*a*).
(*Continued on opposite page.*)

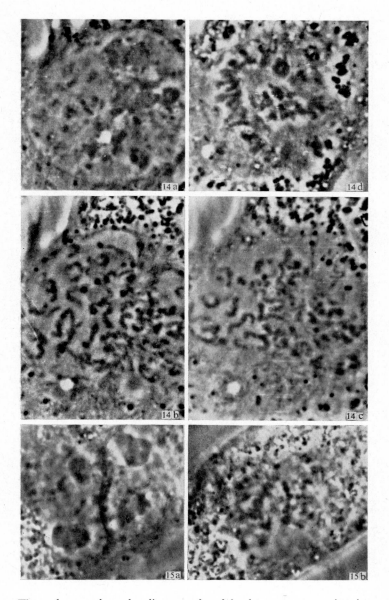

The nuclear membrane has disappeared, and the chromosomes are migrating towards the spindle. (d) Metaphase. 15·8 minutes later than (a). Many of the chromosomes are not yet on the equator of the spindle.

No. 15 Prophase of a binucleate mouse spleen cell in culture. × 2000 (reduction 7/9). (a) Nucleoli and nuclear membrane are still present. (b) 9·5 minutes later than (a). The chromosomes from both nuclei are assembling on a single spindle.

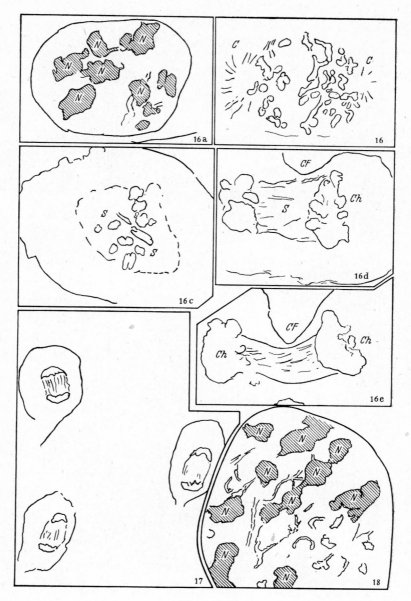

Plate XII

No. **16** Mitosis in mouse spleen cell from prophase to anaphase. × 2000 (reduction 3/4). (*a*) Prophase. Nucleoli still present. (*b*) Very late prophase. 5 minutes later than (*a*). Chromosomes crowding towards asters. (*c*) 25 minutes later than (*a*). Metaphase. (*d*) Anaphase. 29 minutes later than (*a*). The spindle is nearer the upper margin of the cell, where the cleavage furrow has first appeared. (*e*) Late anaphase. 32 minutes later than (*a*). Cleavage markedly asymmetrical. (The further reconstruction of the left-hand group of chromosomes has been shown in FELL and HUGHES[83], Plate VII)

(*Continued on opposite page.*)

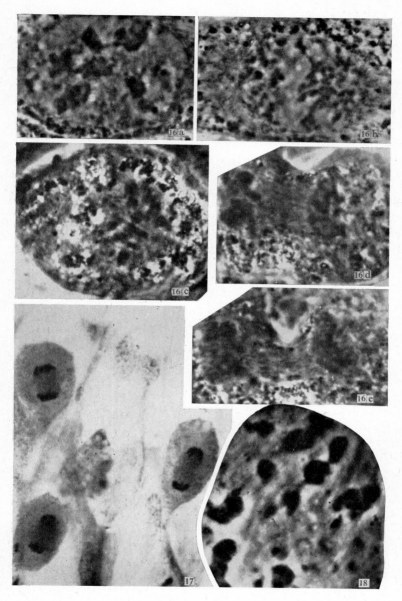

No. 17 Three cells in anaphase from a culture of chick osteoblasts, stained by May-Grunwald-Giemsa. Preparation by Dr W. JACOBSON and reproduced by his kind permission. Between the daughter groups of chromosomes is a 'trail' of basophilic material. × 1750 (reduction 3/4).

No. 18 Mouse spleen cell in interphase, showing some chromonemata visible in the living state. × 4150 (reduction 3/4).

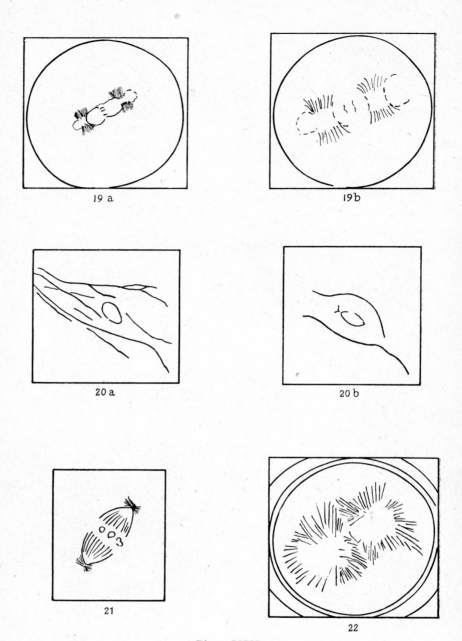

19 a

19 b

20 a

20 b

21

22

Plate XIII

Living spindles in polarized light (reduction 9/9·5).
No. 19 Egg of the sea-urchin *Psammechinus miliaris*, × 450, compensated, fertilization membrane removed. (*a*) 56 minutes after fertilization—metaphase. (*b*) Same egg at 62 minutes—late anaphase.

No. 20 Chick fibroblast, × 800. (*a*) Compensated to show spindle bright. (*b*) Compensated to show spindle dark, small aster visible at left hand spindle pole.

(*Continued on opposite page.*)

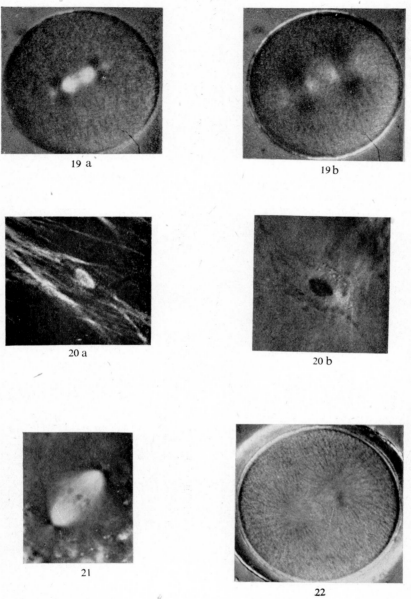

19 a

19 b

20 a

20 b

21

22

No. 21 Egg of *Chaetopterus*, × 800, compensated. Metaphase of first maturation division. Chromosomes are visible at the equator of the spindle. Photograph kindly lent by S. Inoué.

No. 22 Egg of the sea-urchin *Psammechinus miliaris*, × 450, compensated. Late anaphase. Photograph taken at high numerical aperture to show astral rays. Birefringence largely obscured by light scattering.

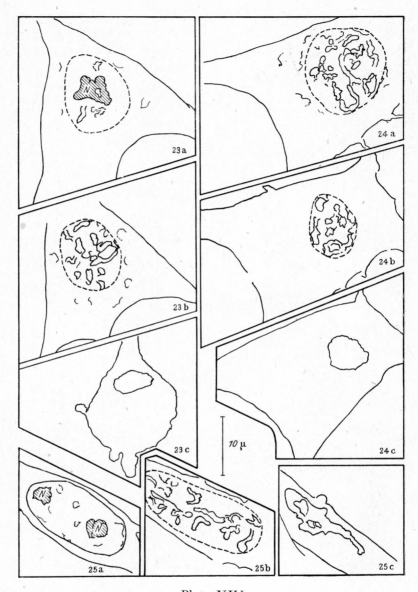

Plate XIV

No. 23 Effect of 0·0027 millimolar colchicine on a cell in prophase. (*a*) 2 minutes after addition. Nucleoli still present. (*b*) 6½ minutes after addition. Nucleoli have just disappeared. (*c*) Fixation after 39 minutes. The chromosomes are tightly clumped.

(Continued on opposite page.)

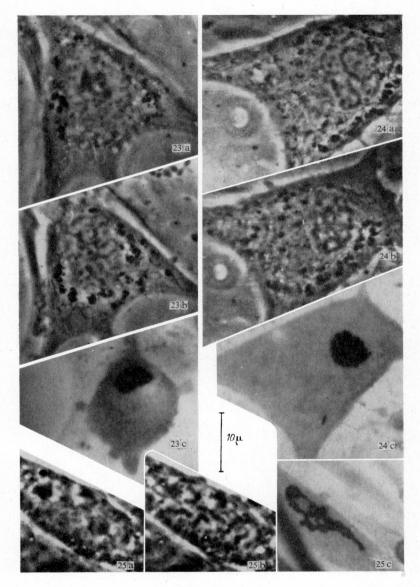

No. **24** Effect of 0·57 millimolar aminopterin on a cell in prophase. (*a*) 7 minutes after addition. Nucleoli have just disappeared. (*b*) 9 minutes after addition. The chromosomes are contracting. (*c*) Fixation after 37 minutes. The chromosomes are tightly clumped.

No. **25** Effect of 0·65 millimolar chloracetophenone on a cell in prophase. (*a*) 1 minute after addition. Nucleoli still present. (*b*) 5 minutes after addition. Nucleoli have just disappeared. (*c*) Fixation after 17 minutes.

Plate XV

No. **26** Effect of 7 millimolar adenine on a chick osteoblast in mitosis. × 2000 (reduction 8/10). (*a*) Cell in metaphase. One minute after addition of adenine. (*b*) Cell in anaphase. 10 minutes later than (*a*). (*c*) Anaphase movement has ceased and cell has not divided. Nuclear reconstruction in progress. 18 minutes

(*Continued on opposite page.*)

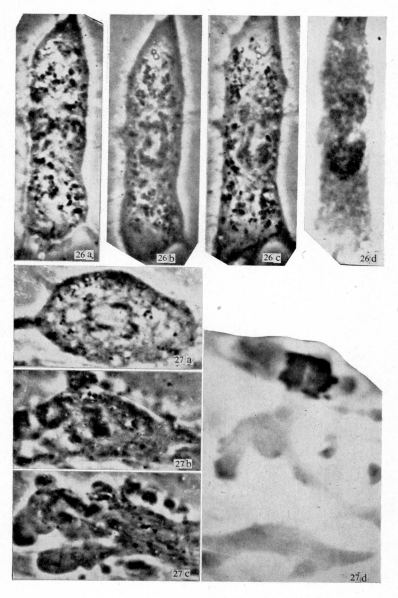

after (*a*). (*d*) Fixation after 35 minutes and stained in Giesma. The two nuclei are joined by a bridge.

No. 27 Effect on a chick osteoblast of 0·13 molar chloracetophenone added to culture as anaphase began. (*a*) Within $\frac{1}{2}$ minute of addition of CAP. Anaphase movement has already ceased. (*b*) 5 minutes later than (*a*). Blebs appear at cell surface. (*c*) $5\frac{1}{2}$ minutes later than (*a*). (*d*) Fixation after 24 minutes. The cell now consists of strands connecting blebs of protoplasm not all of which are shown. In one of these are the unchanged daughter chromosomes.

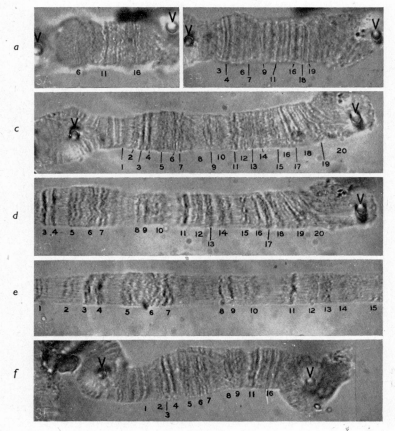

Plate XVI

No. **28** The effect of stretching a salivary chromosome of *Chironomus plumosus* by micromanipulation. × 850. From BUCK *J. Hered.* 32 (1942) 10 (*By courtesy*). The needle points are indicated by V. The numbers indicate positions of same individual bands in successive figures. *a* unstretched, *b-e* elongated 20% (*b*), 80% (*c*), 175% (*d*), 300% (*e*); *f* relaxed again. Notice that most of the elongation is in the interband regions which become longitudinally striated.

constant, to changes in the molecular and micellar arrangement. The decrease, however, is of the order of tenfold or twentyfold, so that the molecular and micellar changes would have to be considerable. On the other hand the fall in the coefficient of birefringence is very approximately an inverse square, which, for simple geometrical reasons, is the relationship to be expected if the spindle and asters consist of a number of distinct unbranching fibrils radiating from the centrosomes. There would seem, therefore, to be two possible structures for the achromatic figure. Either it is orientated throughout, with a varying degree of orientation from point to point, or it consists of discrete fibrils radiating from the centres like the spokes of a wheel. These two structures are illustrated diagrammatically in Figure 48.

So far only a single study of the spindle has been made with the electron microscope (ROZSA and WYCKOFF[257]), but the results are extremely interesting. Using the ordinary precipitating fixatives, these

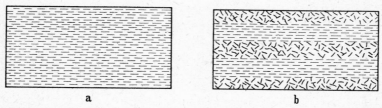

a   b

Figure 48 Diagrams showing possible types of fine structure in the spindle and asters built up from asymmetrical particles of a material present in constant proportions in which the orientated fraction a is constant throughout, and b is variable. In b fibrils are surrounded by an unorientated medium.

authors found that the spindle was irregularly fibrous, bearing in fact a considerable resemblance to its appearance in the light microscope after comparable treatment. With neutral formalin on the other hand, they found that it was entirely homogeneous, with no trace of fibres or orientation of any sort. It is, of course, possible that formalin was not preserving the orientated structure of the spindle, but this is extremely unlikely, since formalin is generally regarded as the best fixative for structures within the cell. Far more probably the living structure was very well preserved. For, as we have seen, there appear to be no significant variations within the spindle, so that we should not necessarily expect a perfectly fixed spindle to show any structure under the electron microscope, unless the resolution was sufficient to show the actual molecules or micelles. In this particular work the resolution was not apparently very high, though appreciably greater than with the light microscope.

From these various lines of evidence, it is possible to draw a number of conclusions about the structure of the living spindle. First of all, it is clear that down to a level of size well below 2,000Å, the spindle is homogeneous, and does not consist of fibres in the ordinary sense of aggregates of high density. On the other hand, it is also clear that some regions of the spindle may be more birefringent than others. A study of the variation of coefficient of birefringence with distance from the centrosomes suggests that the whole achromatic figure may not be uniformly orientated, and that distinct unbranching fibrils may radiate from the centrosomes, the material in between being unorientated. In view of the electron microscope evidence, however, these fibrils, if they exist at all, can only be some tens or hundreds of Ångström units across, so that the birefringent strands found by INOUÉ must be caused by the grouping of numerous fibrils into bundles. It may be significant that fibrils of some hundreds of Ångström units in diameter are known to exist in muscle, flagella, sperm tails and elsewhere, and that in some Protozoa the centrioles generate the spindle during mitosis and the flagella during early interphase. Since, however, it is not possible to be certain of the existence of submicroscopic fibrils without direct evidence from the electron microscope, an alternative explanation is possible, in terms of an orientation throughout the spindle with molecular and micellar arrangement varying from point to point.

The appearance of fibres in the spindle after fixation is easily accounted for on either of these two systems. The effect of most coagulating fixatives is essentially to remove the water layer round protein molecules, so that they can approach each other and precipitate. The precipitated chains may then form fibres. If the whole spindle is orientated, it is to be expected that the more highly orientated regions will produce well marked fibres on fixation, while the less orientated regions will produce fibres that are thinner and less clear cut. If, on the other hand, the spindle consists of submicroscopic fibrils in an unorientated medium, it is still to be expected that large bundles of fibrils will produce visible fibres on fixation. Where the fibrils are more widely spaced, they will not aggregate so readily on fixation, and here the fibres produced will, as before, be thinner and less clear cut.

Since all elongate particles possess a tendency to align themselves parallel, it is not surprising that an aggregation of spindle material, somewhat comparable to that produced on fixation, is occasionally found in life. COOPER[258] has reported that spindle fibres are visible with ordinary light in living *Pediculopsis* spermatocytes, and LEWIS (M. R.)[259] has found that they can be produced reversibly in the cells of the chick by treatment with acid. In both these cases there must have been a sufficient aggregation of material to produce a considerable rise in refractive index. In the same way, HUGHES and SWANN[253] found that delayed metaphase spindles in the chick, examined in polarized light, appeared more fibrous than usual. INOUÉ[256] found that the birefringent strands became more marked in the spindles of *Chaetopterus* eggs that were kept under a coverslip for a long time.

Very little is known of the development of orientation in the spindle, although it has been realized for a long time that focal points such as the centrioles and centromeres are responsible. Classical cytology has been much concerned with such problems as whether the centrioles contain granules, and whether they can arise *de novo*; regrettably little is known, however, of the mechanism by which the orientation is produced. Almost the only significant fact that has emerged is that the orientated region round a centromere or centriole starts by being small and later grows larger by a process of growth or 'crystallization'.

The work of SWANN[254] on the variation of coefficient of birefringence with distance from the centrosome, has already been mentioned. He noticed that the rise in this coefficient at the edge of the centrosome was not as sharp as might have been expected, and concluded tentatively that the orientation is built up gradually over a region of several microns. The significance of this conclusion is obscure, and as SWANN points out, it must be treated with some reserve. The maximum coefficient of birefringence in the sea-urchin spindle or aster is reached at about 5 or 6μ from the centre. Beyond this, there is a rapid fall, which, as was pointed out earlier, may be due to a progressive change in molecular and micellar arrangement, or to a thinning out of fibrils radiating from the centres. In the first case the centrosome is presumably a body which causes general orientation round itself; in the second it must actually generate submicroscopic fibres.

Any individual spindle is, of course, the result of orientation produced by several different centres, namely the centromeres, and in most spindles, the centrioles or centrosomes as well. Because the chromosomes are often small and numerous, the build-up of orientation round the centromeres is seldom clearly visible. The part played by the centrioles is usually much more obvious, as for instance in the sea-urchin egg. Even here, however, where the asters are enormously developed, a significant degree of orientation is also produced by the centromeres (SWANN[254]). The simple notion that the centromere is the point of attachment of the chromosome to the spindle is therefore only part of the truth. The orientated region generated by the centromere does, of course, fuse with the rest of the spindle and thus forms the chromosome attachment. The regions of orientation produced by the centromeres are at the same time collectively involved in generating the whole spindle; in some instances they may even be solely responsible.

The generation of the typical form of the spindle is interesting. Where there are two centrioles, the reason for the characteristic shape is simple enough. When the two regions of orientation meet, it is possible that both systems will continue without regard to each other; but if there is any tendency for the constituent material to aggregate, both lines of orientation will bend round and arrange themselves parallel. Such an effect necessarily produces a spindle shape. At more than 45° from the axis of the centrioles, the lines of orientation would be expected to bend the opposite way, and in the sea-urchin egg, at least, there is clear evidence that this actually happens (Plate XIII (22)). The case of a spindle which is generated without centrioles is rather more complex, and may have to be explained on the lines of tactoids (page 130), where the spindle shape is thought to be due to a compromise between crystallization forces which promote elongation and those of surface tension which tend to cause rounding-up.

Spindle fibres normally include both chromosomal fibres, running from the centrioles to the centromeres, and continuous fibres, running from one centriole to the other. The former are usually more marked than the latter, and this is probably due to the fact, mentioned earlier, that some regions of the spindle are either more orientated, or contain greater amounts of orientated material (e.g., fibrils) than others. It remains to discuss how these differentiated regions of the spindle are formed. Since the essential structure of the spindle is uncertain, it is perhaps unduly speculative to discuss this problem in detail. There seem, however, to be two possibilities, depending on which of the two structures mentioned earlier is the correct one. If the spindle is a solidly orientated body, with centrioles at either pole, and a number of centromeres at the equator, we should expect to find enhanced orientation in the neighbourhood of each centromere, but there would seem to be no reason why this orientation should not melt into the general orientation of the spindle. After fixation there should therefore be a marked fibrillation in the neighbourhood of each chromosome, but no clear evidence of fibres running from the centrioles to the centromeres. If, on the other hand, the centrioles and centromeres both generate sub-microscopic fibrils, those which emanate from the centromeres will fuse with those from the centrioles to give typical chromosomal fibres. Fibrils from the centrioles that fail to fuse with those from the centromeres will meet fibrils from the opposite centriole and form continuous fibres. In this instance there should thus be less tendency for the orientation produced by the centromeres to melt into that of the spindle. It is not possible to say with certainty which of these two schemes is the correct one, but even if we allow for a certain tidying-up of spindle fibres in published diagrams, it appears that continuous fibres, and more particularly chromosomal fibres are usually well differentiated. The evidence from fixed cells would seem therefore to favour the idea of sub-microscopic fibrils as the basic structure of the spindle.

Dynamics of the spindle

The living spindle is usually free of granules, a surprising fact that seems to have attracted very little attention. This may be because the spindle is derived, at least partly, and perhaps in some cases entirely, from the relatively clear nuclear sap (CONKLIN[260]). In many cells there is certainly no great discrepancy between the size of the nucleus and the size of the spindle; but in others, particularly egg cells, there is often a considerable difference, and there can be no doubt that much cytoplasmic material is included in the spindle. It is well known that orientated structures tend to eject foreign bodies, and it seems likely that this is the cause of the absence of granules. The layer of particles that often envelopes the spindle probably consists of inclusions that have been extruded in this way. The tendency to eject particles may also be the cause of the expulsion of loose chromosomes from the spindle, and of the well known centrifugal tendency of chromosomes within the spindle.

Recently ÖSTERGREN[261] has made a valuable study of this and other spindle problems, and has thrown new light especially on metaphase equilibria. He finds that trivalents always lie nearer to that pole with two attachments, and he interprets this as showing that chromosomal fibres exert a force that increases with distance (*i.e.* an elastic tension) since the pull of the two fibres can only be balanced by the pull of one when the two have shortened and the one lengthened.

The idea that chromosomal fibres are elastic attachments between the centromeres and centrioles is an attractive one, but it should not be accepted in too literal a sense. Together with the tendency of the spindle to eject foreign bodies, it may explain the stability of the metaphase plate once it is formed, but it does not explain its initial formation. It has been suggested by DRÜNER[261a] and WASSERMANN[262] and others that the chromosomes are pushed on to the metaphase plate by an advancing wave of gelation, and such an idea is not inconsistent with conditions in many spindles, where orientated growth spreads steadily out from either centriole. It can hardly apply, however, to those spindles where orientated regions form round the separate centromeres, and only later coalesce to give the spindle. In these cases it is not obvious why a metaphase plate is formed at all, and one might rather expect a spindle with chromosomes distributed about at random. An observation of FELL and HUGHES[263] derived from a phase contrast film of early metaphase in mouse cells is interesting in this connexion. Initially the chromosomes are distributed at random in the nucleus, while the beginnings of orientated growth can be seen round either centriole. The nuclear membrane then breaks down, and shortly afterwards the chromosomes move suddenly and more or less simultaneously, on to the spindle

(Plate XI (14)). It is difficult to see how elastic chromosomal fibres could be attached simultaneously to widely scattered chromosomes with the appropriate degree of tension to bring each finally into the metaphase position.

Observations such as this suggest that the metaphase configuration is determined by forces more complex than elastic tensions in the chromosomal fibres, though it is difficult to suggest alternatives. A significant point about the movements of chromosomes is their extreme slowness. It is usual to envisage these movements in terms of their appearance in speeded-up films, but in fact the rates are never more than a few microns, and more often only fractions of a micron per minute. Rates of this order of magnitude are quite incompatible with the existence of tensions as ordinarily understood. They are, however, of the right order for the building up and breaking down of orientated structures. It seems more likely therefore that the metaphase configuration is brought about by the forces of aggregation at work between the various hydrated fibrillar systems combined in the spindle. In trivalents, the existence of two orientated systems on one side of the chromosome and only one on the other, would presumably upset the normal balance and might account for ÖSTERGREN's findings. The observation of HUGHES and SWANN[253] that metaphase chromosomes in chick cells move very slowly up and down the spindle on either side of an equilibrium position may also be relevant to such an idea. Elastic fibres should not give rise to such a slow movement, whereas shifts in the precise patterns of orientation in the spindle might conceivably do so.

Although in one respect there seems to be a case for regarding the metaphase spindle as a complex dynamic system, in another respect it is certainly static. Having grown to a certain size in prophase, it remains so throughout metaphase, whether this lasts for only a few minutes, or for a much longer period. Chick cells in tissue culture for instance, may stick in metaphase for hours; some marine eggs are shed in the metaphase of the first maturation division, in which condition they remain until they are fertilized. In no case, however, does the metaphase spindle show any tendency to increase in size, and as regards the intake and orientation of new material, it is clearly in a state of equilibrium.

With the start of anaphase, this equilibrium is upset, and the birefringence of the spindle declines as the chromosomes move apart. This drop in birefringence was first noticed by SCHMIDT,[251] [252] and was interpreted by him as being due to a contraction of the extended protein elements of the spindle. An essentially similar view has been put forward by SWANN,[255] who has made a quantitative study of the phenomenon. He finds that the drop in birefringence starts from the equator of the spindle, and moves towards each pole; it then spreads outwards through the asters. He concludes that the precise pattern of these changes can only be accounted for by supposing the chromosomes to be responsible, most probably by the liberation of some active substance. If the drop in birefringence is really caused by the release of an active substance from the chromosomes, and if it involves the contraction of the spindle fibres, it follows that the chromosomes bring about of their own movement. A number of cases are now known which clearly demand a degree of chromosome autonomy (SCHRADER[264a]), but as CORNMAN[265] has pointed out, no existing scheme, except perhaps that of BĚLAŘ[248] provides any mechanism for it. In theory at least, SWANN's suggestion seems to allow for this possibility.

The objection is often raised against a traction mechanism, that there is nothing for the chromosomal fibres to pull against. Some authors have tried to overcome this difficulty by supposing the centrioles to be anchored to the cell walls, or to the bulk of the cytoplasm, and in those cells that contain asters this seems not unreasonable; but it is questionable whether any such mechanism is necessary. The spindle is known to be an appreciably rigid body, held together at either pole by centrioles, or possibly by the type of forces operative in tactoids. In either case, it contains, besides the 'chromosome fibre' material, considerable amounts of 'continuous fibre' material, and there is no reason why this interstitial component should not act as the necessary brace against the contraction. The rates of chromosome movement are so slow that the forces involved must be extremely small. Such an idea receives some support from the work on spindle elongation by HUGHES and SWANN.[253] A few of their curves show a perceptible shortening of the spindle at or just before the beginning of anaphase. This shortening is just what might be expected if the contraction of 'spindle fibres' were causing a slight compression in the rest of the spindle. On the other hand the majority of their curves do not show a shortening; nor do the curves of RIS[266][267] or SWANN.[255] It would be interesting to know if perceptible shortening occurs more often in those spindles where the chromosomes are large, and the proportion of 'continuous fibre' material is small.

The extent of the contraction of chromosomal fibres is not always easily determined. In cases where the centriole is small and clearly defined throughout mitosis, measurement presents no great problem; but where the centrosomes are large and ill defined, as in the sea-urchin, it is more difficult. In Table IV that follows some figures are given for the extent of this contraction, measured from the centre of the centriole or centrosome. In no case is the contraction particularly large compared with that of smooth muscle, which may contract down to about one-tenth of its extended length.

Curves of the anaphase movement of chromosomes have been obtained by a number of workers. HUGHES and SWANN[253] found in the chick, that the rate of separation fell off steadily (Figure 44). However, Ris[267] found an initial sigmoid inflection with the spermatocytes of *Chortophaga*, and Hughes and Preston[268] found a similar inflection with Amphibian cells. It is hard to know what significance to attach to these curves. Hughes and Swann[253] pointed out that the general form of their curves suggested a contractile mechanism, but it is questionable how far chromosomes can be treated as bodies being pulled through a viscous medium. The fact that both large and small chromosomes move at the same rate, for instance, suggests that ordinary dynamic considerations may not be relevant. It is clear, however, that it would be difficult to account for any of the curves on the basis of a repulsive force between chromosomes. If Swann's hypothesis about the cause of chromosome movement is correct, the velocity, though depending to some extent on the response of the contractile elements, will be largely

TABLE IV. EXTENT OF CHROMOSOMAL FIBRE CONTRACTION

Material	Contraction (length at metaphase/length at anaphase)
Psammechinus egg (Swann, unpublished)	3·5
Chick tissue culture cell (Hughes and Swann[253])	4·5
Chortophaga spermatocytes (Ris[267])	4·0–4·5
Tamalia Primary spermatocytes (Ris[266])	2·0
Protenor Primary spermatocytes (Ris[266])	5·0

determined by the rate of release of the active substance. If this is so, it is of doubtful value to search for any mechanical significance in such curves.

It is well known that chromosome separation is due not only to a contraction of the chromosomal fibres, but in some cases, to a general elongation of the spindle as well. Ris[266] [267] recognizes that in most cells, anaphase movement is due to a combination of the two. The idea that chromosomes may be pushed as well as pulled apart is an old one. It forms part of several theories of mitosis, in particular that of Bělař, who postulated in his earlier papers a definite body, the 'Stemmkorper' which forces the daughter groups apart. Ris, however, maintains that growth is nowhere localized.

If a spindle is to elongate it must either take in new material, or, if the volume remains constant, it must become thinner. Only the observations of Bělař[248] give any indication of thinning, and there is no doubt that the spindle normally increases in volume as it lengthens. Curves of elongation, taken from the data of Ris,[267] Hughes and Swann,[253] and Swann,[255] all agree in showing that it remains more or less constant in size at metaphase, whereas it grows rapidly during anaphase. The spindle, having previously been unable to take in new material, is suddenly enabled to do so. An exactly similar state of affairs was observed by SWANN[255] in the asters of the sea-urchin egg. Having been constant in size throughout prophase and metaphase, they start growing rapidly in anaphase.

Anaphase evidently involves a drastic change in the capacity of the cytoplasm to aggregate and orient. SWANN[255] has related this to the release by the chromosomes of a second active substance, with rather different properties from the one responsible for the decline in birefringence of the spindle. The argument for postulating a second substance, however, is not easily summarized, and the reader is referred to the original paper for details.

For whatever reason, the spindle does take in new material at anaphase; it remains to decide how it does so, for growth of the spindle would be expected to lead mainly to an increase in diameter, whereas in fact there is only an increase in length. This, like many other properties of the spindle, can probably be explained in terms of a hydrated system of asymmetrical particles. Such particles tend to aggregate linearly, but for reasons discussed earlier, a certain curvature is imposed on them in the spindle. If extra material is then taken in, as the result of some change in the conditions governing aggregation, the spindle will tend to acquire a greater curvature. This, however, will be opposed by the tendency towards linear arrangement of particles. Providing that internal rearrangement can take place (and for a highly hydrated system this is almost certainly the case) a new equilibrium will be established, and the spindle will elongate. It might be expected that the original curvature would be restored, though in fact the spindle at the end of anaphase is usually less curved than at metaphase (p 132). Presumably therefore there must also be an increase in the forces tending towards linear arrangement; in view of the increased tendency to aggregate new material this is not unexpected.

Many different factors must be involved in the growth and elongation of spindles. The strength of the various forces involved in aggregation, the nature of the centrioles, the size, shape and degree of hydration of the molecules and micelles taking part may all be important. It is possible, however, to make one or two rough guesses at the behaviour of elongating spindles. It is likely, for instance, that strongly curved spindles will elongate more than those that are long and thin. In the case of four spindles for which data are available, this seems to be true (Table V).

The relative sizes of the metaphase spindle and of the whole cell must also influence the degree of spindle elongation. In most somatic cells, for instance, the metaphase spindle more than half fills the cell, so that the amount of new material that can be incorporated inevitably limits

its elongation. In *Amoeba* on the other hand, the metaphase spindle is only about one-fifth the diameter of the cell, so that very considerable amounts of fresh material can be taken in. The extent of the elongation is, in fact, about fivefold (see figures in LIESCHE[269]).

Spindles and tactoids

A discussion of the spindle in terms of a hydrated system of elongate particles, inevitably raises the question of the tactoid hypothesis (BERNAL[270]). A tactoid is not only the name given to the lenticulate aggregates in tobacco mosaic virus solutions, described by BERNAL and FANKUCHEN,[271] but to any similar body, provided it has a corresponding internal structure (not all lenticulate crystals do). This is a wide definition which certainly covers the spindle, and frequent statements can be found that 'the spindle is a tactoid'. Such assertions, however, when the definition of tactoids is so wide, are not particularly illuminating. The

TABLE V.

RELATION BETWEEN SPINDLE CURVATURE AT METAPHASE
AND SPINDLE ELONGATION IN ANAPHASE

Material	Curvature (measured as breadth/length)	Elongation (anaphase length/ metaphase length)
Sea-urchin egg (SWANN, unpublished)	0·49	1·25
Chick tissue culture cell (HUGHES and SWANN[253])	0·54	1·40
Chortophaga Primary spermatocyte (RIS[267])	0·58	1 42
Chortophaga Secondary spermatocyte (RIS[267])	0·66	1·50

need is rather to find out whether the spindle has any properties in common with tactoids, and whether a general study of these bodies can throw any light on the spindle. These are questions that have been consistently shirked by cytologists.

The only tactoids that have been much studied are those of tobacco mosaic virus, which first led BERNAL to put forward his hypothesis. These are birefringent, lenticulate bodies that form spontaneously in the lower layers of tobacco mosaic virus solutions. X-ray diffraction studies show that they consist of particles about 150Å across, and some ten times as long, separated by an amount of water that depends on the strength of the solution and on the ions present. The particles are arranged lengthwise in the tactoid, but conform to the lenticulate shape. The tactoids have a general tendency to grow; small ones are thin and needle-shaped, larger ones are longer and relatively thicker.

BERNAL and FANKUCHEN[271] examined in some detail the reasons for their characteristic shape. Because of the wide separation between the constituent particles, they concluded that simple primary and secondary valence forces could not be responsible and they suggested that the structure is held together by long range forces generated by the ionic atmosphere round each particle. The shape appears to be due to a compromise between the tendency of the highly asymmetrical virus particles to produce linear aggregates, and the rounding-up tendency of the surface tension at the edges of the tactoid.

The familiar 'positive' tactoids are not the only form of aggregate to be found in these solutions. There are also lenticulate cavities or 'negative' tactoids within more or less uniformly orientated masses of virus solution, and various other aggregates, regular and irregular.

Since both spindles and tactoids are similar in shape, and consist of asymmetrical elements that give rise to birefringence, BERNAL suggested that the parallel between the two structures might be a close one. He went on to suggest that since they both have a tendency to elongate, the study of tactoids might throw light on the anaphase separation of chromosomes. He also made a few tentative suggestions about the possibility of the chromosomes generating negative tactoids, which grew in size at the expense of the spindle, and in so doing, moved the chromosomes to the poles, and disorientated the whole mitotic structure. These ideas, however, have seemed too speculative to be of much value, and as a hypothesis of anaphase movement, the tactoid hypothesis has met with considerable criticism (SCHRADER[264 274]). On the other hand, the spindle is still often referred to as a tactoid, and it is a question of some importance to decide whether such a comparison has any justification. The three points of similarity between spindles and tactoids have already been mentioned. It remains to discuss the points of difference, which are more numerous.

Tactoids consist of large asymmetrical particles which are all more or less identical, and give rise to extremely well defined X-ray patterns. The nature of the particles within the spindle is uncertain, and X-ray diagrams have yet to be obtained. In such protoplasmic structures as have been examined by this means, however, the X-ray patterns are very diffuse, and there is no evidence for precisely arranged particles of constant size.

The forces holding the virus particles together are long range ionic ones. As a result, tactoids are extremely labile, and can be disintegrated merely by shaking. For this reason they cannot, of course, be fixed. Spindles and protoplasmic structure in general, on the other hand, are certainly held together by secondary valence forces, and probably by primary valence forces as well (FREY-WYSSLING[272]). In consequence, they are far more robust than tactoids; spindles, for instance, can be pushed round the cell, or even squeezed out of it (FOOT and STROBELL[272a]), and they can be preserved by fixation.

Whereas tactoids grow and fuse with great ease, spindles and asters apparently do not. Every spindle is the product of a number of definite orientating centres without which it cannot form. Tactoids, on the other hand, have no centres.

The shape of many spindles, as was discussed earlier, can be explained by the action of the two centrioles; but in many cells, particularly those of the higher plants, centrioles are apparently absent, and in these cases tactoid forces may be involved. It is by no means certain, however, that centrioles are really absent in plant cells, while in a number of cells where centriolar activity is undeniably absent, the spindle poles remain permanently diffuse. It is not certain, therefore, that the characteristic shape of the spindle is necessarily due to the same effects as the shape of the tactoid.

Since spindles only form from a number of orientating centres, they show a different pattern of early growth from tactoids. Whereas small tactoids are needle-shaped, spindles form in a number of ways, none of which resembles the growth of a tactoid except perhaps the small acuminate spindles that form round individual chromosomes in species such as *Acroschismus* (HUGHES-SCHRADER[273]). Since tactoids do not possess orientating centres, they never, of course, produce asters.

Once again, as the result of orientating centres, the internal structure of the spindle is complicated by regions of greater and lesser birefringence. Except for the rather doubtful possibility that tactoids may contain within them negative tactoids, there is no reason to suppose that the internal structure of the tactoid varies from point to point, and considerable reason to suppose that it does not.

Even the similarity between the two bodies as regards birefringence is superficial. The polarized light photographs given by BERNAL and FANKUCHEN show that tactoids are uniformly bright, whereas spindles are always less birefringent at the equator. The reasons for this have been discussed by SWANN[254] and briefly also in the present section. It must be due either to a thinning out of sub-microscopic fibrils or to a change in molecular and micellar arrangement. Neither of these effects is to be found in the tactoid.

Finally, there is the question of the lengthening of the spindle in anaphase. Whereas the tactoid grows markedly thicker as it elongates, the spindle does not. Measured from the photographs of BERNAL and FANKUCHEN, the smaller tactoids appear to have a ratio of length to breadth of 4:1, which decreases to about 2:1 in the larger tactoids. From the evidence of RIS,[266] HUGHES and SWANN[253] and SWANN[254] [255] it appears that the metaphase spindle has a length to breadth ratio of between 1·5:1 and 2:1, while in late anaphase this ratio rises to between 2:1 and 3:1.

If the differences between spindles and tobacco mosaic virus tactoids have been unduly laboured, it is only because they have not been made sufficiently clear in the past. It should now be evident that there are very considerable differences, which arise mainly because different particles are held together by unlike forces in the two cases; in one, moreover, the structure is built around a number of definite orientating centres, while in the other it is not. It might be argued that although there are differences in detail between the two systems, nevertheless spindles fall within the definition of tactoids given earlier, and the general nature of the forces that govern the patterns of aggregation is the same in both cases. This may be so; but if the tactoid hypothesis has to be whittled down to such vague generalities, it becomes doubtful whether it is worth having. In short, while it is not incorrect to call the spindle a tactoid, providing the definition of tactoids is wide enough, there is little point in doing so.

GENERAL CYTOPLASMIC CHANGES DURING MITOSIS

It is probably safe to say that all activities and features of a cell are affected by mitosis. The visible changes are most marked in non-spherical cells, which lose their characteristic shape and become rounded during division. This is seen in columnar epithelia, as in the gut wall of the lower vertebrates (COHEN and BERRILL[275]) and to a variable extent in the flattened fibroblastic type of cell in tissue culture, where the angular prolongations of the cell are withdrawn, leaving behind fine filaments which connect one cell with another; at the same time, the cell increases in thickness. These changes proceed slowly during prophase, but when the nuclear membrane suddenly disappears at the end of this period, there is an equally rapid rounding of the whole cell.

During mitosis some specialized functions both of the external surface and of the cytoplasm are suspended. Cilia are lost from the epithelial cells of the frog oesophagus (KINDRED[276]); in the hypotrichous ciliates, all the motor organelles are resorbed during fission and two new sets are formed in the daughter individuals. This fact was realized by STEIN[277] in 1859; CALKINS[278] is of the opinion that similar events occur in all the main group of the Protozoa. CLEVELAND[279] has described the complex events which occur during cytokinesis in flagellates such as *Holomastigotoides* where the daughter nuclei separate as the spiral flagellar band to which one nucleus is attached unwinds round the organism (Figure 49).

The changes at the surface of *Acanthamoeba* during division are described by COMANDON and DE FONBRUNE[280] in these terms: "ce n'est qu'immediatement avant la mitose qu'elle cesse de se nourrir et de ramper. Alors son contour s'arrondit et se hérisse de nombreux, courts, et fins pseudopodes qui sont de moins en moins mobiles'.

The pulsations of the contractile vacuole cease during anaphase, and are resumed in telophase. In *Amoeba proteus* during metaphase, fluid is actually reabsorbed from the contractile vacuole into the cytoplasm (CHALKLEY[280a]).

Within the intestinal epithelial cells of the frog, the secretory granules disappear during mitosis (COHEN and BERRILL[275]). The long filamentous mitochondria of fibroblastic cells in tissue culture are changed into short rods; in the malignant cells studied by LUDFORD *et alii*[281] the mitochondria are normally short, but they become granular after the nuclear membrane has broken down at the end of prophase. At that

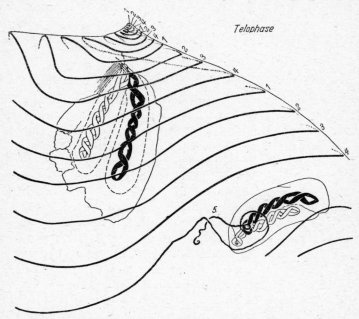

Telophase

Figure 49 Early telophase in *Holomastigotoides tusitala* x 2100. From CLEVELAND[279] (*By courtesy, Trans. Amer. Phil. Soc.*). Showing separation of daughter nuclei by the unravelling of the 5th spiral band, to which s attached the smaller nucleus.

time, according to these authors, the mitochondria 'are seen to have a peripheral layer of nucleic acid. The cytoplasm itself contains little or no absorbing material. It appears to have been deposited on the surface of the mitochondria'. In dividing cells of several tissues, DALTON[281a] finds that the mitochondria decrease in either number or size during prophase or metaphase. The osmophilic Golgi material disappears entirely in hepatoma cells during mitosis. In the pollen mother cells of *Lilium*, the cytoplasmic lipoidal granules aggregate during metaphase (SAKAMURA;[282] KATÔ[283]). Similar changes are described by PEKAREK[284] in the cytoplasm of the end-cell of the rhizoid of

Chara during this period of mitosis. Protoplasmic streaming within the staminal hair of *Tradescantia* ceases (SCHAEDE,[285] KATÔ[283]); BARBER[286] states that 'at metaphase and early anaphase the "boiling" of the protoplasm as seen in the (cinematograph) films of prophase stops completely'. The internal motion of the cell is later resumed.

It is well known, though as yet inexplicable, that some of these changes resemble the responses of the cell to injury; cell permeability is apparently increased in both instances, though observations of this change in cells during mitosis are largely restricted to marine eggs. That the heightened sensitivity of dividing cells to external agents cannot be due to this cause alone, however, is sufficiently demonstrated by their response to radiation.

Permeability

Several methods have been used to demonstrate these variations in permeability of the egg. The most extended study in this field is that of HERLANT,[287] who among many other experiments, followed the permeability of the *Paracentrotus* egg to water by plasmolysis in hypertonic sea water. LILLIE[288] studied the resistance to cytolysis by hypotonic media, while HARVEY[289] allowed eggs of *Toxopneustes* to take up neutral red, and then followed the penetration of sodium hydroxide by the change in colour of the indicator. Most workers have studied the susceptibility to various agents by exposing separate batches of eggs thereto for a short time at different periods after fertilization, and have then observed the extent to which the eggs in each batch continued development. In this way were examined the effects of ether (SPAULDING[290]), cyanide (MATHEWS[291]), higher alcohols (BALDWIN[292]) and ethylene glycol (STEWART and JACOBS[293]). Susceptibility and permeability are not necessarily directly related, but their correlation may be admitted from the agreement between results obtained by the different methods. In the eggs of *Arbacia, Toxopneustes,* and *Paracentrotus,* soon after fertilization permeability is generally high; this later decreases and remains low during the early part of the first mitosis. Just before cleavage, the permeability sharply rises, and equally rapidly decreases again when cytoplasmic division is complete. In other eggs, however, these generalizations do not seem to apply. Less clear cut results in *Asterias* were found by MATHEWS[291] and by STEWART and JACOBS;[293] SHAPIRO[294] finds a very slight increase in permeability to water of the egg of *Chaetopterus* after fertilization, and a marked decrease in that of the frog is described by KROGH *et alii*.[295]

I have only been able to find one instance of a research on the permeability of any other type of cell during mitosis. STERN[296] studied the penetration of sucrose into isolated pollen mother cells of *Trillium*. These were placed in a 1·5 molar solution, and became plasmolysed;

they recovered from this state as the solute entered the cells, and the inverse of the 'deplasmolysis time' was used as a measure of the rate of penetration (Figure 50). In the early mitotic divisions of these cells, permeability to sucrose is at a maximum during metaphase and appears to fall during anaphase. During meiosis, STERN finds that in the pre-leptotene stages, sucrose enters so readily that plasmolysis cannot be induced by this solute. Further investigations of this kind would be of much interest, particularly if another means of measuring permeability

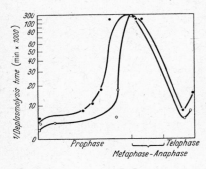

Figure 50 Permeability changes during mitosis of pollen cells of *Trillium erectum*. Time for deplasmolysis in sucrose solutions (inversely proportional to permeability) plotted against stage of mitosis. ● 1·0 Molar; ○ 1·5 Molar. From STERN[296] (*By courtesy, Trans. R. Soc. Canada*).

were also used. The deplasmolysis method is not entirely without objection (WEBER[297]). SHIMAKURA[298] found that sucrose very readily enters the pollen mother cells of *Tradescantia*.

Viscosity

The implications of these variations in permeability we shall later discuss in relation to our next topic in mitotic physiology, namely the changes in protoplasmic viscosity within the dividing cell. There are numerous descriptions of a decrease in the viscosity of cells at different phases of mitosis, based either on the centrifugation of readily stratifiable cells, or the observation of changes in the extent of Brownian motion of cytoplasmic granules. A third method relies on subjective impressions of cytoplasmic fluidity during microdissection. Most observers agree that viscosity is low during metaphase or anaphase. HEILBRUNN[299] maintains that in the eggs of *Arbacia* and *Cumingia* and of *Chaetopterus* (HEILBRUNN and WILSON[300]) 'the appearance of the mitotic spindle is preceded by an increase in protoplasmic viscosity and is followed by a decrease in protoplasmic viscosity'. He says 'it is as though the spindle were coagulated out of the protoplasm'. FRY and PARKS[301] put the minimum in *Arbacia* and *Cumingia* at an earlier point; their results are more in agreement with the subjective observations of CHAMBERS.[302] [303] To the criticisms of FRY and PARKS, HEILBRUNN has replied with some acerbity (HEILBRUNN and WILSON[300]). It is probable that the difficulties of timing the mitotic cycle in marine eggs are responsible for these differences in results. A minimum viscosity at anaphase is found by CARLSON[304] in the grasshopper neuroblast, and between metaphase and anaphase by KATÔ[283] in the pollen mother cells of the lily; the results of these two workers were based on observations of Brownian movement. KOSTOFF[305] centrifuged the flower buds of *Nicotiana* and finds that here also the minimum viscosity is between metaphase and anaphase in both of the meiotic divisions. ZIMMERMANN[306] places the minimum in the Alga *Sphacelaria* at metaphase. LEWIS[306a] states that in the ova of vertebrates the movement of granules in the cytoplasm markedly increases during prophase.

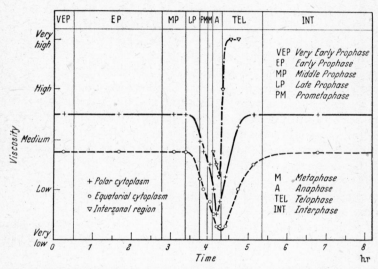

Figure 51. Cytoplasmic viscosity at various points (Figure 25) in the neuroblast of *Chortophaga viridifasciata* during mitosis, judged from observations of Brownian movement. From CARLSON[304] (*By courtesy, Biol. Bull.*).

The measure of agreement between these various observers is more noteworthy than are their points of difference. It is to be expected that the general viscosity of a sea-urchin egg would rise in late anaphase when the asters are attaining their full size; it is not obvious why there should be a similar increase in a plant cell without asters and in which the cell divides by a wholly different method. Centrifugation gives an indication of general cytoplasmic viscosity; in the grasshopper neuroblast CARLSON[304] find that Brownian movement becomes more pronounced during anaphase at each of six sites in the cell (Figure 51). The absolute values of viscosity which are compared by these two methods are probably of the same order; they refer to the lower end of the whole range of protoplasmic viscosities. The centrifugal forces used in these stratification experiments vary from 490 × g for 15 minutes (KOSTOFF[305]) to 12,065 × g for 20 seconds (*Arbacia*, FRY and PARKS[301]),* whereas BEAMS and KING[307] found that as much as 150,000 × g for 10 minutes was necessary to distort the contents of the cells of chick embryos; under these conditions both dividing and resting cells were equally affected. In preliminary experiments in which the magnetic particle method of CRICK and HUGHES[308] was applied to chick cells in culture, there seemed to be no regular differences in protoplasmic consistency between cells in interphase and mitosis.

It has long been customary to relate these and other changes in living protoplasm to reversible gelation; in this way some of the general concepts of colloid chemistry have been applied to living material both in relation to the dividing cell and to protoplasmic activity such as amoeboid movement. The physiology of mitosis has been discussed in these terms by SPEK[309] for example, and by BUJARD.[310] The study of the effect on these changes of applied hydrostatic pressures by MARSLAND, BROWN and PEASE has lifted this subject from a purely descriptive phase into one of experimental analysis, and has enabled these workers for instance to distinguish between different types of sol-gel equilibria, according to whether volume changes are involved therein. The effect of applied pressure on such equilibria can be deduced from the principle of LE CHATELIER. (General reviews of this field are given by MARSLAND[311] [311a].)

Pressures of the order of thousands of atmospheres reversibly inhibit such biological activities as amoeboid movement, protoplasmic streaming in plant cells and cell cleavage. As far as can be judged from the available evidence, however, other features of the mitotic process are not uniformly affected to the same extent. MARSLAND[312] states that if the first cleavage is suppressed in the egg of *Paracentrotus*, two nuclei are afterwards found within the undivided egg; during the next cleavage period such an egg divides into four blastomeres if the pressure is released. There must thus be some anaphase movement of the chromosomes under pressure although cleavage is prevented. PEASE[313] found that the fibrous structure of the asters and spindle disappears in eggs of *Urechis* when fixed after the application of 210 atmospheres, but at this pressure, the chromosomes still move in anaphase, though at a much retarded rate. They often then coalesce into vesicles and PEASE suggested that this effect on the chromosomes is due to liquefaction of the sheath. The same author (PEASE[314]) later found that the spindle of the pollen mother cells of *Tradescantia* can be reversibly solated by pressure. The salivary chromosomes of the *Drosophila* larva are apparently insensitive to hydrostatic pressure (PEASE and REGNERY[315]).

* The changes in consistency of the gelated cortex of the sea-urchin egg will be discussed in the pages that follow.

Cortical changes

The cortex of the sea-urchin egg is a structure of great importance and interest. By studying the effects of temperature and high pressure upon it, MARSLAND[316] has shown that cortical gelation is an endothermic process, and the energy needed for cleavage is stored in the gelated cortex previous to this period of mitosis.* It is to be hoped that MARSLAND will tell us whether the same is true of the mitotic spindle.

In the *Arbacia* egg, the pigment granules migrate into the cortex within ten minutes after fertilization (HARVEY[317]) and are not displaced therein by the centrifugal forces which suffice to statify the yolk granules in the inner zones at ordinary pressures. MARSLAND's[326] observations on this point show that at the equator the cortex is especially rigid:

> Although it is evident that the plasma gel over the entire surface of the egg undergoes a setting process just prior to and during cleavage, some evidence has appeared . . . which indicates that a maximum rigidity is present in the equatorial region. When eggs are centrifuged for a long period (10 minutes) at 68 atmospheres, there is some tendency for the pigment granules of the poles to be dislodged centrifugally, whereas those in the equatorial region remain fixed. This leaves a fairly conspicuous pigment band girdling the equator of the egg.

CORNMAN and CORNMAN[317a] suggest that a 'furrow-determining substance' released by the nucleus at the end of prophase is carried in a nearly symmetrical pattern to the cell cortex'. The plane of the cleavage furrow may be determined at a time even before this, for E. B. HARVEY[318a] found that if the nucleus of the egg of *Parechinus* was displaced by centrifuging at a stage before the dissolution of the nuclear membrane, the egg cleaved nevertheless in a plane through the original position of the nucleus.

In an apparatus described by BROWN[318] eggs can be centrifuged while under pressure, and in these circumstances the pigment granules in the egg cortex can be displaced, both at the equator and elsewhere. BROWN has compared the readiness with which they move at various times after fertilization, and has constructed a cortical viscosity curve at 408 atmospheres which can be compared with that of HEILBRUNN for the inner zones at ordinary pressures, for which the absolute rigidity is enormously lower (Figure 52). The interesting fact emerges from this comparison that there is an increase in cortical rigidity some time before the rise in general viscosity during cleavage; before and during cleavage therefore, when permeability of the surface is high, the cortex of the egg is especially stiff. It is of interest to compare this state of affairs with that which immediately follows fertilization, where again permeability is high, and the whole egg has become

---

* ZEUTHEN[316a] has shown that when cleavage is in progress in the eggs of *Psammechinus* and *Urechis*, the rate of oxygen uptake is then decreasing. It rises again during the next mitotic cycle.

comparatively rigid. MIRSKY[319] finds that the proportion of protein soluble in molar potassium chloride within the egg is decreased on fertilization from about 83 per cent to about 70 per cent; this is correlated with a decrease in the proportion of bound calcium by about 15 per cent (MAZIA[320]). This observation forms part of the evidence for a general theory of protoplasmic stimulation which has been advanced by HEILBRUNN and his colleagues (HEILBRUNN[321]), some comments on which have recently been made by DANIELLI.[321a] According to this theory, the reaction of the living cell to a stimulus is to release calcium from the cortex into the interior, where the heightened concentration of this ion provokes an increased viscosity, which HEILBRUNN calls 'protoplasmic clotting'. The effect of calcium in decreasing surface permeability is well known. This general theory has been developed by HEILBRUNN in relation to the effects of various stimuli on amoeboid movement, on protoplasmic streaming in plant cells, and

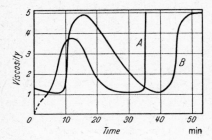

Figure 52. Curves of viscosity against time during first cleavage period of egg of *Arbacia punctulata* obtained by centrifugal sedimentation. **A** in pigment zone of cortex at 408 atmospheres; **B**, HEILBRUNN's curve for whole egg. In **A**, the arbitrary units are very much larger than in **B**. (*From original of fig 4 by Dr. D. E. S. Brown, J. Cel. comp. Physiol,* 5 (1934) 342.

on muscle and nerve fibres. The evidence is most detailed for the stimulus of fertilization, and it is tempting to inquire whether similar events occur during division of the egg cell. There are close analogies between the events which follow fertilization and those which occur during the later stages of mitosis, in respect to the astral cycles, the changes in viscosity and permeability, and also in the birefringence and light scattering properties of the egg membrane (SWANN and MITCHISON[322]). The refractive index of the whole egg, according to VLÈS[323] falls after fertilization, and rises to a maximum just before cleavage (Figure 53). ODDO and ESPOSITO[323a] have shown that an uptake of potassium follows fertilization in both *Arbacia* and *Paracentrotus*. This event is followed by a loss of this ion, which again is succeeded by an uptake reaching a maximum immediately before cleavage.

HEILBRUNN and WILSON[324] have proposed the generalization that protoplasmic clotting is the primary cytoplasmic change in mitosis and have observed that heparin prevents both mitotic gelation and cell division in the eggs of *Chaetopterus*. To this subject we shall return in a later chapter (p 194). It would be of interest to know whether any change in the proportion of free and bound calcium occurs at cleavage, for MAZIA[320] did not extend his observations beyond fertilization. MIRSKY states that there is no further change in the solubility of the egg proteins for two hours after this point. However, one piece of evidence of some importance can be cited. SHAPIRO[325] has shown that *Arbacia* eggs undergo cleavage more rapidly in the absence of calcium in the medium and more slowly when an excess of this ion is added. This observation is thus consistent with the view that calcium is normally withdrawn from the surface of the egg before cleavage. In other types of cell, the order of events may well differ from those in

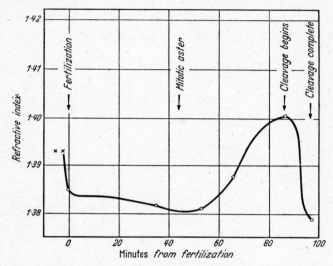

Figure 53 Changes in the refractive index of the whole egg of the sea urchin, from fertilization to the 1st cleavage. From VLÈS.[323]

the egg; the evidence from plant cells, such as it is at present, does not suggest that during the mitotic cycle a high internal viscosity coincides with an increased permeability.

Cleavage in animal cells

The part played by the gelated cortex in the cleavage of the egg cell has received prominence in recent years.

SCHECHTMAN[329] showed that in the eggs of the Newt *Triturus torosus*, the first event in cleavage is an equatorial infolding of the egg surface; this was demonstrated by the fact that marks made on either side of the equatorial great circle were invaginated within the egg (Figure 54). The cortical furrow which is formed grows by the gelation of subcortical cytoplasm which flows beneath the cortex into the equatorial plane.

* The Nematode egg appears to provide a remarkable combination of an impermeable surface with a cleavage 'uniquely resistant to the effects of hydrostatic pressure' (PEASE and MARSLAND[330] with reference to *Ascaris*).

Such streaming movements, demonstrated by the movement of granules, were observed in the eggs of small Nematodes* by von ERLANGER[331] in 1897 and in several other eggs by SPEK.[332] They were believed until recently to be analogous to the streaming movements seen at the surface of an oil-drop when the surface tension is locally lowered. This analogy was the main evidence for the theory that cleavage of the cell was caused by a decrease in surface tension at the cleavage furrow. It is now, however, certain that the surface of living cells is not a liquid protoplasmic interface, and evidence from a number of sources has shown that the tension at the cell surface is very low indeed; this evidence is admirably reviewed by DANIELLI.[333] The streaming movements in the egg at cleavage are now regarded by SCHECHTMAN[329]

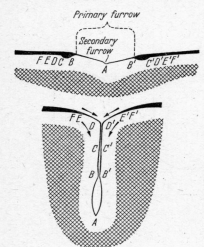

Figure 54 Two stages of the ingrowth of the cortex of the egg of *Triturus torosus* during cleavage, revealed by experiments with vital stains. Cortical pigment black, remainder of cortex white; subcortical cytoplasm cross-hatched. The letters indicate the same sites in the cortex at each stage. From SCHECHT-MAN[329] (*By courtesy, Science*).

and by MOTOMURA[334] to be located below the gelated cortex. At the egg surface, movement on a lesser scale does occur. DAN *et alii*[335] [336] [337] have shown that in several eggs at the time of cleavage a wave of expansion spreads from the poles of the surface which is most marked in the cleavage furrow (Figure 55). SWANN and MITCHISON believe that this expansion begins at the poles because an active substance, released from the chromosomes in anaphase, first reaches the cell surface in these areas (p 127). The cleavage of the egg is thus a complex process, involving the co-operation of several events, the relative importance of which may well vary from species to species. GRAY (1931) was of opinion that the growth of the asters played a large part, for as he says 'any irregularity in the size or position of these structures is invariably accompanied by an irregularity in the form and position of the cleavage furrow.' PAINTER[339] found that if the formation of the asters in the *Arbacia* egg were suppressed by the action of phenyl urethane, cleavage subsequently did occur, but only in an extremely irregular fashion. In the delayed and irregular cleavages which follow the inhibition of the spindle of sea-urchin eggs by podophyllin, however, CORNMAN and CORNMAN[317a] conclude that 'furrow' activity maintains a relationship with chromatin and not with 'asters'. In the sand dollar (*Echinarachnius*), FRY,[340] compared the behaviour after activation of nucleated and enucleated halves of the egg, and showed that the asters divide and form a spindle only when they are in contact with chromosomes and that cleavage is always extremely irregular in an enucleated half. DALCQ[350] succeeded in depriving some of the achromatic figures in Frog's eggs of all chromosomes by first treating the sperm with trypaflavine, which renders the male chromosomes incapable of division after fertilization, and then cauterizing the animal pole of the egg to eliminate the maternal chromatin. Successive cycles of 'cinèses achromosomiales' could occur, but these were never followed by cleavage. In *Arbacia punctulata*, however, HARVEY[341] succeeded in obtaining almost normal

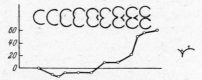

Figure 55. Displacement of particles on the surface of the egg of the sea-urchin, *Mesphilia globulus* to one side of the cleavage furrow as indicated, expressed as percentage changes. The fertilization membrane was first removed. *From* DAN et alii[335] (*By courtesy, Protoplasma*).

cleavages of activated 'red half eggs' which had no nucleus, and observed a cleavage furrow in the normal relation to an amphiaster. Cleavage of enucleate blastomeres within parthenogenetic embryos of *Artemia* has been described by GROSS.[342] In European species of sea-urchins, SWANN (unpublished) found that only the most irregular divisions of enucleated halves of eggs could be obtained.

In normal cleavage, the mitotic spindle of late anaphase in some way influences the progress of cytokinesis. If, as a slight abnormality, the spindle is placed asymmetrically and lies nearest to the cell surface at one point, the cleavage furrow will advance most rapidly in this direction. This fact was observed in the sea-urchin egg by TEICHMANN.[342a] It is also true of cells in tissue culture (Plate XII (16d)), when the advancing furrow bends the spindle before it. In the eggs of coelenterates, this is the normal sequence of events (DAN and DAN[343]).

An approach to the problems of the dividing egg unrelated to its structural features has been made by RASHEVSKY and his school of mathematical biophysics. They postulate that the metabolism of the egg sets up differences in the concentration of metabolites between various parts of the egg. Such differences result in diffusion of particular substances; these diffusion currents in turn exert forces on the cell by an unequal molecular bombardment and by a viscous drag. These tend to deform the cell, while the surface forces in the membrane oppose any changes from the spherical shape; if the diffusion forces are greater than those at the surface the cell becomes unstable and elongates. Elongation is followed by cell division (BUCHSBAUM and WILLIAMSON[344]). From this basic reasoning, these authors derive equations for both the axial elongation, and the equatorial constriction of the dividing egg, and compare their theoretical curves with data obtained from photographic observations of the dividing *Arbacia* egg. The agreement between theory and practice is remarkably close for the elongation during cleavage, though less so for the constriction of the cleavage furrow. However, it is hardly possible for us to conclude that the structural features of the egg cortex, spindle and asters do not play an essential role in the process of division. That it is unlikely that metabolic factors alone are predominant in cleavage is suggested by other evidence. CALLAN[345] has shown that in four species of sea-urchins from Naples, there is no correlation between cleavage rate and oxygen consumption. According to MOORE,[346] eggs deprived of part of their cytoplasm cleave at the normal rate; it is hardly to be expected that the concentrations of metabolites within an egg fragment would be identical with those in a whole egg. Several agents are known which both inhibit cell division and at the same time increase the rate of respiration in the sea-urchin egg (KRAHL and CLOWES;[347] CLOWES and KRAHL[348]). Meanwhile, the results of BUCHSBAUM and WILLIAMSON remain to be explained if they are due neither to coincidence nor to the forces which these authors have postulated.

The geometrical cleavage of the egg seems to provide a contrast to the type of cell division seen in such irregularly shaped cells as the tissue culture fibroblast. This latter type of cleavage GRAY[338] calls 'disjunctive'. The non-regular form of the dividing fibroblast is correlated with the small size of its asters (HUGHES and SWANN[349]). The daughter fibroblasts clearly separate by an active pulling apart; and the stretching of the connecting stalk between the two cells leads to a secondary birefringence of the interzonal region of the spindle (HUGHES and SWANN[349]), which is not seen in the dividing egg. A further point of difference is the characteristic 'bubbling' at the surface of the fibroblastic cell in cleavage; this, however, does not provide a fundamental distinction for several reasons. 'Bubbling' can occur in a spherical cell, as in the egg of *Sabellaria* during the maturation divisions (NOVIKOFF[351]); the process has also been observed in the dividing spermatocytes of grasshoppers and crickets by BAUMGARTNER.[352] Secondly, the process extends equatorially from the poles of the cell where, presumably, the cortex is less rigid. CHAMBERS[328] states that bubbling at the surface of the dividing fibroblast follows this course; this observation I can confirm from frequent observation. It was shown by JUST[327] that *Echinarachnius* eggs when placed in hypotonic sea water during cleavage burst most readily at the poles. CHAMBERS[328] finds that the spermatocytes of the grasshopper *Dissosteria* during cleavage can be readily provoked to extrude polar blebs by touching them at this point with a microdissection needle; elsewhere on the cell surface this reaction does not occur. A further point of resemblance between cleavage in a fibroblast and in an egg is revealed in an observation of JACOBSON (unpublished) who has seen in cells in tissue culture before cleavage a narrow equatorial band of basophilic cytoplasm comparable to the ring of cortical gel in the *Arbacia* egg which marks out the site of the cleavage furrow.

Thus, although the statement of GRAY[338] that 'no comprehensive theory of disjunctive cell division has yet been put forward' is still true, some points of similarity with geometrical cleavage have since become clearer. Little, however, has since been learnt concerning the most obvious feature of the process, namely the surface 'bubbling' during cleavage. Of this the present writer is painfully aware, for in the course of demonstrating films of mitosis in cells in tissue culture to scientific meetings over a considerable period, it has been invariable that this aspect of the process attracts an undue share of notice, diverting attention from other points, and leads to questions to which no satisfactory answer is yet possible.

The phenomenon was first observed by PEREMESCHKO,[353] who noticed an amoeboid movement of cell extrusions from epithelial cells of *Triton* in cleavage, which he was observing in the living state. Study of film records of the division of fibroblastic cells in culture reveals some details of the 'bubbling' process. A clear bleb of cytoplasm is extruded from the cell surface and assumes a rounded outline. For several seconds it rapidly grows in size to a diameter of 3–5μ and then the process is reversed. The bleb decreases in size, usually at a slower rate (Figure 56). There is a strong tendency for repeated 'bubbling' at the same site. The blebs grow larger as cleavage of the cell proceeds; the largest become virtually pseudopodial expansions of the cell wall. Treatment of the culture with any of a number of chemical agents exaggerates the degree of bubbling, some to a fantastic extent (p 196).

It may be suggested that the bleb is formed by the escape of fluid endoplasm through a local weakness in the cell wall, and that its surface gelates in contact with the external medium. Outward flow ceases when the pressure resulting from the elastic tension in the bubble wall balances the general hydrostatic pressure in the cell; further gelation of the wall will result in an excess pressure within the bubble which causes the contents to re-enter the cell once again. Sometimes when an appreciable proportion of the endoplasm is being extruded into a large bubble, the contents of one will be sucked out by the formation of another; the older bubble will then shrink and collapse and lose its rounded outline during the return stroke. Before any further analysis of the phenomenon could be attempted it would be necessary to know something of the hydrostatic pressure within the cell at the time of cleavage.

Cytokinesis in plants

In plants, as in animals, there is no uniform pattern of cell division. A classification of the various methods in plants by which the daughter cells are separated is given by YAMAHA.[354] The most usual course of

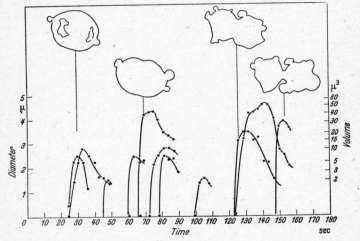

Figure 56 'Bubbling' in a chick cell during anaphase and cleavage. Dimensions of bubbles measured from frames of a film record. The four outlines of the cell refer to the times indicated.

events is that a cell plate is formed midway between the daughter nuclei; this is formed by the coalescence of a row of granules which are either formed, or take up their position in this plane. In the flowering plants, it seems that it is not the anaphase spindle which forms the cell plate, but another orientated body which succeeds it; to this the name 'phragmoplast' is given. According to BECKER[355] [356] there is some variation in the degree to which this body is distinct from the anaphase spindle. These events in the living *Tradescantia* staminal hair cell (Plate V (9 P-R)) are described by BARBER:[286]

During metaphase and anaphase it is extremely difficult to make out any definite spindle in the living cell. Whilst the chromosomes are contracting to form the telophase nuclei the whole cell undergoes very vigorous cytoplasmic movements.

146

Granules appear to flow down from the poles and penetrate between the two telophase nuclei right into the spindle region. They may show vigorous Brownian movement. This granular state lasts only a short time (5–10 minutes) and then a narrow secondary spindle . . . connecting the two telophase nuclei appears. It rapidly grows in width and contracts in length, drawing the two telophase nuclei nearer to each other. The cell plate appears in the centre of it and rapidly grows across the cell (cell plate formation is usually complete 40 minutes after the beginning of anaphase and takes on the average 10 minutes from its first appearance to divide the cell completely.)

DARLINGTON and THOMAS[357] describe the abnormalities of cell division in the pollen mother cells of a *Festuca-Lolium* derivative, in which although the chromosomes are normally duplicated, at the first anaphase the daughter sets may be divided irregularly into two incomplete groups, between which a cell wall is subsequently formed, although no spindle has previously connected them. A fibrillar condition of the cytoplasm is seen in the region where the irregular cell wall develops, recalling the normal arrangement of the phragmoplast and cell plate. These authors consider that 'an orientation of the cytoplasm is in plants generally necessary for the regular orientated deposition of particles to make the cell wall'. In living material this orientation probably resides at micellar orders of magnitude as is true of the mitotic spindle, in which the microscopically visible spindle fibres of the stained preparation are aggregated during fixation and dehydration. ROBYNS[358] states that the fibrous appearance of the normal phragmoplast originates in this way.

In *Spirogyra*, and some other filamentous Algae, a new transverse wall between daughter cells develops by the ring-like ingrowth of a 'girdle wall'. The process was first described by VON MOHL[359] in 1837 in '*Conferva glomerata*' (*Cladophora* sp.), and its duration measured by MITSCHERLICH[360] in 1848. This form of cytokinesis superficially resembles the formation of a cleavage furrow in an animal egg, but is really a variety of the phragmoplastic method. MCALLISTER[361] has described how in one species of *Spirogyra* the late anaphase spindle becomes vacuolated in the interzonal region, where water continues to accumulate within to such an extent that the structure reaches the wall of the cell. It is then a hollow phragmoplast and becomes thickened and striated in the region of the developing diaphragm (Figure 57). Cell division in *Cladophora* (BRAND[362]) and in *Closterium* (LUTMAN[362a]) also follows a similar course.

VAN WISSELINGH[363] showed that if the tannins of the living cells of *Spirogyra* in mitosis were precipitated by any of a number of agents, cell division was then more readily arrested than was nuclear division. It is possible that the effect of tannins in forming electrovalent links (BROWN[364]) may play a part in the extension of protoplasmic surfaces during the formation of the girdle wall.

147

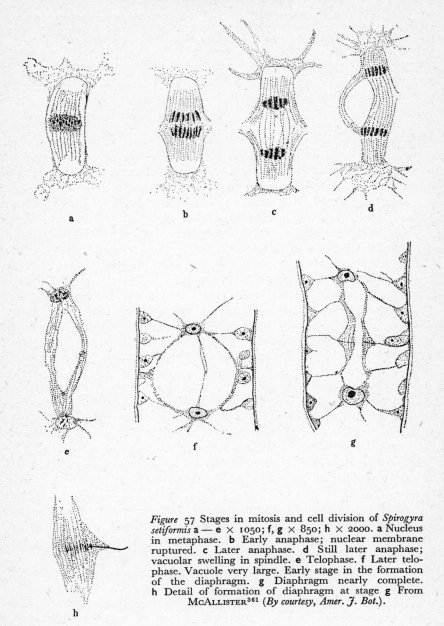

Figure 57 Stages in mitosis and cell division of *Spirogyra setiformis* a — e × 1050; f, g × 850; h × 2000. a Nucleus in metaphase. b Early anaphase; nuclear membrane ruptured. c Later anaphase. d Still later anaphase; vacuolar swelling in spindle. e Telophase. f Later telophase. Vacuole very large. Early stage in the formation of the diaphragm. g Diaphragm nearly complete. h Detail of formation of diaphragm at stage g From McAllister[361] (*By courtesy, Amer. J. Bot.*).

It is probable that our general understanding of cell division could be deepened by an extended comparison of the process seen in plants and in animals. The difference in the nature of the cell wall in both groups necessitates a divergent course of cytokinesis, yet, for example, a preceding period of enhanced cytoplasmic motion often seems common to both. Circulatory streaming in the leaf cells of *Elodea* is sensitive to hydrostatic pressure (MARSLAND[365]); it would be of great interest to study the division of plant cells under the influence of high pressures from several points of view. Possibly something more would also be learnt about the nature of the colloidal changes involved in the first formation of the plant cell wall.

MODIFICATIONS OF MITOSIS

In this section will be discussed examples of variation in the normal course of mitosis in cellular organisms in which the great majority of somatic cell divisions elsewhere follow their usual course. We shall leave out of account the special forms of nuclear division in the Protista, of which those in Protozoa have been so admirably and fully described by BĚLAŘ.[366]

Changes in ploidy

First we may consider modifications of somatic mitosis in which the size or number of the chromosomes is increased or diminished. In the former, duplication of chromosomal material is not followed by cell division; the least modified instance of this is where an otherwise

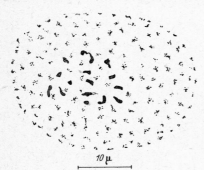

Figure 58 Nucleus of a cell from the testis septum of *Gerris lateralis* × 1750. The number of heterochromatic X chromosomes (16) indicate the degree of heteroploidy. From GEITLER[371] (*By courtesy, Z. Zellsforsch.*).

10 μ

normal nuclear division is not succeeded by cleavage. Binucleate cells can be formed in this way in the regenerating mammalian liver (BEAMS and KING;[367] WILSON and LEDUC[368]). As such cells again enter mitosis, the chromosomes of both nuclei join a common metaphase plate, and after a normal anaphase and telophase, large daughter nuclei are formed which are probably tetraploid; this process has been observed in living spleen cells of the mouse in tissue culture by FELL and HUGHES[369] (Plate XI (15)). Thus a tetraploid nucleus is formed in two mitotic stages. A less indirect duplication of chromosomes is seen in the

149

process which GEITLER[370] first described as 'endomitosis', which takes place within an intact nuclear membrane. This is especially character-istic of insect tissues in which histological differentiation is accompanied by increase in nuclear size. In the pond skater *Gerris lateralis* the degree

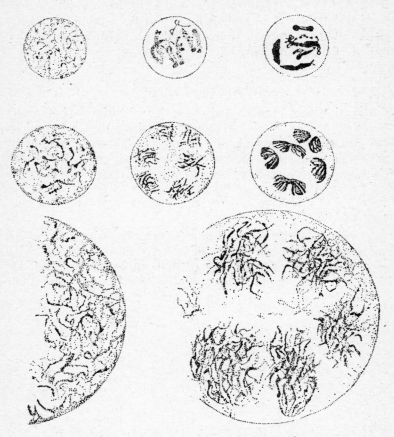

Figure 59 Endomitosis in the ovarian nurse cells of *Drosophila melanogaster*. Upper row: a reticular, an early, and a late prophase (not all elements shown). Middle row: similar sequence of changes, association of chromatids looser in late prophase. Lower row: details of largest nuclei. Many hundred chromosomes must be present in the felt-like aggregations seen in the lower right figure. From PAINTER[372a] (*By courtesy, J. Roy. micr. Soc.*).

of polyploidy in such large nuclei in interphase is indicated by the num-ber of heterochromatic X-chromosomes (GEITLER;[371] Figure 58). During prophase these nuclei contain bundles of chromosome threads which are inferred to be undergoing reduplication. In the nurse cells of the ovary of *Drosophila* (PAINTER and REINDORP[372]) the homologous chromosomes are closely associated (Figure 59), a condition which seems to be another example of the tendency towards 'somatic pairing' in the *Diptera* (METZ[373]). In *Gerris*, homologous chromosomes are usually found in the same part of the nucleus, but there is no tendency towards a closer association (GEITLER[374]). No further stages of mitosis are seen, and it is therefore concluded that the reduplicated chromosomes must resume their interphase condition after this modified prophase. GRAFL[375] has described instances of endomitosis in plant tissues; in mouse tumours, BIESELE *et alii*[376] have figured nuclei with an intact membrane, within which are fully formed chromosomes and without nucleoli; such nuclei they regard as endomitotic. Phase counting should reveal whether this is a stage of some duration, as would be expected if the view of these authors is correct, or whether it represents a brief and variable epoch at the end of prophase.

COOPER[377] and PAINTER[378] consider that the development of the polytene condition of the salivary gland chromosomes in larval Diptera is to be regarded as an endomitotic process. During the larval period in *Culex*, the nuclei of the ileum increase in size and their chromosomes are reduplicated, yet remarkably enough, the resting condition is maintained throughout (BERGER;[379] GRELL[380]). At metamorphosis the polyploid condition of these nuclei is revealed; they then enter prophase and undergo a series of 'reduction divisions' in which the number of chromosomes is reduced successively from 48 or 96 to the normal diploid number of six (BERGER[381] [382]). In the prophase of these mitoses, there is again synapsis of the sister chromonemata. They contract, and separate at metaphase into pairs; there are no chiasmata to be seen during prophase. BERGER suggests that the implication of this observation is that 'chiasmata in germ cells are the result of previous crossing over, rather than that crossing over results from chiasma formation'.

Should it ever prove possible to follow these variants of mitosis in the living nucleus, such observations would undoubtedly be of very great interest. An adequate technique of cultivating insect tissues might make it possible to study the factors which determine the onset of reductional mitoses in the ileum of the larval mosquito at metamorphosis. It would not be easy to find many problems in experimental cell biology of equal fascination and importance.

Amitosis

We pass now to consider the evidence for a form of nuclear division in which the study of the living cell has not yielded so far a uniform answer. Amitosis is known to occur in some cells, but many instances where the 'direct' division of nuclei have been described have subsequently been doubted. In 1887, ARNOLD[383] published a paper on the amitotic division of living leucocytes of the frog. His technique was an interesting one; with aseptic precautions, he inserted into the dorsal lymph-sac of a frog a fragment of elder pith, which became infiltrated by wandering cells. It was subsequently removed and mounted in a moist chamber on the stage of the microscope; the leucocytes then wandered out and could be observed in such preparations for a period of four or five days. ARNOLD deserves a place in the history of tissue culture, and his experiments would be well worth repeating with the use of the phase microscope. In his paper, ARNOLD gives several series of drawings of leucocytes in amitosis. Each begins when the process is already well advanced, and both the nucleus and cell have elongated and are constricting in the middle (Figure 60). The later stages from this point to the separation of the two cells occupied 30–45 minutes. It is rare for the amitotic division of a nucleus to be followed by the cleavage of the cell; another instance where this seems to occur is provided by the erythrocytes of *Necturus*, according to CHARIPPER and

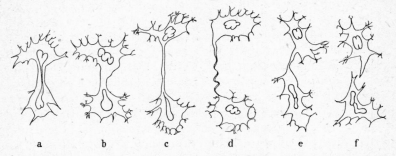

   a   b   c   d   e   f

Figure 60 Stages in the amitotic division of a living Frog leucocyte. **b** 15 mins.; **c** 30 mins.; **d** 40 mins.; **e** 45 mins.; **f** 50 mins. later than **a**. From ARNOLD.[383]

DAWSON,[384] who however did not observe the process in living material. More often, a binucleate cell results from the amitotic division of a nucleus. This event was followed in cultures of heart fibroblasts of the chick embryo by MACKLIN[385] [386] who found that indentation of the nucleus was sometimes followed by its direct division. In one cell, the extent of the indentation opposite the central body varied over a period of more than two hours, but finally the cleft pushed right through the nucleus and divided it into two. This event is a rare one in such cultures; it has never been observed by the present writer. In the study by WERMEL and PORTUGALOW[387] on the rhythmic growth in size of nuclei in tissue culture, one nucleus which they followed for a period of over five hours finally divided amitotically (Figure 23). LEWIS and WEBSTER[388] report that in their cultures of human lymph nodes 'one clear case was seen of amitotic division of the nucleus in one of the large wandering cells', and suggest that multinucleate giant cells may possibly originate by repetition of this process. In order to prove from a series of nuclear outlines in fixed material that direct division is occurring, one must be sure that they never otherwise can become lobulated or dumb-bell shaped. This is certainly not true of tissue cultures, for living nuclei can remain in such forms for many hours.

The clearest instances of the formation of binucleate cells by amitosis are seen in glandular tissues of Arthropods where the cells of the adult organ become binucleate at a time long past that when normal mitosis has ceased. KATER[389] gives as examples of this the hepato-pancreas of the Crustacean *Porcellio*, and the Malpighian tubules of the cricket. Amitotic division in these tubules in the walking-stick insect (*Diapheromera*) is described by MARSHALL.[390]

It has been argued that amitosis must occur in some growing tissues because normal mitotic division is insufficient to account for the observed rate of cell multiplication. STOUGH[391] computed mitotic indices in the 1–3 day chick embryo, and calculated the expected increase in the number of cells in the embryo after a given time. His reasoning suggested that the rate of cell multiplication by mitosis was inadequate to account for the cellular growth of the embryo, and so a 'cryptomitotic' modification of normal nuclear division described in a previous paper (STOUGH[392]) was called upon to make up the deficit. The main difficulty in counting mitoses in tissues such as those of the embryo chick is to judge between nuclei in interphase and in early prophase. Mainly for this reason, mitotic counts of different observers vary; those of STOUGH are consistently well below those of SCHULTZ[393] for the same tissue and time of development. It is thus probable that a mitotic time of one hour which STOUGH used in his calculations is not relevant to his data. He suggests that a shorter time of 27–37 minutes would be consistent with his calculations, but rejects such a figure for the duration of mitosis; yet it would probably be more appropriate for the purpose.* A more incisive example of this argument for direct nuclear division is that of the adult mammalian liver, where mitoses are said either to be absent (MÜNZER[396]) or very rare (BRUES and MARBLE[397]). Yet the organ grows by increase in cell number, and the frequency of binucleate cells increases (CLARA[398]). WILSON and LEDUC[368] are of the opinion that the mitotic process in the liver cell is gradually slurred over with advancing age of the tissue. In the young animal there are full and typical mitosis; later binucleate cells are formed by the suppression of cytoplasmic cleavage. Next in this series, large nuclei arise by an endomitotic process, and finally binucleate cells are formed in a cryptotic or amitotic manner. MACMAHON[402] considers that mitosis and amitosis are interchangeable in the liver.

* WOODARD[394] has criticized STOUGH's reasoning along the same lines. He considers that the intermitotic period in the chick embryo may be more constant than the duration of mitosis. STOUGH's photomicrographs of sections of his material suggest that some of his 'modified mitoses' may be degenerating nuclei, which are often found in embryonic tissues (GLÜCKSMANN[395]).

Apart from the difficulty of demonstrating direct nuclear division, the main objection to admitting that it occurs rests on the question of how far a cell is viable if the nucleus does not contain a full complement of chromosomes. It is inconceivable that the complex procedure of mitosis whereby two equal sets of chromosomes are formed and distributed to two equivalent daughter nuclei can also take place in a concealed fashion during a simple constriction of the nucleus into two portions. Yet the mammalian erythrocyte shows that some cells can exist even without any nuclear component; generally, however, circulatory cells have a limited life and no further potentialities of development. If amitosis can occur in embryonic tissues, then the possibility must be admitted that cells arising in such a manner can beget a persistent lineage of other cells, which might even contribute to the germ line. Among Western biologists, the evidence for this is not considered sufficient to overthrow the chromosome theory of heredity. Nevertheless, rather than brush aside all observations of direct nuclear division with a theoretical objection however strong, we should address ourselves to further consideration of the problem of what deviation from the normal complement of chromosomes, or 'aneuploidy' as BIESELE[39] terms it, can be tolerated by different cells during the various stages of the life cycle. Early embryos soon deviate from normal development when the full complement of chromosomes are not present in the nucleus (POULSON[400]), but there is increasing evidence that irregular numbers of chromosomes may be found in nuclei at later stages of development (TIMONEN and THERMANN[401]). If more were known on this topic, the problem of amitotic division could be more surely approached.

REFERENCES

Somatic prophase and telophase in the living cell

[1] FLEMMING, W., *Arch. Mikr. anat.*, 16 (1879), 302
[2] SCHLEICHER, W., *ibid*, 16 (1879), 248
[3] STRASBURGER, E., *Jena. Z. Naturw.*, 13 (1879), 93
[4] —, *Zellbildung und Zelltheilung* Jena, 1875 (1st ed.), 1880 (3rd ed.)
[5] NORDENSKIOLD, E., *The History of Biology*. Transl. by L. B. EYRE, New York, 1928
[6] SUTTON, W. S., *Biol. Bull. Wood's Hole*, 4 (1902), 24; 4 (1903), 231
[7] BĚLAŘ, K., *Z. Zellforsch.*, 10 (1929), 73
[8] LEWIS, W. H., *Amer. J. Cancer*, 35 (1939), 408
[9] —, In *The Structure of Protoplasma*, p 163, Iowa, 1942
[10] ZERNICKE, F., *Z. tech. Phys.* 16 (1935), 454
[11] TAYLOR, E. W., *J. R. micr. Soc.*, 66 (1946), 1
[12] RICHARDS, O. W., *J. biol. photo. Ass.*, 16 (1947), 29
[13] HUGHES, A. F., In *Progress in Biophysics*, p 137, ed. by J. A. V. BUTLER and J. T. RANDALL, Vol. 1, London, 1950
[14] CANTI, R. G., *Arch. Exp. Zellforsch*, 6 (1928), 86
[15] MICHEL, K., *Naturwiss.*, 29 (1941), 61
[16] HUGHES, A. F., *J. R. micr. Soc.*, 69 (1949), 215

[17] HUGHES, A. F., *Quart. J. micr. Sci.*, 91 (1950), 351
[18] TELEZYŃSKI, H., *Acta. Soc. Bot. Polon.*, 7 (1930), 381
[19] MARTENS, P., *Cellule*, 38 (1927), 67
[20] BECKER, W. A., *Bot. Rev.*, 4 (1938), 446
[21] BROWN, R., *Trans. Linn. Soc.*, 16 (1833), 685
[22] SCHAEDE, R., *Beitr. Biol. Pflanz.*, 14 (1925), 231
[23] LISON, L., and PASTEELS, J., *Bull. Acad. Roy. Belg.*, 5th Ser., 36 (1950), 348
—, —, *Arch. Biol.*, 62 (1951), 1
[24] KUWADA, U. and NAKAMURA, T., *Mem. Coll. Sci. Kyoto.* (B), 9 (1934), 343
[25] NEBEL, B. R., *Cytologia, Tokyo*, 5 (1933), 1
[26] KUWADA, U., *ibid*, 10 (1939), 213
[27] RABL, C., *Morph. Jb.*, 10 (1885), 214
[28] SHIGENAGA, M., *Cytologia, Tokyo*, Fujii Jub. vol. I (1939), 464
[29] PEKAREK, J., *Planta*, 16 (1932), 788
[30] —, *Protoplasma*, 17 (1932), 1
[31] KARLING, J. S., *Bull. Torrey. bot. Cl.*, 55 (1928), 11
[32] GREGORY, W. C., *Amer. J. Bot.*, 27 (1940), 687
[33] STERN, H., *J. Hered.*, 37 (1946), 46
[34] SHIMAKURA, K., *Cytologia, Tokyo*, 5 (1934), 363
[35] TAYLOR, J. H., *J. Hered.*, 40 (1949), 87
[36] DARLINGTON, C. D., and LA COUR, L. F., *The Handling of Chromosomes*, London, 1942
[37] BĚLAŘ, K., *Erg. Fortsch. Zool.*, 6 (1926), 235
[38] HERTWIG, R., *Jena Z. Naturw.*, 17 (1884), 490
[39] BĚLAŘ, K., *Arch. Protistenk*, 43 (1921), 431
[40] —, *ibid*, 46 (1922), 1
[41] CHALKLEY, H. W. and DANIEL, G. E., *Physiol. Zool.*, 6 (1933), 592
[42] DAWSON, J. A., KESSLER, W. R. and SILBERSTEIN, J. K., *Biol. Bull. Wood's Hole*, 72 (1937), 125
[43] —, —, —, *ibid*, 69 (1935), 447
[44] COMANDON. J. and DE FONBRUNE, P., *C. R. Soc. biol.*, 124 (1937), 1299
[45] CARLSON, J. G., *Symp. quant. Biol.*, 9 (1941), 104
[46] — and HOLLAENDER, A., *J. cell. comp. Physiol.*, 31 (1948), 149
[47] JOLLY, J., *C. R. Soc. Biol.*, 53 (1901), 1183
[48] COMANDON, J. and JOLLY, J., *ibid*, 75 (1913), 457
[49] —, DE FONBRUNE, P. and JOLLY, J., *ibid*, 117 (1934), 975
[50] HUGHES, A. F. and PRESTON, M. M.'E., *J. R. micr. Soc.*, 69 (1949), 121
[51] DEARING, W. H., *J. Morph.*, 56 (1934), 157
[52] JACOBSON, W. and WEBB, M., *J. Physiol.*, 112 (1951), 2P
[53] ALFERT, M., *J. cell comp. Physiol.*, 36 (1950), 381
[54] CASPERSSON, T., *Cell Growth and Cell Function*, New York, 1950
[55] BIESELE, J. J., POYNER, H. and PAINTER, T. S., *Univ. Texas Publ.*, 4243 (1942)
[56] ENGSTRÖM, A., in *Progress in Biophysics*. ed. J. A. V. BUTLER and J. T. RANDALL, Vol. 1, London, 1950, p 164
[57] BĚLAŘ, K., *Arch. f. Entw.Mech.*, 118 (1929), 359
[58] AISENBERG, E. J., *Bull. Histol. Tech. micr.* appl., 12 (1935), 100
[59] GRAY, J., *Quart. J. micr. Sci.*, 58 (1913), 447

Time scale of the mitotic cycle

[60] MITSCHERLICH, E., *J. prakt. Chem.*, 43 (1848), 158
[61] FAURÉ-FREMIET, E., *Arch. Anat., micr.*, 15 (1913), 435
[61a] — *ibid* 20 (1924), 211
[62] WRIGHT, G. P., *J. R. micr. Soc.*, — (1925), 414
[63] GRAY, L. H., and SCHOLES, M. E., *Brit. J. Radiol.*, 34 (1951)
[63a] BROWN, R., *J. exp. Bot.*, 2 (1951), 96
[64] LAUGHLIN, H. H., *Carn. Int. Wash.* Publ. 265 (1919), 488
[65] COOPER, Z. K. and SCHIFF, A., *Proc. Soc. exp. Biol., N.Y.*, 39 (1938), 323
[66] — and FRANKLIN, H. C., *Anat. Rec.*, 78 (1940), 1

[67] BLUMENFELD, C. M., *ibid*, 72 (1938), 435
[67a] LOEB, J., *Arch. ges. Physiol.* 124 (1908) 411
[68] BULLOUGH, W. S., *Proc. roy. Soc.* (B), 135 (1948), 212
[69] MÖLLERBERG, H., *Acta. anat. Basel.*, 4 (1948), 393
[70] BULLOUGH, W. S., *J. Endocrinl.*, 6 (1950), 350
[71] COMANDON, J. and DE FONBRUNE, P., *C. R. Soc. Biol.*, 124 (1937), 1299
[72] BĚLAŘ, K., *Erg. Fortsch. Zoologie.*, 6 (1926), 235
—, *Arch. Protistenk.*, 46 (1922), 1
[73] STERN, C., *ibid*, 48 (1924), 436
[74] ZIMMERMANN, W., *Z. Bot.*, 15 (1923), 113
[75] MARTENS, P., *Cellule*, 38 (1927), 67
[76] BARBER, H. N., *Chromosoma*, 1 (1939), 33
[77] CARLSON, J. G. and HOLLAENDER, A., *J. cell comp. Physiol.*, 31 (1948), 149
[78] JOLLY, J., *Arch. Anat. micr.*, 6 (1904), 455
[79] WASSERMANN, in VON MÖLLENDORF, W., *Handbuch der Mikroskopisches Anatomie des Menschens* I Pt. 2. Berlin, 1929
[80] HUGHES, A. F. and FELL, H. B., *Quart. J. micr. Sci.*, 90 (1949), 37
[81] —, *J. R. micr. Soc.*, 69 (1949), 215
[81a] — and PRESTON, M. M. E., *J. R. micr. Soc.*, 69 (1949), 121
[82] HUETTNER, A. F., *Z. Zellforsch*, 19 (1933), 119
[83] FELL, H. B. and HUGHES, A. F., *Quart. J. micr. Sci.*, 90 (1949), 355
[84] METCALF, M. M., *Bull. U.S. nat. Mus.*, Bulletin 120 (1923)
[85] CLEVELAND, L. R., *Trans. Amer. phil. Soc.*, 39 (1949), 1
[86] BUSCHKE, W., FRIEDENWALD, J. S. and FLEISCHMANN, W., *Bull. Johns Hopk. Hosp.*, 73 (1943), 143
[87] DE WILDEMAN, E., *Ann. Soc. Belge Micros.*, 15 (1891), 5
[88] HEILBRUNN, L. V., *An Outline of General Physiology*, Philadelphia, 1943
[89] HÖBER, R., *Physical Chemistry of Cells and Tissues*, London, 1946
[90] EPHRUSSI, B., *Protoplasma*, 1 (1926), 105
[91] FRY, H. J., *Biol. Bull., Wood's Hole*, 70 (1936), 89
[92] BUCCIANTE, L., *Arch. exp. Zellforsch.*, 5 (1927), 1
[93] GRAY, J., *Brit. J. exp. Biol.*, 4 (1927), 313
[94] RUGH, R., *Experimental Embryology*, Minneapolis, 1948
[95] PINCUS, G., *Proc. roy. Soc. B.*, 107 (1930), 132
[96] LEWIS, W. H. and GREGORY, P. W., *Science*, 69 (1929), 226
[97] OLIVO, O. M. and SLAVITCH, E., *Arch. EntwMech.*, 121 (1930), 96
[98] SCHULTZ, A. F., *Proc. Okla. Acad. Sci.*, 2 (1922), 45
[99] TISCHLER, G., *Allgemeine Pflanzenkaryologie*, 1921, Berlin
[100] FRIESNER, R. C., *Amer. J. Bot.*, 7 (1920), 380
[101] WINTER, J. M., *Trans. Amer. micr. Soc.*, 48 (1929), 276
[101a] MILLETTI, A., *Arch. Ital. Anat. Embryol.*, 54 (1950), 339

Structure of the chromosomes

[102] DARLINGTON, C. D., *Cytologia, Tokyo*, 7 (1936), 242
[103] SHARP, L. W., *Introduction to Cytology*, New York, 1934
[104] CLEVELAND, L. R., *Trans. Amer. phil. Soc.*, 39 (1949), 1
[105] HUGHES-SCHRADER, S. and RIS, H., *J. exp. Zool.*, 87 (1941), 429
[106] HIRSCHLER, J., *Naturwiss.*, 30 (1942), 105
[107] SERRA, J. A., *Symp. quant. Biol.*, 12 (1947), 192
[108] METZ, C. W., *Proc. nat. Acad. Sci. Wash.*, 20 (1934), 159
[109] SCHRADER, F., *Z. wiss. Zool.*, 142 (1932), 520
[110] —, *Cytologia, Tokyo*, 6 (1935), 422
[111] KAUFMAN, B. P., *Bot. Rev.*, 14 (1948), 125
[112] KUWADA, Y., *Cytologia, Tokyo*, Fujii Jub., vol. 1 (1939), 389
[113] NEBEL, B. R. and RUTTLE, M. L., *Amer. J. Bot.*, 23 (1936), 652
[114] MICKEY, G. H., *Amer. Nat.*, 80 (1946), 446
[115] KAUFMAN, B. P., *J. Morph.*, 56 (1934), 125
[116] CREIGHTON, M., *Cytologia, Tokyo*, 8 (1938), 497

[117] FELL, H. B. and HUGHES, A. F., *Quart. J. micr. Sci.*, 90 (1949), 355
[118] MANTON, I., *Amer. J. Bot.*, 32 (1945), 342
[119] DARLINGTON, C. D., *Recent Advances in Cytology*, 2nd ed., London, 1937
[120] LEA, D. E., *Actions of Radiations on Living Cells*, Cambridge, 1946
[121] BARANETSKY, J., *Bot. Zeit.*, 38 (1880), 241, 265 and 281
[122] RUCH, F., *Chromosoma*, 3 (1949), 357
[123] MANTON, I., *Biol. Rev.*, 25 (1950), 486
[124] —, *Nature, Lond.*, 155 (1945), 471
[125] NEBEL, B. R., *Symp. Quant. Biol.*, 9 (1941), 7
[126] WHITE, M. J. D., *J. Genet.*, 40 (1940), 67
[127] MANTON, I. and SMILES, J., *Ann. bot. Lond. N.S.*, 7 (1943), 195
[128] PÄTAU, K., *Cytologia, Tokyo*, Fujii Jub. vol. II (1939), 667
[129] CLEVELAND, L. R., *Biol. Bull., Wood's Hole*, 74 (1938), 1
[130] RIS, H., *ibid*, 89 (1945), 242
[131] PAINTER, T. S., *Symp. quant. Biol.*, 9 (1941), 47
[132] HINTON, T., *J. Hered.*, 37 (1946), 99
[133] PAINTER, T. S., *ibid*, 25 (1934), 465
[134] BERGER, C. A., *ibid*, 31 (1940), 3
[135] KOSSWIG, C., and SHENGÜN, A., *ibid*, 38 (1947), 235
[136] METZ, C. W. and LAWRENCE, E. G., *Quart. Rev. Biol.*, 12 (1937), 135
[137] —, *Amer. Nat.*, 73 (1939), 457
[138] RIS, H. and CROUSE, H., *Proc. Nat. Acad. Sci. Wash.*, 31 (1945), 321
[139] CHAMBERS, R. M., *General Cytology*. Ed. by COWDRY, E. V., Chicago, 1924
[140] BUCK, J. B., *J. Hered.*, 33 (1942), 10
[141] D'ANGELO, E. G., *Biol. Bull., Wood's Hole*, 90 (1946), 71
     —, *Ann. N.Y. Acad. Sci.*, 50 (1950), 910
[142] PALAY, S. L. and CLAUDE, A., *J. exp. Med.*, 89 (1949), 431
[143] PEASE, D. C. and BAKER, R. F., *Science*, 109 (1949), 8
[144] SCHULTZ, J., MACDUFFEE, R. C., and ANDERSON, T. F., *ibid*, 110 (1949), 5
[145] PICKEN, L. E. R., *Biol. Rev.*, 15 (1940), 133
[146] FREY-WYSSLING, A., *Submicroscopic Morphology of Protoplasm and its Derivatives*, Amsterdam, 1948
[147] CASPERSSON, T., *Chromosoma*, 1 (1939), 605
[148] SCHMIDT, W. J., *Z. wiss. Mikr.*, 56 (1939), 1
[149] SCHMITT, F. O., *J. App. Phys.*, 9 (1938), 109
[150] PAINTER, T. S., *Proc. Nat. Acad. Sci. Wash.*, 26 (1940), 95
[151] DODSON, E. O., *Univ. Calif. Publ. Zool.*, 53 (1948), 281
[152] DURYEE, W. R., *Ann. N.Y. Acad. Sci.*, 50 (1950), 920
[153] RÜCKERT, J., *Anat. Anz.*, 7 (1892), 107
[154] FLEMMING, W., *Zellsubstanz, Kern und Zelltheilung*, Leipzig, 1882
[155] CLARK, G. L., BARNES, M. R., and BAYLOR, E. R., *Science*, 95 (1942), 250
[156] KOLLER, P. C., *Symp. Soc. exp. Biol.*, 1 (1947), 270
[157] RUCH, F., *Viert. Naturf. Ges. Zürich*, 90 (1945), 214
[158] OURA, G., *Z. wiss. Mikr.*, 53 (1936), 36
[159] KUWADA, Y., SINKE, N. and OURA, G., *ibid*, 55 (1938), 8
[160] SHIGENAGA, M., *Jap. J. Bot.*, 10 (1940), 383
[161] ELVERS, I., *Ark. Bot.*, 30 B (1941), 1
[162] BUCHHOLZ, J. T., *Science*, 105 (1947), 607
[163] ROZSA, G. and WYCKOFF, R. W. G., *Biochim. Biophys. Acta.*, 6 (1950), 334
[164] HOVANITZ, W., *Genetics*, 32 (1947), 500
[165] POLLISTER, A. W. and MIRSKY, A. E., *ibid*, 28 (1943), 86
[166] MIRSKY, A. E., *Symp. Quant. Biol.*, 12 (1947), 143
[167] CLAUDE, A. and POTTER, J. S., *J. exp. Med.*, 77 (1943), 345

Composition of the Chromosomes

[168] SCHMIDT, G., HECHT, L. and THANNHAUSER, S. J., *J. gen. Physiol.*, 31 (1948), 203
[169] LEUCHTENBERGER, C., *Chromosoma*, 3 (1950), 449
[170] CASPERSSON, T., *ibid*, 1 (1939), 147

[171] RIS, H., *Symp. quant. Biol.*, 12 (1947), 158
[172] SWIFT, H. H., *Physiol. Zool.*, 23 (1950), 169
[173] ALFERT, M., *J. cell comp. Physiol.*, 36 (1950), 381
[174] OGUR, M., ERICKSON, R. O., ROSEN, G. U., SAX, K. B and HOLDEN, C., *Exp. Cell Res.*, 2 (1951), 73
[174a] LISON, L., and PASTEELS, J., *Bull. Acad. Roy. Belg.*, 5th Ser. 36 (1951), 384
—, —, *Arch. biol.*, 62 (1951), 1
[175] RIS, H., and MIRSKY, A. E., *J. gen. Physiol.*, 33 (1949), 125
[176] HOWARD, A., and PELC, S. R., *Nature*, 167 (1951), 599
[177] JACOBSON, W. and WEBB, M., *J. Physiol.*, 112 (1951), 2P Proc. Physiol. Soc., May 1950
[178] MAZIA, D., *Symp. quart. Biol.*, 9 (1941), 40
[179] —, *Ann. Acad. Sci., N.Y.*, 50 (1950), 954
[179a] DALY, M. M., MIRSKY, A. E., and RIS, H., *J. gen. Physiol.*, 34 (1951), 439
[180] CASPERSSON, T., *Chromosoma*, I (1940), 562
[181] HEINE, L., *Hoppe-Seyl. Z.*, 21 (1895), 494
[182] MIRSKY, A. E. and POLLISTER, A. W., *J. gen. Physiol.*, 30 (1946), 47
[183] STEDMAN, E. and STEDMAN, E., *Nature, Lond.*, 166 (1950), 780
[184] HORNING, E. In *Cytology and Cell Physiology*, ed. BOURNE, G., Oxford, 1942 (p 160)
[185] SCOTT, G. H., *C. R. Acad. Sci.*, 190 (1930), 1323
[186] —, *Bull. Histol. Tech. micr.*, 7 (1930), 251
[187] FUNAOKA, S. and OGATA, H., *Folia anat. japon.*, 8 (1930), 169
[188] BARIGOZZI, C., *Z. Zellforsch.*, 26 (1937), 462
[189] LUCAS, N. S., *Proc. Soc. Exp. Biol., N.Y.*, 27 (1930), 258
[190] KRUSZYNSKI, J., *Bull. int. Acad. Cracovie*, 2 (1934), 105
[191] —, *Z. Zellforsch.*, 28 (1938), 35
[192] BAGINSKI, G., *Bull. Histol. Tech. micr.*, 11 (1934), 17
[193] SCOTT, G. H. and PACKER, D. M., *Anat. Rec.*, 74 (1939), 17
[194] —, In Biological Symposia X., *Frontiers in Cytochemistry*, (1943), p 277
[195] UBER, F. M. and GOODSPEED, T. H., *Bot. Gaz.*, 97 (1935), 416
[196] GULLAND, J. M., *Symp. quant. Biol.*, 12 (1947), 95
[197] ENGSTRÖM, A., *Acta physiol. Scand.*, 8 (1944), 137
[198] —, *Chromosoma*, 2 (1943), 459
[198] WILLIAMSON, M. B. and GULICK, A., *J. cell. comp. Physiol.*, 23 (1944), 77
[198a] JUNGNER, G., *Science*, 113 (1951), 378
[199] DURYEE, W. R., In *Cytology, Genetics and Evolution*, Philadelphia (1941), p 129
[200] D'ANGELO, E. G., *Biol. Bull.*, 90 (1946), 71
[201] ENGSTRÖM, A., In *Progress in Biophysics*, ed. J. A. V. BUTLER and J. T. RANDALL, vol. I, London (1950), p 164

The central body

[202] DERBÈS, M., *Ann. Sci. nat. Zool.* Ser. 3, 8 (1847), 80
[203] VAN BENEDEN, E., *Bull. Acad. Roy. Belg.* Ser. 2, 41 (1876), 1160
[204] — and NEYT, A., *ibid*, Ser. 3, 14 (1887), 215
[204a] LEWIS, W. H., *Ann. N.Y. Acad. Sci.*, 51 (1951), 1287
[205] BOVERI, TH., *Jena Z. Naturw*, 35 (1901), I
[206] WILSON, E. B., *The Cell in Development and Heredity*, 3rd ed., New York, 1925
[207] GRAY, J., *Experimental Cytology*, Cambridge, 1931
[208] FISCHER, A., *Fixierung, Farbung, and Bau des Protoplasmas*, Jena, 1899
[209] FRY, H. J., *Biol. Bull.*, Wood's Hole, 54 (1928), 363
[210] —, *ibid*, 56 (1929), 101; 57 (1929), 131
[211] —, *ibid*, 63 (1932), 149
[212] POLLISTER, A. W., *Science*, 75 (1932), 390
[213] HUETTNER, A. F., *Z. Zellforsch.*, 19 (1933), 119
[214] —, and RABINOWITZ, M., *Science*, 78 (1933), 367
[215] CLEVELAND, L. R., *ibid*, 81 (1935), 598
[216] —*Trans. Amer. Phil. Soc.*, 39 (1949), I

[217] JOHNSON, H. H., *Z. wiss. Zool.*, 140 (1932), 115
[218] STURDIVANT, H. P., *J. Morph.*, 55 (1934), 435
[219] SHARP, L. W., *Bot. Gaz.*, 54 (1912), 89
[220] YUASA, A., *Bot. Mag. Tôkyô*, 49 (1935), 868
[221] —, *Proc. imp. Acad. Japan*, 12 (1936), 266
[222] —, *Jap. J. Bot.*, 10 (1939), 259
[223] FRY, H. J., *J. exp. Zool.*, 43 (1925), 49

Chromosomes and the achromatic figure

[224] FELL, H. B. and HUGHES, A. F., *Quart. J. micr. Sci.*, 90 (1949), 355
[225] SCHRADER, F., *J. Morph.*, 69 (1941), 587
[226] SMITH, S. G., *Canad. J. Res.*, 20 (1942), 221
[227] RABL, C., *Morph. Jb.*, 10 (1885), 214
[228] HUGHES-SCHRADER, S., *Biol. Bull.*, *Wood's Hole*, 85 (1943), 265
[228a] GELEI, J., *Arch. Zellforsch.*, 16 (1921), 88
[229] SCHRADER, F., *J. Morph.*, 68 (1941), 123
[230] HUGHES-SCHRADER, S., *Chromosoma*, 3 (1947), 1
[231] SWANSON, C. P., *Amer. Nat.*, 76 (1942), 593
[232] WHITE, M. J. D., *Proc. R. Soc. B*, 119 (1935), 61
[233] BĚLAŘ, K., *Arch. EntwMech.*, 118 (1929), 359
[234] BERNAL, J. D., *Publ. Amer. Ass. Sci.*, 14 (1940), 199
[235] RIS, H., *Biol. Bull.*, *Wood's Hole*, 85 (1943), 164
[236] HUGHES, A. F. and SWANN, M. M., *J. exp. Biol.*, 25 (1947), 45
[237] CORNMAN, I., *Amer. Nat.*, 78 (1944), 410
[238] ÖSTERGREN, G., *Bot. Notis.* (1945), 767
[239] LEWIS, W. H., *Science*, 89 (1939), 400
[240] ÖSTERGREN, G., *Hereditas*, 31 (1945), 498
[241] HUGHES-SCHRADER, S., *Chromosoma*, 3 (1948), 257
[242] SCHRADER, F., *ibid*, 3 (1947), 22
[243] METZ, C. W., *Biol. Bull.*, *Wood's Hole*, 64 (1933), 333
[244] —, *Cytologia, Tokyo*, 7 (1936), 219
[245] McCLENDON, J. F., *Arch. EntwMech.*, 31 (1910), 80
[246] HARDY, W. B., *J. Physiol.*, 47 (1913), 108
[247] HARRIS, J. E., *J. exp. Biol.*, 16 (1939), 258

The spindle

[248] BĚLAŘ, K., *Arch. EntwMech.*, 118 (1929), 374
[249] DARLINGTON, C. D., *Recent Advances in Cytology*, London, 1937
[250] OETTLÉ, A. C., *J. R. micr. Soc.*, 70 (1950), 232
[251] SCHMIDT, W. J., *Die Doppelbrechung von Karyoplasma, Metaplasma und Zytoplasma*, Berlin, 1937
[252] —, *Chromosoma*, 1 (1939), 253
[253] HUGHES, A. F. and SWANN, M. M., *J. exp. Biol.*, 25 (1948), 45
[254] SWANN, M. M., *ibid*, in press
[255] —, *ibid*, in press
[256] INOUÉ, S., Personal communication (1950)
[257] ROZSA, G. and WYCKOFF, R. W. G., *Biochim. Biophys. Acta.*, 612 (1950), 334
[258] COOPER, K. W., *Proc. Nat. Acad. Sci. Wash.*, 27 (1941), 480
[259] LEWIS, M. R., *Bull. Johns Hopk. Hosp.*, 34 (1923), 373
[260] CONKLIN, E. G., *Ann. N. Y. Acad. Sci.*, 51 (1951), 1281
[261] ÖSTERGREN, G., *Hereditas*, 37 (1951), 85
[261a] DRUNER, L., *Z. Naturw.*, 29 (1895), 271
[262] WASSERMANN, F., *Wachstum und Vermehrung*, Berlin, 1929
[263] FELL, H. B. and HUGHES, A. F., *Quart. J. micr. Sci.*, 90 (1949), 37
[264] SCHRADER, F., *Mitosis*, New York, 1944
[264a] —, In *Symposium on Cytology*, Mitchigan, 1951

[265] CORNMAN, I., *Amer. Nat.*, 78 (1944), 410
[266] RIS, H., *Biol. Bull.*, *Wood's Hole*, 85 (1943), 164
[267] —, *ibid*, 96 (1949), 90
[268] HUGHES, A. F. and PRESTON, M. M'. E., *J. R. micr. Soc.*, 69 (1949), 121
[269] LIESCHE, W., *Arch. Protistenk*, 91 (1938), 135
[270] BERNAL, J. D., *Publ. Amer. Ass. adv. Sci.*, 14 (1940), 199
[271] — and FANKUCHEN, I., *J. gen. Physiol.*, 25 (1941), 111
[272] FREY-WYSSLING, A., *Submicroscopic morphology of Protoplasm and its derivatives*, Elsevier (1948)
[272a] FOOT, K., and STROBELL, E. C. *Amer. J. Anat.*, 4 (1905), 199
[273] HUGHES-SCHRADER, S., *J. Morph (Amsterdam)*, 39 (1924), 157
[274] SCHRADER, F., *Chromosoma*, 3 (1947), 22

Cytoplasmic changes during mitosis

[275] COHEN, A. and BERRILL, N. J., *J. Morph.*, 60 (1936), 243
[276] KINDRED, J. E., *ibid*, 43 (1927), 267
[277] STEIN, F., *Der Organismus der Infusionthiere*, Abt. I., Leipzig (1859)
[278] CALKINS, G. N., *The Biology of the Protozoa*, London, 1926
[279] CLEVELAND, L. R., *Trans. Amer. Phil. Soc.*, 39 (1949), 1
[280] COMANDON, J. and DE FONBRUNE, P., *C. R. Soc. Biol.*, 124 (1937), 1299
[280a] CHALKLEY, H. W., *Ann. N.Y. Acad. Sci.*, 51 (1951), 1303
[281] LUDFORD, R. J., SMILES, J., and WELCH, F. V., *J. R. Micr. Soc.*, 68 (1948), 1
[281a] DALTON, A. J., *Ann. N.Y. Acad. Sci.*, 51 (1951), 1295
[282] SAKAMURA, T. U., *Protoplasma*, 1 (1927), 537
[283] KATÔ, K., *Mem. Coll. Sci. Kyoto. Imp. Univ.* (B), 8 (1933), 201
[284] PEKAREK, J., *Planta*, 16 (1932), 788
[285] SCHAEDE, R., *Beitr. Biol. Pfl.*, 14 (1925), 231
[286] BARBER, H. N., *Chromosoma.*, 1 (1939), 33
[287] HERLANT, M., *Arch. Biol.*, 30 (1920), 517
[288] LILLIE, R. S., *J. exp. Zool.*, 21 (1916), 369
[289] HARVEY, E. N., *ibid*, 10 (1911), 507
[290] SPAULDING, E. G., *Biol. Bull.*, *Wood's Hole.*, 6 (1904), 224
[291] MATHEWS, A. P., *ibid*, 11 (1906), 137
[292] BALDWIN, F. M., *ibid*, 38 (1920), 123
[293] STEWART, D. R. and JACOBS, M. H., *J. cell comp. Physiol.*, 1 (1932), 83
[294] SHAPIRO, H., *Biol. Bull.*, *Wood's Hole*, 77 (1939), 317
[295] KROGH, A., SCHMIDT-NIELSEN, K. and ZEUTHEN, E., *Z. vergl. Physiol.*, 26 (1938), 230
[296] STERN, H., *Trans. R. Soc.*, *Canad.*, 40, Sect. 5 (1946), 141
[297] WEBER, F., *Protoplasma*, 15 (1932), 522
[298] SHIMAKURA, K., *Cytologia*, *Tokyo*, 5 (1934), 363
[299] HEILBRUNN, L. V., *J. exp. Zool.*, 34 (1921), 417
[300] — and WILSON, W. L., *Biol. Bull.*, *Wood's Hole*, 95 (1948), 1
[301] FRY, H. J. and PARKS, M. E., *Protoplasma*, 21 (1934), 473
[302] CHAMBERS, R., *Anat. Rec.*, 11 (1917), 491
[303] —, *J. gen. Physiol.*, 2 (1919), 49
[304] CARLSON, J. G., *Biol. Bull.*, *Wood's Hole*, 90 (1946), 109
[305] KOSTOFF, D., *Protoplasma*, 1 (1930), 177
[306] ZIMMERMANN, W., *Z. Bot.*, 15 (1923), 113
[306a] LEWIS, W. H., *Ann. N.Y. Acad. Sci.*, 51 (1951), 1287
[307] BEAMS, H. W. and KING, R. L., *Biol. Bull.*, *Wood's Hole*, 71 (1936), 188
[308] CRICK, F. H. C. and HUGHES, A. F., *Exp. Cell Res.*, 1 (1950), 37
[309] SPEK, J., *Verh. dsch. zool. Ges.*, 28 Jahresversammlumg (1923), 14
[310] BUJARD, E., *Arch. Sci. phys. nat.*, 23 (1941), 194
[311] MARSLAND, D. A., *Symposium on Structure of Protoplasm*, ed., SEIFRIZ, W., Iowa (1942), 127
[311a] —, *Ann. N.Y. Acad. Sci.*, 51 (1951), 1327
[312] —*J. cell. comp. Physiol.*, 12 (1938), 57

[313] PEASE, D. C., *J. Morph.*, 69 (1941), 405

[314] —, *Biol. Bull.*, *Wood's Hole*, 91 (1946), 145

[315] — and REGNERY, D., *J. cell comp. Physiol.*, 17 (1941), 397

[316] MARSLAND, D., *ibid*, 36 (1950), 205

[316a] ZEUTHEN, E., *Biol. Bull.*, *Wood's Hole*, 98 (1950), 144 and 152

[317] HARVEY, E. N., *J. exp. Zool.*, 8 (1910), 355

[317a] CORNMAN, I., and CORNMAN, M. E., *Ann. N.Y. Acad. Sci.*, 51 (1951), 1443

[318] BROWN, D. E. S., *J. cell. comp. Physiol.*, 5 (1934), 335

[318a] HARVEY, E. B., *Biol. Bull.*, *Wood's Hole*, 69 (1935), 287

[319] MIRSKY, A. E., *Science*, 84 (1936), 333

[320] MAZIA, D., *J. cell comp. Physiol.*, 10 (1937), 291

[321] HEILBRUNN, L. V., *An outline of General Physiology*, 2nd ed., Philadelphia, 1937

[321a] DANIELLI, J. F., In BOURNE, G. H., *Cytology and Cell Physiology*, 2nd ed., Oxford, 1951, p 168

[322] SWANN, M. M. and MITCHISON, J. In press (1951)

[323] VLÈS, F., *C. R. Soc. Biol.*, 85 (1921), 492

[323a] ODDO, A. M., and ESPOSITO, *J. Gen. Physiol.*, 34 (1951), 285

[324] HEILBRUNN, L. V. and WILSON, W. L., *Biol. Bull.*, *Wood's Hole*, 97 (1949), 242

[325] SHAPIRO, H., *J. cell comp. Physiol.*, 18 (1941), 61

[326] MARSLAND, D. A., *ibid*, 13 (1939), 15

[327] JUST, E. E., *Amer. J. Physiol.*, 61 (1922), 505

[328] CHAMBERS, R., *J. cell. comp. Physiol.*, 12 (1938), 149

[329] SCHECHTMANN, A. M., *Science*, 85 (1937), 222

[330] PEASE, D. C. and MARSLAND, D. A., *J. cell comp. Physiol.*, 14 (1939), 407

[331] VON ERLANGER, R., *Biol. Zbl.*, 17 (1897), 152

[332] SPEK J., *Arch. EntwMech.*, 44 (1918), 1

[333] DANIELLI, J. F., *Essays presented to D'A. W. Thompson*, Ed. LE GROS CLARK and MEDAWAR (1945), 295

[334] MOTOMURA, I., *Rep. Tôhoku Imp. Univ.*, 4th ser., 10 (1935), 212

[335] DAN, K., YANAGITA, T. and SUGIYAMA, M., *Protoplasma*, 28 (1937), 66

[336] — DAN, J. C., and YANAGITA, T., *Cytologia*, *Tokio*, 8 (1938), 1951

[337] — — *Cytologia*, *Tokyo*, 12 (1942), 246

[338] GRAY, J., *Experimental Cytology*, Cambridge (1931)

[339] PAINTER, T. S., *J. exp. Zool.*, 18 (1915), 299

[340] FRY, H. J., *ibid*, 43 (1925), 49

[341] HARVEY, E. B., *Biol. Bull.*, *Wood's Hole*, 79 (1940), 166

[342] GROSS, F., *Quart. J. micr. Sci.*, 79 (1936), 57

[342a] TEICHMANN, E., *Arch. EntwMech.*, 16 (1903), 243

[343] DAN, K. and DAN, J. C., *Biol. Bull.*, *Wood's Hole*, 93 (1947), 163

[344] BUCHSBAUM, P. and WILLIAMSON, R. R., *Physiol. Zool.*, 16 (1943), 162

[345] CALLAN, H. G., *Biochim. Biophys. Acta.*, 3 (1949), 92

[346] MOORE, A. R., *J. exp. Biol.*, 10 (1933), 230

[347] KRAHL, M. E. and CLOWES, G. H. A., *J. gen. Physiol.*, 20 (1936), 173

[348] CLOWES, G. H. A. and KRAHL, M. E., *ibid*, 23 (1940), 401

[349] HUGHES, A. F. and SWANN, M. M., *J. exp. Biol.*, 25 (1948), 45

[350] DALCQ, A., *C.R. Ass. des Anatomistes*, 24 (1929), 176

[351] NOVIKOFF, A. B., *J. exp. Zool.*, 82 (1939), 217

[352] BAUMGARTNER, W. J., *Trans. Kansas Acad. Sci.*, 36 (1933), 209

[353] PEREMESCHKO, —, *Arch. mikr. Anat.*, 16 (1879), 437

[354] YAMAHA, G., *Jap. J. Bot.*, 3 (1926), 139

[355] BECKER, W. A., *Acta Soc. Bot. Polon.*, 11 (1934), 139

[356] — *Cytologia*, *Tokyo*, 6 (1935), 337

[357] DARLINGTON, C. D. and THOMAS, P. T., *Ann. Bot. N.S.*, 1 (1937), 747

[358] ROBYNS, W., *Cellule*, 39 (1929), 85

[359] VON MOHL, H., *Flora Jena*, 1837, —, p. 1

[360] MITSCHERLICH, E., *J. prakt. chem.*, 43 (1848), 158

[361] McALLISTER, F., *Amer. J. Bot.*, 18 (1931), 838

[362] BRAND, F., *Ber. dtsch. bot. Ges.*, 26 (1908), 114

[362a] LUTMAN, B. F., *Bot. Gaz.*, 51 (1911), 401

[363] VAN WISSELINGH, C., *Bei. Bot. Centralbl.* 1 Abt., 32 (1915), 155
[364] BROWN, C. H., *Quart. J. micr., Soc.*, 91 (1950), 331
[365] MARSLAND, D. A., *J. cell. comp. Physiol.*, 13 (1939), 23

Modifications of mitosis
[366] BĚLAŘ, K., *Erg. Fortschr. Zool.*, 6 (1926), 235
[367] BEAMS, H. W. and KING, R. L., *Anat. Rec.*, 83 (1942), 281
[368] WILSON, J. W. and LEDUC, E. H., *Amer. J. Anat.*, 82 (1948), 353
[369] FELL, H. B. and HUGHES, A. F., *Quart. J. micr. Sci.*, 90 (1949), 355
[370] GEITLER, L., *Chromosomenbau—Protoplasma Monographien* Bd., 14, 1938
[371] —, *Z. Zellf rsch.*, 26 (1937), 641
[372] PAINTER, T. S. and REINDORP, E. C., *Chromosoma*, 1 (1939), 276
[372a] —, *J. Roy. micr. Soc.*, 60 (1940), 161
[373] METZ, C. W., *Biol. Bull., Wood's Hole*, 43 (1923), 369
[374] GEITLER, L., *Chromosoma*, 1 (1939), 1
[375] GRAFL, I., *ibid*, 1 (1939), 265
[376] BIESELE, J. J., POYNER, H., and PAINTER, T. S., *Univ. Texas Publ.*, 4243 (1942)
[377] COOPER, K. W., *Proc. Nat. Acad. Sci. Wash.*, 24 (1938), 452
[378] PAINTER, T. S., *Symp. quant. biol.*, 9 (1941), 47
[379] BERGER, C. A., *Amer. Nat.*, 71 (1937), 187
[380] GRELL, M., *Genetics*, 31 (1946), 60 and 77
[381] BERGER, C. A., *J. Hered.*, 29 (1938), 351
[382] —, *Symp., quant. Biol.*, 9 (1941), 19
[383] ARNOLD, J., *Arch. mikr. Anat.*, 30 (1887), 205
[384] CHARIPPER, H. A. and DAWSON, A. B., *Anat. Rec.*, 39 (1928), 301
[385] MACKLIN, C. C., *Contr. Embryol. Carneg. Instn.*, 13 (1916), 71
[386] —, *Biol. Bull., Wood's Hole*, 30 (1916), 445
[387] WERMEL, E. M. and PORTUGALOW, W. W., *Z. Zellforsch.*, 22 (1935), 185
[388] LEWIS, W. H. and WEBSTER, L. T., *J. exp. Med.*, 33 (1921), 349
[389] KATER, J. McA. *Bot. Rev.* 6 (1940), 164
[390] MARSHALL, W. S., *Biol. Bull., Wood's Hole*, 14 (1908), 89
[391] STOUGH, H. B., *J. Morph.*, 58 (1935), 221
[392] —, *ibid.*, 52 (1931), 535
[393] SCHULTZ, A. F., *Proc. Okla. Acad. Sci.*, 2 (1922), 45
[394] WOODARD, T. M., *Amer. Nat.*, 82 (1948), 129
[395] GLÜCKSMANN, A., *Biol. Rev.*, 26 (1951), 59
[396] MÜNZER, F. T., *Arch. mikr. Anat.*, 104 (1925), 138
[397] BRUES, A. M. and MARBLE, B. B., *J. exp. Med.*, 65 (1937), 15
[398] CLARA, M., *Anat. Anz.*, 72 (1931), 219
[399] BIESELE, J. J., *Cancer Rev.*, 4 (1944), 232
[400] POULSON, D. F., *J. exp. Zool.*, 83 (1940), 271
[401] TIMONEN, S., and THERMANN, E., *Nature Lond.*, 166 (1950), 995
[402] MacMAHON, H. E., *Jb. Morph. Mikro. Anat.*, 32 (1933), 413

5

EXPERIMENTAL ANALYSIS

NATURE OF THE STIMULUS TO MITOSIS

It is well to make clear at the start that the chemical and physical factors which determine the onset of the process of cell division are completely unknown. All that can be done is to consider mitosis as one of the events (certainly one of cardinal importance) contributing to growth; to indicate some of the factors that appear to be implicated in the whole complex of processes which comprise tissue growth; and to speculate upon the question whether or not some of these factors may act directly or indirectly as stimuli to mitosis.

The literature bearing upon such factors—variously known as 'growth factors', 'growth hormones', 'trephones', 'cell division complexes' *etc*—is full of confusion. This can be attributed principally to the deceptive simplicity of the term 'growth'. Although it has been repeatedly pointed out (*e.g.*, by HAMMETT;[1][2] CUNNINGHAM and KIRK;[3] RICHARDS and CAVANAGH;[4] MAYER[5] and WEISS[6][7]) that the number of meanings of 'growth' is nearly as great as the number of investigators, publications on 'growth' still regularly appear, in which no explicit definition is supplied.

Mitosis and growth

Growth can comprise increase in mass, volume, area or length of cells, tissues or organisms; and any of these can take place without cell division contributing at all. It is true that it frequently does contribute importantly to growth in its commonly accepted senses. But, in reviewing the literature on 'growth stimuli', it is often impossible to discover whether the action studied has been on mitosis or on some other aspect of growth. As WEISS[6] says: 'the relation between cell division and growth is by no means as close as the widespread habit of treating them interchangeably would make it appear.' Nevertheless, serious attempts have been made to abstract the process of mitosis or cell proliferation from the closely related activities of tissue growth and differentiation. If these attempts have not wholly achieved the aim of demonstrating effects on mitosis alone, TYLER[8] gives the pertinent reminder 'that the developing embryo, although it is not in a steady state, also exhibits maintenance in addition to processes resulting in increase in amount of living material (growth) and in change of form and composition (differentiation). That maintenance, growth and differentiation can be distinguished conceptually does not necessarily mean that they are distinct in the embryo'—or, it might be added, in any tissue or in the cell itself.

Mitosis takes place in tissues in process of normal development, repair and regeneration, and in tumours. It is probable that the basic conditions leading to cell division are the same in all these states. So the question why cell division happens is part of the larger problem of why it sometimes ceases to occur. If it were understood why cell division largely ceases in maturity, or when repair and regeneration are achieved, it might become clearer how cells are released from this control in tumours and, rather similarly in tissue cultures (BERRILL[9]).

Research on cell growth, especially in tissue culture, has often been conducted on the assumption (stated or implied) that there is a single growth substance or 'growth hormone', the addition of which to a system otherwise favourable physically and chemically acts as 'the' stimulus to cell division. It is not in fact known whether such a single substance exists. There may be one key point at which the metabolism of the cell may regularly be altered, by the application of one special stimulus (or perhaps one of several), in the direction leading inevitably to mitosis. BERRILL[9] is one of those who do not regard cell division as the result of a single, simple stimulus. On the contrary, it is 'the climax of a complex process of growth and duplication of a multitude of cell components, while inhibition of the process *in vivo* is clearly not due to lack of nutritive substances or to any deficiency on the part of the cell.' It is probable that a combination of external and internal conditions is necessary. NEEDHAM[10] suggested that the 'growth-promoting factor is probably no more than a right conjunction of nutrient materials and the appropriate capacities for making use of them.' Synthesis of new protoplasm precedes or accompanies each mitosis, so the raw materials for this synthesis must be provided. It appears, therefore, to be axiomatic that, for cell division to be possible, adequate nutritional conditions for supplying energy and materials must first be fulfilled. Whether the 'appropriate capacities' include a special type of stimulus over and above availability of nutrients in optimal amounts, remains uncertain. BAKER and CARREL[11] made the distinction between substances required for cell nutrition and those for cell multiplication, having already shown that chick embryo extracts are an excellent source of both for fibroblast tissue cultures. The problem is already clearly defined: 'Whether there is in embryonic extract a specific substance with a function of initiating or producing cell division, or whether embryonic extract simply contains the essential nutrient substances required by the cells is not known. Neither is there any knowledge concerning the chemical nature of the substances present in the extract which are utilized by the cells.' Twenty years later FISCHER[12] can only say: 'It would be of great interest were we able to separate the forces acting in preparing the division and those which act in releasing the division process.' It is of importance, too, to distinguish between factors which may initiate the process of mitosis and those influencing the division rate under conditions where division would in any case occur. The effects of suitable doses of radiations, *e.g.*, heat (which may increase) and ultraviolet (which may increase or decrease) division rate, are of the second kind (GIESE;[13] [14] LOOFBOUROW[15]).

There appear to be certain optimal dimensions to which a given type of cell must approximate and, that being so, 'the question arises whether the cells are induced to continue growing and consequently keep dividing to maintain optimal dimensions or whether they are induced to divide and must grow to maintain the same surface-volume ratios' (BERRILL[9]). THOMPSON[16] is committed only to the general statement that 'the phenomenon of division of the growing cell, however it be brought about, will be precisely what is wanted to keep fairly constant the ratio between surface and mass, and to retain or restore the balance between surface-energy and the other forces of the system', but BERRILL[9] goes a little farther in concluding that 'cell proliferation is itself primarily a response to changing surface relationships' and 'Cell division must therefore occur when the cell size exceeds a certain critical value.' To state this, however, only raises questions about how the cell increases in size, and whether *mere* increase in size would really be a sufficient stimulus to mitosis. The increase in size which is correlated with mitosis is more probably itself merely one of the more obvious manifestations of complex activities in which the whole cell and its immediate environment are taking part.

Plant growth substances

In plants, as in animals, the phenomena usually grouped under the name 'growth' are multiple. At the cellular level, cell enlargement, cell division and cell organization may occur separately and independently or simultaneously and perhaps interdependently. The plant 'growth substances' of the auxin group—indolylacetic acid and its analogues, appear to act, in low concentrations, on cell size only; at higher concentrations the principal response (*e.g.*, in the rooting response of woody cuttings) is cell division. At still higher concentrations, cell enlargement and cell division may be so much accelerated that the tissues grow faster than the roots can supply food to them. The result is necrosis, and this mechanism accounts for the weed-killing properties of '2, 4-D'. One of the first effects of auxin on the plant cell is to increase the rate of cyclosis and possibly of the cell metabolism in general. This increased cytoplasmic activity in the plant cell may well correspond to the increased cell movement (of the cell as a whole, and of the cell contents) which JACOBY,[17] MEDAWAR[18] and FISCHER[19] believe to be intimate and necessary accompaniments of cell division in animal cells. The *demonstrable* effects of the auxins, as of other 'growth stimulants', whether visible (*e.g.*, on cell size) or chemical (*e.g.*, on respiration) must be related to the primary stimulus by chemical mechanisms which are only partly understood and may be quite indirect. When the effects of clearly defined chemical compounds are, as in the case of the plant 'growth hormones', so obviously multiple and complex, it would be capricious and dogmatic to assign to them, predominantly or only, a special mitosis-stimulating action. It seems necessary still to agree with THIMANN:[20] 'It does not seem at present that there is any specific hormonal stimulus for cell division *per se*.'

TABLE VI. PLANT GROWTH SUBSTANCES

Nuclear and cytoplasmic stimuli

If one assumes that there is a master reaction controlling cell division, its seat might be in the nucleus or in the cytoplasm. LUDFORD[21] believes that 'the stimulus to divide originates within the nucleus, and that to a large extent the process of cell division is independent of the state of functional activity of the cytoplasm.' Others proclaim the importance of the cytoplasm (*e.g.*, FISCHER[19]) and DARLINGTON and MATHER[22] pronounce that: 'it should not be lost sight of that the cytoplasm is in immediate control of all the everyday details of mitosis.' There is, however, not enough evidence to prove the predominance of either in initiating mitosis and the probability is that the interdependence of nucleus and cytoplasm is too intimate for it to be possible to say that one controls the other (JENNINGS[23]).

Both nuclear and cytoplasmic components are certainly synthesized in the cell during the maturing process which precedes cell division (FISCHER[12]). SWIFT[24] has shown that deoxypentose nucleoprotein is built up in the interphase nucleus and that no synthesis takes place during the visible stages of mitosis. Pentose nucleoproteins also increase in tissues preparatory to cell division.[25-29] Among other components, great importance has been attached to the increase in —SH groups in proliferating tissues; this subject was critically reviewed by NEEDHAM.[10]

In a discussion of the factors involved in wound healing, CARREL[30] recalls that WEIGERT denied the power of any agent exterior to the cells to stimulate their proliferation, but VIRCHOW thought that inflammatory growth was stimulated by irritants which incited the cells to proliferate, and WELCH regarded these irritants as chemical in nature. CARREL argues that as there is no evidence for inhibitory agents able to overcome an inherent tendency to growth, direct growth-promoting action, such as that associated *in vitro* with embryonic and leucocytic extracts, must be responsible for stimulating proliferation.

Cell division and differentiation

Whereas in the early stages of embryonic development all the cells of an organism are able to divide, as differentiation proceeds, this ability may be reduced or lost as the result of a kind of 'physiological division of labour' (FISCHER[12]). The seeming antagonism or incompatibility between proliferation and functional differentiation has been recognized at least since 1905 (SCHAPER and COHEN[31]) and has been frequently restated, *e.g.*, by STRANGEWAYS,[32] LORRAIN SMITH,[33] REIMANN,[34] NEEDHAM[10] and NICHOLSON.[35] The relationship between cell division and differentiation is discussed by DAWSON,[36] especially in the light of the views of BLOOM[37] and WEISS.[38] BLOOM states the thesis that 'cellular multiplication and cellular differentiation are distinct processes, each of which usually takes place only in the absence of the other'. The emphasis may differ, as when FISCHER and PARKER[39] state that 'reproductive quiescence is an important factor in differentiation', while WEISS[38] puts it: 'In general it can be said that, the more specialized a cell is in its structure and function, the less apt it is to divide.' There is no hard and fast rule. Though always stated with cautious reservation, the conclusion is invariably the same. 'Cellular differentiation and cellular multiplication are two processes which, if not strictly mutually exclusive, are nevertheless markedly antagonistic in their tendencies' (WEISS[38]) and 'proliferation does not interfere with differentiation, but it does impede the elaboration of certain manifest products of differentiation' (WEISS[6]). DAWSON,[36] while agreeing with WEISS that 'a differentiating cell . . . gradually loses its capacity to divide and factors promoting differentiation automatically reduce proliferation', points out the fallacy of the converse supposition, found in the literature, that the apparent inability of certain cells to divide can be accepted as primary evidence of their high degree of specialization, and he emphasizes the effect of the environment in determining whether or not a cell will divide. He states the problem, that 'we must determine whether the incapacity to divide is due to intrinsic or extrinsic factors, or to an interaction between them', and suggests that the capacity to divide may simply be suppressed by unfavourable environmental conditions. A similar idea is expressed by LITTLE,[40] who agrees that 'it has been a well established habit to speak and think of the differentiated cell in mammals as having largely lost its power of cell division', but argues that 'the fact that a cell does not use its power to divide is no indication that it does not possess that power.' In LITTLE's opinion, cell division is the 'natural objective and climax of activity of the healthy, fully-equipped animal cell', and vast numbers of cells in the differentiated tissues of an organism fail to achieve this end because there is a 'battle between chemical and mechanical products of an organized community of cells on the one hand, and on the other the tendency of those cells to return to the function of cell division and independent metabolism inherent in all complete animal cells.' The influence of one tissue or its secretions on another in the organism, and of one cell on another in the tissues, is clearly of very great significance in regulating the conditions which can permit cell division or not. That cell multiplication and cell differentiation appear to be mutually exclusive, so far from indicating, as BLOOM[37] thought, that they are 'distinct processes', may show that they form two aspects of a single kind of cellular activity, differently conditioned by the environment. The animal organism as a whole may be regarded as being in a state of maintenance, striking a balance between continuous disintegration of protoplasm and its continuous repair. Growth, in the sense of an increase in amount of living tissue, can be looked upon as an extension of normal maintenance which results when the building up processes are in excess of breakdown (TYLER[8] [41]).

Effects of hormones

The study of the effects of hormones on growth of parts of the whole organism provides one approach to the problem of growth stimuli. PULLINGER[42] observed a quantitative relation between the developmental growth of the mammary glands of castrated mice and dosage of oestrogen. Mammary tumours also require oestrogen for the initiation of growth but such tumours, grafted into ovariectomized females or into males, will continue to grow without further oestrogen. Since cell division and functional differentiation in these tumours are thus independent of an external source of ovarian hormone, PULLINGER suggests that the simplest assumption to account for the autonomy of the tumours is that a stimulant to mitosis, functional differentiation and secretion, with oestrogen-like properties, 'must be elaborated intracellularly' and transmitted heritably by the tumour cells. Assuming for the purpose of hypothesis that cell division in multicellular organisms does require some positive stimulus other than adequate nutrition, though agreeing that 'our ignorance of stimuli to division of somatic cells is very great', she suggests that 'the response of the histospecific hormones' of which oestrogen is an example, are 'pointers to the existence of actual positive stimuli'. On this view the tumour cell is one which has acquired the ability to elaborate its own stimulus to cell division and to transmit this ability in perpetuity. The nature of the stimuli can only be a matter for conjecture, both in the case of the postulated self-perpetuating stimulus in tumours and that operating in normal cell division. PULLINGER considers the possibility (which would make identification very difficult) that the hypothetical substances might not be extractable because they form an integral part of the cell structure.

Based on the perspective, already quoted, that cell division is the normal and natural consummation of cell activity, LITTLE's belief[40] is that in metazoan organisms, subordination of parts to the whole introduces an intricate pattern of controlling and inhibiting influences on cells and tissues. Hormone interactions have been studied in relation to this conception. Castration of mice one to three days after birth produces, in adult life, different degrees of compensatory endocrine activity according to the strain of mouse (WOOLLEY et alii[43]). In C57 black mice, no unusual growth or hormone activity was observed. After about six months, dba mice of both sexes showed some oestrogenic effects and hypertrophy of the adrenal cortex (WOOLLEY, et alii[43 44 45]). Mice of strain ce developed adrenal cortical carcinoma in 100 per cent of the animals (WOOLLEY et alii[46 47]), and the sex hormone activity displayed at six months in both sexes was male in character. LITTLE[40] believes that, in normal ce mice, 'the gonads act as inhibitors to the uncontrolled and cancerous growth of the adrenals. When the gonads are removed such growth always occurs. When gonads are present it *never* occurs', and suggests that this may be a particular example of a quite general phenomenon.

Tissue culture provides systems in which cells are released from the controls exerted by the whole organism. It has therefore been possible to study, *in vitro,* what conditions are *sufficient* for growth by cell proliferation. It is in general found that the limits of permissible variation of the physical environment, for most of the animal cells investigated, are rather narrow. That is, the temperature, pH, osmotic pressure, *etc*, must fall within a range close to those of the cells' natural environment. The chemical variations which can be tolerated by different types of cell are much less fully known—but it is certain that different types of cell have different nutritional requirements for optimal proliferation (STRANGEWAYS;[32] PARKER[48]). Thus while we know with certainty that continued cultivation of a particular strain of cells can be achieved in an empirically selected medium containing, say, chicken plasma, horse serum and chicken embryo extract, we still know little about which chemical components of such a mixture supply the nutrients to maintain the cells alive and healthy, and which may

M

be necessary for the special function of inducing cell division to occur. Both of the possible approaches to the study of the components of media for the growth and maintenance of tissue cultures, the analytic and the synthetic, have been made. Attempts have been made to determine, by analytical methods, which components of media known to be growth supporting are in fact essential. Chemically defined media have been synthesized (WHITE;[49] [50] MORGAN et alii[51]). More often, a combination of both methods has been used (e.g., FISCHER).

Leucocyte secretions

The first media for cultivating animal tissues *in vitro* were composed of lymph, serum, plasma, tissue extracts, or some combination of these biological fluids. Early in the history of the tissue culture technique, a clear and simple distinction seemed possible between (i) media which could support the proliferation of leucocytes—probably monocytes and lymphocytes, indistinguishable in cultures from the tissue macrophages —consisting of dilute serum or plasma alone; and (ii) media for normal connective tissue (fibroblasts) and epithelial tissues, in which it seemed essential to include extracts of embryonic tissue (CARREL and EBELING.[52] [53] Some tumours can also grow in serum alone (STERN[54]), but while normal connective tissue can remain alive and healthy for prolonged periods with no other nutrient (CARREL[55]), if increase by mitotic division is to take place, some additional source of 'growth-promoting factor', such as embryo extract (CARREL[56] [57]) or extract of leucocytes (CARREL[58]) or of spleen (CARREL;[57] CARREL and EBELING[52] [60]) is necessary. Fibroblasts will grow if they are placed together in the same culture medium with macrophages (CARREL and EBELING;[59] FISCHER[19]). From these observations the conclusion was drawn (CARREL[61]) that the macrophages are themselves able to produce from serum some factor or factors of which the normal fixed tissues require an exogenous source. These leucocyte secretions were named 'trephones' (CARREL[58] [62] [63]) and their action was originally regarded as purely nutrient (CARREL;[58] CARREL and EBELING;[64] DES LIGNERIS[65]). LUDFORD[66] believes that their action is to stimulate enzymes which break down the serum proteins to units of a size assimilable by the fibroblasts and FISCHER[12] regards the leucocytic trephones, not as nutrients, but as specific growth hormones with the special function of stimulating mitosis.

CLAUDE BERNARD (quoted by FISCHER[67]) and RENAUT (1893, quoted by CARREL and EBELING[59] [60]) were among the first to suggest that the main function of the leucocytes was to transport food material to the fixed tissue cells, and DES LIGNERIS[65] discusses the 'trephocytes' which can make and generate CARREL's trephones from serum and plasma and act as intermediaries for the nutrition of more differentiated cells.

Recent studies of the trephocytes, which 'have the function of carrying nutrients to all parts of the organism' and 'produce and ultimately liberate nutritive growth substances', have been made by LIEBMAN[29 68 69]). Vertebrates have two types of trephocyte, the lymphocytes and the mast cells, and LIEBMAN[68] draws particular attention to their probable importance in protein synthesis and growth, and to the fact that 'it is apparently common that mitotically active tissues contain lymphocytes'. The role of the thymus in regulating growth has been the subject of much speculation (ROWNTREE;[70] TYLER[41]), and one finds such suggestions as that 'the thymus and other organs of the lymphoid system are to be regarded as a "cyto-regulatory system", inasmuch as they would decisively determine processes of cell division and consequently growth, by storing or making available nucleoproteins' (STERN and WILLHEIM[71]).

The addition of more than a small amount of embryo extract to cultures of macrophages causes their rapid disintegration and death. This could be due to over-stimulation by factors similar to those elaborated by the macrophages themselves and does not invalidate the hypothesis that the growth-promoting actions of both types of extract may be similar. Evidence suggesting that an external supply of labile, macro-molecular trephones or components of the 'embryonin' type (FISCHER;[72] FISCHER and ASTRUP[73]) may not be indispensable for proliferation of fibroblasts is given by LASER,[74] who found that, in spite of smaller areas, fibroblast cultures in serum alone could reach greater dry weights in a three to four day period of observation than cultures in media containing embryo extract. This does not necessarily mean that mitosis has contributed to a growth effect which may be mostly due to increase in cell size. In addition, however, BAKER[75] has described a medium in which rapid and prolonged growth of fibroblasts took place. This contained only serum, Witté peptone, haemin, insulin, thyroxin, cysteine, ascorbic acid, glutathione, vitamins A and D, glucose and salts. It is conceivable that fibroblasts are capable of producing the 'embryonin' type of factor, but usually only in subliminal amounts, and that a medium such as BAKER's stimulates its production to a level above the threshold required to induce mitosis. That such factors are indeed present in fibroblasts, but not readily available, is suggested by FISCHER's[76 77] demonstration that fibroblast cultures which are repeatedly 'wounded' release growth-promoting substances from some cells at the expense of which others can proliferate. Such 'wounded' cultures grow much faster than undamaged controls. The macrophages seem able to produce and release the 'growth-promoting factors'.

The circulating leucocytes, and especially the lymphocytes, are short-lived cells which have about them something of the character of embryonic cells. The immature leucocytes possess a certain plasticity and pluripotentiality and are capable of producing many types of protein (serum globulins, including specific antibodies). LUDFORD[66] is among those who link the activity of the leucocytes *in vitro* with their ability to cause breakdown of proteins for cell nutrition. It is necessary, therefore, to examine the evidence concerning the mitosis-stimulating effects of partial and complete breakdown products of proteins.

Protein breakdown products

Embryo extracts have been shown to have proteolytic activity (GUILLERY;[78] ALBERT and HECHT;[79] SANTESSON[80]). It has been claimed that protein breakdown products—*e.g.*, proteoses—are capable of contributing to very extensive increase in area of fibroblast colonies, by stimulating migration (WILLMER and KENDAL[81]), but that they do not promote cell multiplication in the absence of the thermolabile materials of embryo extract (BAKER[82]). In the presence of embryo extract, however, various fractions from Witte peptone (BAKER and CARREL[83]) or from partial digestion of purified proteins (CARREL and BAKER[84 85]) cause exceptionally extensive and vigorous growth of fibroblast colonies. FISCHER[86] found that peptides from chicken plasma, in contrast to those from heterologous proteins, promoted the growth of normal chick fibroblasts in the presence of dialysed plasma and dialysed embryo extract. Proteolytic enzymes, either on the cell surface or in the plasma, are believed by FISCHER[87] to attack, after activation, *e.g.*, by glutathione, proteins which are fixed and partially denatured on the cell surface. HUEPER and RUSSELL[88] found that ultraviolet irradiation of chick embryo extract did not destroy its growth-promoting power, nor did the addition of glutathione or cysteine enhance the activity of the irradiated extracts. VERNE and VERNE-SOUBIRAN[89] on the other hand inactivated embryo extract by heat (100°) and found that it could be to some extent reactivated by glutathione. Stored embryo extract, which also lost its growth-promoting power, could not be reactivated in this way. HUEPER *et alii*[90] could find no evidence that the —SH group *per se* has a selective mitosis-stimulating effect. However, a strong, if not necessarily casual, relationship between the presence of reduced sulphydryl groups and the activities of cell division has been firmly established by the work of HAMMETT,[91 92 93] VOEGTLIN and CHALKLEY,[94] RAPKINE[95] and others. The fact that the —SH group is an activator of many enzymes, including proteolytic enzymes (HAMMETT and LAVINE[96]) leaves it an open question whether the influence is indirect and nutritional or rather, as HAMMETT[91] stated earlier, that sulphydryl exerts its effect 'through its specific stimulation of cell division and not through a forwarding influence on assimilative or cell size growth'. An optimal concentration of protein breakdown products may be a limiting factor in the cell environment, either as nutrients or as specific growth stimuli. FISCHER[97] has reported his intention to make 'a closer investigation of the mitosis-stimulating effect of higher peptides', and suggests that earlier evidence points to the probability that 'components possessing maximal activity in respect of the induction of cell proliferation' lie within definite limits of molecular weight, in that they are non-dialysable but not precipitated by trichloroacetic acid. BOHUS JENSEN has found (FISCHER[98]) that the 'presence of large peptides in the medium causes a remarkable increase in the frequency of cell divisions'. Proteins completely broken down to amino acids have an important nutritional function for the tissues (FISCHER[99] [100]), but there is no evidence for an effect of any single amino acid, or combination of them, specifically on cell division.

Chicken embryo extracts

By far the greatest amount of work on the growth of fibroblasts in tissue culture, from 1912 onwards (CARREL[56]) has been done with chicken embryo extracts as source of growth-promoting factors. Special interest therefore attaches to their mode of action. The activity of chick embryo extracts is not restricted to homologous tissue, and extracts of other embryos (and of adult tissues) have been used for cultivating chick tissues. It can therefore be concluded that there is no species-specific growth-promoting factor. Extracts of chick embryos promote growth of cultures of duck fibroblasts (FISCHER;[101] KIAER[102]), rat tissues (MOTTRAM[103]) and mouse, rat, rabbit, guinea-pig and human tissues (FISCHER[72]). Bovine tissue extracts have been used for chick (FISCHER[72]) and human (GEY and GEY[104]) tissue cultures. Chick tissues have been grown in extracts of mouse, guinea-pig and rabbit embryos (CARREL and EBELING;[105] LANDSTEINER and PARKER[106]). No significant difference in growth-promoting power has been noted between extracts prepared from whole chick embryos and those from broadly separated regions (*e.g.*, head, eyes, body) of the embryo (HUEPER *et alii*;[90] FOWLER[107]), though FISCHER[72] found extracts of internal organs less active than those from whole embryos. GAILLARD[108] [109] has shown that extracts from embryos of different ages may differ in their effects *in vitro*. Extracts from embryos of successive ages were tested, each at several dilutions, for their growth-promoting effects on tissues from embryos of various ages. Optimal growth of periosteal fibroblasts from 10-day embryo was attained in a 1:8 dilution of 10-day embryo juice; of similar tissue from 15-day embryo in a 1:64 dilution of 15-day embryo juice. Optimal growth in extracts from embryos of the same age as the tissue cultivated was not, however, a general finding—*e.g.*, heart fibroblasts from a 7-day embryo grew best in a 1:16 dilution of 18-day embryo juice (Figure 61). Progressive differentiation, instead of unorganized growth, of osteogenetic cells into true bone was achieved *in vitro* by the 'ascending range' method of cultivation in extracts from successively older embryos with each renewal of the culture medium (GAILLARD[109]).

Adult tissue extracts

Conclusions about the effects of adult tissue extracts vary widely. This may be due to differences in technique and in methods of measuring 'growth'. CARREL[57] reported adult spleen extracts to be more active than kidney, muscle or thyroid and found extracts of the Rous chicken sarcoma effective. HEATON[110] found adult spleen the least effective of a series of tissues of which bone marrow was the best, followed by brain, kidney, heart, voluntary muscle, pancreas, intestine, thymus, lung, ovary and testis. In agreement with WALTON,[111] he found that the

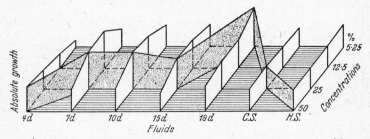

Figure 61 3-dimensional representation of the effect on the growth of heart fibroblasts from a 7-day chick embryo of different concentrations of press juice from 4-, 7-, 10-, 15- and 18-day chick embryos, and also from hatched chick (C.S.) and from adult (H.S.). From GAILLARD[109] (*By courtesy, Hermann et Cie*).

growth of fibroblasts was inhibited by liver extracts. The order of activity of adult and growing fowl tissue extracts given by TROWELL and WILLMER[112] descends from brain to thyroid, thymus, testis, ovary, bone marrow, liver, kidney and muscle. Brain was found by HOFF-MANN[113] to be the only effective extract from a series of rat tissues tested on chick tissue cultures: heart extracts had no effect and liver, kidney, lung and spleen were inhibitory. The only claims for greater activity in an adult tissue than in embryo extracts are those of DOL-JANSKI and HOFFMANN[114] and HOFFMANN *et alii*[115] [116] who obtained more rapid growth of chick fibroblast cultures with adult chicken heart extract than with the usual chick embryo extract; optimal concentrations of the two extracts stimulated mitosis to the same degree (MARGOLIASH and DOLJANSKI[117]). Area increases of the same order as produced by chick embryo extracts were achieved with adult sheep, cow, rabbit and dog heart extracts (DOLJANSKI *et alii*[118]). Sustained growth of adult fowl heart tissue has been achieved in a medium of entirely adult origin (DOLJANSKI and HOFFMANN[119]).

HUEPER *et alii*,[90] are among those who have made determined attempts to dissociate the different effects of embryo extracts on growing tissue cultures. They recognized that a growing culture may be affected by numerous endogenous and exogenous factors, and they distinguish carefully between (i) survival without proliferation, (ii) 'cell multiplication without increase in protoplasmic matter, due to the presence of substances stimulating mitosis and the absence of the proper nutritive elements in the culture medium' and (iii) proliferation with formation of new protoplasm. They found no evidence of significantly different activities in extracts from different anatomical regions of the embryo, and concluded that the value of embryo extracts for supporting the growth of tissue cultures lies in their great complexity, in that they contain 'not only substances for the stimulation of cell division, but also nutritive material which can be assimilated by the explanted cells and used for the synthesis of new protoplasmic matter'. It is indeed precisely this complexity that has reduced so many investigators to despair. Success in determining whether any one (or a few) of the components of an extract is responsible for the growth-promoting effect has been very elusive. FISCHER[12] [72] believes that the effect of embryo extracts in promoting cell division is to a great extent indirect, through accelerating cell migration (WILLMER;[120] GAILLARD[109]). DOLJANSKI and GOLD-HABER[121] believed that, because migratory activity can be stimulated by embryo extract after mitosis has been inhibited by X-radiation, migration and cell division are separately affected. The experiments of MEDAWAR[18] [122] on fibroblast inhibitors have shown the importance of cell movement in the growth of connective tissue. MEDAWAR believes the inhibitors he has studied act on cell movement through a surface active effect and that this is the basis for the differential action on fibroblasts and not on epithelial cells, in which amoeboid movement does not accompany cell division. Movement of epithelial sheet as a whole precedes cell division in cultures of kidney epithelium (EPHRUSSI and LITVAC[123]).

Substances necessary for fibroblastic growth

The importance of the distinction between 'survival of tissue and active growth' was already emphasized by CARREL and EBELING[124] in 1923 and FISCHER has made a descriptive classification of the substances required for the growth of fibroblasts into (i) low molecular 'accessory growth factors' necessary for cell nutrition (ASTRUP *et alii*[125]) and (ii) high molecular, labile substances associated with a nucleoprotein fraction and called 'embryonin' (FISCHER and ASTRUP[73]). By dialysing plasma and embryonic extract,[99] he freed an otherwise wholly adequate medium from 'accessory growth factors', so that it no longer supported life or growth. Supplementation of the dialysed medium with synthetic mixtures of amino acids, vitamins, etc. (FISCHER *et alii*[100] [127]) or with extracts of kidney, yeast or malt (FISCHER *et alii*[126] [128-131]) restored the deficient medium to an extent that growth was again possible. Although it has been demonstrated (WHITE and LASFARGUES[132]) that dialysis does not achieve a clear cut distinction between accessory factors and others, inasmuch as some activity can be restored to the dialysed mixture by dilution with Tyrode solution containing no additional supplements, FISCHER's experiments are of great importance in demonstrating the requirements of cells for certain low molecular nutrients, and particularly

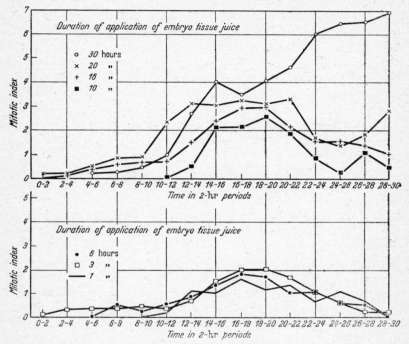

Figure 62 Mean curves showing the effect on the mitotic index of applying 15 per cent embryo juice to cultures of chick periosteal fibroblasts for different lengths of time, from 1–30 hours. From JACOBY *et alii*[135] (*By courtesy, J. exp. Biol.*).

for amino acids. Other evidence, especially from the work with fully synthetic media (WHITE;[49] [50] MORGAN *et alii*[51]), demonstrates that the low molecular 'accessory growth factors' with which FISCHER supplements his medium are precisely those of primary importance for maintenance. It underlines again the fact that, for cell division to be able to take place, the nutritional requirements of the cells must first of all be supplied. In a medium completely optimal except for the omission of a single component, restoration of that one limiting factor would raise it to the status of 'the' chemical stimulus to cell division.

On the basis of a long experience, starting with fractionation experiments in 1925 (FISCHER[133]) which already demonstrated that some of the active components of embryo extracts were very labile, FISCHER[12] has come to regard 'embryonin' as a true 'growth catalyst'. Many attempts at purification of this fraction have resulted in reduction of its activity, and FISCHER has not succeeded in identifying any single chemical entity possessing the embryonin activity. The embryonin fraction, prepared by the method of HAMMARSTEN[134] for isolating nucleoprotein from pancreas, is heterogeneous in character, showing four main and many minor components on electrophoresis (FISCHER and ASTRUP[73]).

In a study of the stimulating effect of embryo extracts on fibroblast cultures, JACOBY et alii[135] demonstrated that an extract need not be

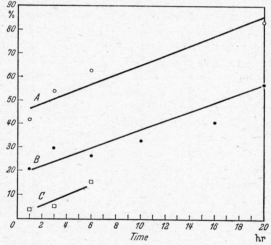

Figure 63 Graph showing the relation between the duration of the application of embryo juice to cultures of chick periosteal fibroblasts and the amount of growth which is produced. Ordinates: the aggregate percentage of cells which divide between the 10th and 20th hours after the application of the juice. Abscissae: time in hours **A** 40 per cent, **B** 15 per cent, and **C** 5 per cent embryo juice. From JACOBY et alii[135] (*By courtesy, J. exp. Biol.*).

present in appreciable amounts during the actual process of cell division. It is required only to initiate a process which, after a latent period of 10 to 12 hours, culminates in cell division. Short contact with embryo extract (less than 10 hours) produces only one crop of mitoses (Figure 62), but the number of mitoses is more dependent on the concentration of extract than the time for which it acts (Figure 63). TOMPKINS et alii[136] showed that the stimulus to division produced by fresh embryo extract disappeared between 48 and 72 hours. To obtain a fresh crop of mitoses, renewal of the medium is necessary. WILLMER[137] thinks that: 'in any given colony there are some cells which need high concentrations of juice before they will divide, while others have more modest requirements.' It is perhaps possible to see an analogy between the latent period after application of embryo juice to a culture and the onset of mitosis, and the latent period which intervenes between infection of cells with a virus and the reproduction of the virus (HORSFALL;[138] LURIA[139]). The analogy with virus reproduction is worth examining. Indeed, FISCHER[12] has suggested that the growth-promoting factors 'may display biological activity somewhat akin to that of the virus-proteins' and a similar idea had already been put forward in 1936 by DES LIGNERIS.[140] The nucleoprotein-containing particles of embryonic cells have a number of properties which may support the idea that they are concerned in the mitosis-stimulating activity of the extracts. Embryo extracts are essentially cytoplasmic extracts and contain pentose nucleoprotein but (depending on the method of preparation) no detectable deoxypentose nucleic acid (WAYMOUTH, unpublished) or very small amounts (DAVIDSON and WAYMOUTH[141]). From extracts prepared from 9-day embryos by extracting one volume of tissue pulp with one volume of Tyrode solution, 80 per cent of the pentose nucleic acid can be sedimented in one hour at $100,000 \times g$ (GILBERT, MEIKLEJOHN and WAYMOUTH, unpublished). The major part of the pentose nucleoprotein can be spun down from adult tissue extracts at much lower speeds, at which only about 50 per cent of the embryonic particulate material may be sedimentable (BRACHET[142]). CLAUDE[143-145] first isolated particles from 8-day chick embryos, and compared the preparations with the particulate fraction, isolated under similar centrifugal conditions ($18,000 \times g$ for 90 minutes) with which the Rous sarcoma (chicken tumour I) activity is associated. A particulate fraction from 8-day chick embryos ($67,000 \times g$ for 30 minutes) was tested on cultures of mouse fibroblasts in chicken plasma and rat serum (TENNANT et alii[146 147]), and the 'expansion rate' (i.e., area increase in 30 hours) measured. The activity (in this sense) was not very great and appeared to be increased by heating the pellet material at 100° C. for 15 minutes. FISCHER[12] reported that high molecular components of embryo extract, separated in the ultracentrifuge, possessed growth-promoting activity, but 'in no way exceeding that of the supernatant fluid', and he does not regard the activity detected by TENNANT et alii[147] as that of a specific growth promoting substance, but rather as due to an 'ordinary nutrient . . . substance'.

Macromolecular complexes

During the last decade much new information about the composition and functions of the cytoplasm has come to light. It is now clear that macromolecular complexes containing phospholipines and pentose nucleoproteins are characteristically found in the cytoplasm of cells. The notion that the cell cytoplasm contains a few microscopically visible formed elements, such as the mitochondria, but consists in the main of a structureless matrix in which a bewildering number of substances is more or less randomly distributed has been giving way to a concept of a high degree of organization at the submicroscopic level. NILSSON[148] and COMMONER[149] have drawn attention to the importance of cell structure in the orientation of cellular metabolic systems, especially those concerned with oxidations. This idea had already been put forward by WARBURG[150] in 1913; he was perhaps the first to insist on the importance of structural arrangement of cell constituents in respiration. Before anything was known about the fine structure of the ground substance of the cytoplasm, HOPKINS[151] discerned that 'although the microscope may detect no heterogeneity in the cytoplasm', 'the micelles or particles which form the internal phase in the cytoplasm *must* be diverse in respect of their surfaces, and a proportion, probably no small proportion, of these surfaces, must have catalytic properties'. HOPKINS envisaged the possibility that the catalytic agencies in cells might, because their activities depended so completely on configuration and localization in a structural framework, be incapable of isolation. The centrifuged sediment of a muscle suspension was however shown by BANGA[152] to possess respiratory enzyme activities. At about this time CLAUDE[153] first isolated macromolecular particles from normal and malignant tissues, and was followed by KABAT and FURTH[154] and by STERN[155-157] and others. STERN considered that the macromolecular material, though heterodisperse, consisted of 'subcellular functional units' and believed 'that the active groups of the various component catalysts are arranged in or on them in an orderly fashion so as to ensure a smooth functioning of the highly complex process of cell respiration'. The dependence of enzyme activities on the structural integrity of cytoplasmic particles is now well established (SCHNEIDER and HOGEBOOM[158]). CLAUDE[28,159] classified cytoplasmic particles into two broad categories: 'large granules', precipitable at 2,000 $\times$ g in 25 minutes and of size 0·5 to 2·0μ; and 'microsomes' brought down at 18,000 $\times$ g in 90 minutes, with a size range of 100 to 200mμ. Enzymatic activities of many kinds have been found associated with the particles, and in general the larger the particle size, the higher the probability of finding a greater variety of enzymes. The size of particle isolated is a function of the conditions of centrifugation, and CLAUDE,[160] while he supports the idea that there are several distinct types of particle in most cells, noted that the mitochondria and large granules stood at the end of a continuous series of cytoplasmic elements. CHANTRENNE[161] demonstrated, in extracts of mouse liver, a continuous range of particle size, the smallest particles containing the highest proportion of pentose nucleic acid and the lowest enzyme content. The smallest particles, in common with virus particles, seem to possess no enzymatic activities.

Embryonic tissues contain a larger proportion of pentose nucleic acid not sedimented at high speeds than do adult tissues (JEENER and BRACHET[162]). Suspensions of granules from 2-day chick embryos, or from frog neurulae, applied to the chorio-allantoic membrane of the chick embryo, produced marked thickening (SHAVER and BRACHET[163]). The results of irradiating with ultraviolet, and of heating the material, were not conclusive. The integrity of the granules is hardly likely to survive heating for 10 minutes at 80° C., treatment which did not always cause inactivation. It was therefore thought unlikely that the particles multiply in the membrane as viruses do, and SHAVER and BRACHET suggest that the particulate material contains some constituent which stimulates pentose nucleic acid synthesis. The concept of normal cytoplasmic particles penetrating normal cells and behaving like a virus is nevertheless developed by BRACHET,[164] who had already[165] stressed the probable importance of nucleoprotein-containing particles as agents of protein synthesis.

Enzymatic activity

MOOG and STEINBACH[166][167] studied the enzymatic activities of granules isolated from chick embryo cells, on the hypothesis that 'incorporation of enzyme into these granules during the embryonic period would . . . be an aspect of the building up of an 'activity structure', a fundamental sort of differentiation on which more overt differentiation may be founded'. The evidence shows that embryonic 'development involves the construction of increasingly complex associations of biochemical constituents, and it seems reasonable to assert that, from an embryological point of view, the most important enzymes are those which become linked with, and presumably oriented upon, such granular associations.' Cellular differentiation is conceived (BRACHET[168][169]) as a process associated with the development of increased size, organization and complexity of the cytoplasmic granules, and a differentiated cell as one which has acquired a certain stability. There may be stability at two levels: 'dynamic' stability of particle population, resulting in stable morphological and functional characteristics in the cell; and stability of differentiated particles in each cell, with consequent loss of pluripotentiality and of ability to initiate reduplication. It is suggested that the metabolic and synthetic activities of the cell may be stimulated or controlled by the pluripotent undifferentiated small particles in a direction which leads to cell division. The hypothesis rests on the unproven assumption that the smallest particles, characteristic of embryonic tissues, resemble viruses in their ability to promote reproduction of their own kind, but differ from viruses in their ability to undergo a directed differentiation into the subcellular functional units of STERN. As CLAUDE[159] suggests, there are two alternative hypotheses which could account for the reproduction of the great variety of known cytoplasmic structures. Either each separate kind of element is self-reproducing, or it is produced by an independent agency which must itself be self-perpetuating. As a working hypothesis CLAUDE chooses the second alternative, which permits the greatest economy of assumption, namely that the 'existence of a reservoir of self-perpetuating microsomes from which the specific granules may develop would provide a satisfactory answer to this problem'. Self-perpetuation is, in his view (CLAUDE[170]), more likely to be the result of 'rigidly ordered chains of reactions' and biochemical cycles than of the self-duplication of highly complex substances by any kind of template replication. It is not excluded that the microsomes may take their origin in the nucleus (CASPERSSON and SCHULTZ;[171] SCHNEIDER and HOGEBOOM;[158] WEISS;[172] JEENER and SZAFARZ[173]) which WEISS believes may be the ultimate source of all cytoplasmic systems. In leukaemic spleen, in which the total pentose nucleic acid is 2·5 times the normal value, a parallel increase is found in the smaller submicroscopic particles and in the nuclei (PETERMANN et alii[175]). WEISS[174] postulates that 'what have appeared to be self-reproducing bodies in the cytoplasm would simply become model centers of adsorption, aggregation, alignment and conversion', originating in the nucleus but differentiating in the cytoplasm. He agrees with CLAUDE in proposing that such bodies are 'self-perpetuating' rather than 'self-reproducing'. Extracts of embryonic tissue display much greater activity, perhaps in stimulating mitosis, certainly in promoting 'growth' and enhancing metabolic activity, than extracts of adult tissues (CARREL and EBELING[105] pp 173, 174). It is possible that the particulate fractions, and especially the smallest particles, which are much more abundant in embryonic cells, may be associated with the activity. BRACHET[176] asks the question: 'A-t-on des raisons de penser que les particules déplacables par ultracentrifugation jouent un role dans la mitose?' and gives evidence which leads him to an affirmative answer, while CLAUDE[170 177] draws attention to the possibility that anaerobic respiration, mediated by the microsomes and the nucleolus, supplies at least part of the energy for the exacting requirements of growth.

Conclusion

The older cytologists studied the static morphology of the cell at the different stages of mitosis. Today cells are being studied dynamically and in relation to their environment. For, 'the living cell is an unstable system which can have neither existence nor form except in relation to its environment' (WEISS[6]). The cultivation of tissues *in vitro* has helped to emphasize that 'cells and medium are an indivisible whole. . . To each modification of the medium corresponds a structural and functional change of the tissues' (CARREL[178]). It is also from tissue culture that most of the evidence has come that many limiting factors affecting the metabolism of the cell can unequivocally be described as nutritional. If nutrition is defective, mitosis is only one of the activities of the cell which is inevitably restrained. Certain other factors, *e.g.*, the hormones, some of the higher peptides and the labile cytoplasmic particulate fractions, could have a specific, overriding stimulating function on cell division. But until more is known about the chemical and enzymatic reactions in which they take part, as well as those which initiate and accompany mitosis, it is difficult even to guess whether the effects of these stimuli (if such they are) are just those required to set in motion the train of events which culminates in cell division. It can still be argued that to designate as 'growth-promoting factors' those substances whose precise function in the cell metabolism is at present unclear or unknown is to use the term as a curtain for ignorance of some vital chapters of cell nutrition. But difficulties arise if too rigid a classification is adopted in describing cell metabolites, for 'a given substance, required as a component of one of the essential metabolic processes, might appear in three different roles . . . (1) as an "essential nutrient", when its rate of synthesis by the cell was so slow as to be insignificant; (2) as a growth stimulant, when its rate of synthesis was somewhat faster but still slow enough to be a limiting factor; or (3) as a substance not required at all for nutrition, because the cell could synthesize it so fast that it was not a limiting factor in growth. It is the metabolic process which is the essential thing. . .' (KNIGHT[179]). The cell and its environment form a single, dynamic metabolizing system, 'a complex interwoven series of processes' (KNIGHT[179]) which is the life of the cells. It is suggested by one biologist that 'the nutrient of some animal cells . . . appears to be made up of both chemical as well as biological components. It may thus become rather difficult to explain nutrition of the animal cell in purely chemical terms' (LIEBMAN[69]). It is true that certain nutrients (in a wide sense) are too complex in their structure and organization to be accessible to exact analysis by the present techniques of the chemist. But such 'biological components' need not, because of this difficulty, be lifted out of the field of biochemistry. The chemical and enzymatic activities of the complex separable and morphological parts of the cell, and their interactions, are being elucidated (CLAUDE;[170] SCHNEIDER and HOGEBOOM[158]). Not only are the activities of the cell and its environment closely integrated; so are those within the cell itself (WEISS[174]). 'A living cell acts as a whole, and it is difficult to imagine an element, be it a gene or a mitochondrion, that would not be in some way under the influence of other components of the cell. On the other hand, each element of the cell possesses a considerable degree of independence and stability.' (CLAUDE[180]). Each stimulus and reaction must be fitted into the dynamic pattern of complex trans-mutations which makes up the life of the cell. To find out exactly what changes in this pattern lead to the process of mitosis and how these changes are brought about is the task for the imaginative insight of the biochemist—for still, 'even now those who think in terms of mole-cular events may have visions of progress denied to those whose thought is guided by the visible alone' (HOPKINS[181]).

INHIBITORY STUDIES ON MITOSIS

In this section, it is proposed to review some of the literature on the effects of chemical substances upon dividing cells. A very large number of papers relate to this subject, but many of them are studies which are primarily concerned with medical or agricultural problems. With the development of chemotherapeutical research in recent years, there has been a considerable increase in the number and complexity of the organic compounds which have been tested on growing tissues, though much of this work relates more to the toxicology of these substances than to the physiology of the dividing cell.

Each line of inquiry tends to develop its own body of theories and ideas into which fresh information is incorporated; not always has each school of thought been ready to admit the validity of the results and conceptions of the other. A brief reference to some of the main branches of research may be made. The chief school of research which uses the whole animal, usually the mouse, as experimental material is that of A. P. and P. DUSTIN and their collaborators, which has been studying for over 25 years the effect of injected substances on the main sites of cell division in the animal. Reviews on the work of this school have been given by DUSTIN (P.).[182] [183] The chief limitation of this type of research is that in sectioned tissues of the experimental animals there are seen only the end results of the reaction of the cell to the agent, the detailed course of which can only be inferred. DUSTIN has made the distinction between substances which inhibit the mitotic spindle and those which affect mainly the chromosomes; the latter type of agent has been termed 'radiomimetic', since ionizing radiations have an apparently similar effect. The cell is believed to be specially sensitive to the action of such substances when it is about to enter prophase. Not always, however, do different types of dividing cell react in the same way to mitotic poisons, and the distinction between DUSTIN's two categories is not invariably maintained.

The analogy with the effect of radiation has been enhanced by the well-known discovery that mustard gas both provokes mutations (AUERBACH and ROBSON[184-186]) and causes cytological abnormalities in germ cells (DARLINGTON and KOLLER[187]) and also in somatic cells in mitosis (HUGHES and FELL[188]). The essential feature common to these effects is a disturbance of the normal pattern of chromosome reproduction, which persists in subsequent cycles of mitosis. This principle has led to researches on the action of chemical substances on the cell nucleus in which effects on the chromosomes of genetical significance have been stressed (LOVELESS and REVELL[189]).

It seems probable that the structures within the dividing cell differ in their sensitivity towards particular agents, the overall action of which may be due to effects on the cell at many points. Moreover, it is now clear that the end result can vary with different types of cell; for the relative effects on the spindle and on the chromosomes of some agents are not uniformly the same. Other substances have been shown to inhibit dividing cells with an equal facility at any point in the mitotic cycle. The present topic, therefore, in common with most aspects of cell biology has the property of becoming increasingly complex with time.

Studies on the living cell of the influence of agents offer the obvious advantage of a direct approach to the problems of mitotic pharmacology. Where marine eggs are used as experimental material, the effects of the treatment on other aspects of cell physiology such as respiration and protoplasmic viscosity may be investigated in parallel. Such combined studies have yielded information of much interest. In a preceding chapter (p 70) has been given an account of the normal mitosis of some cells in which fine detail can be observed in life. Further studies of the action of chemical agents have been made on each of these types of cell. The effects of colchicine in *Acanthamoeba* have been studied by COMANDON and DE FONBRUNE,[190] and on the grasshopper neuroblast by GAULDEN and CARLSON,[191] though research on this material has been mainly concerned with the effects of radiation. Experimental studies on the staminal hair cells of *Tradescantia* in division have been made by WADA[192 193] and on the petal cells of the same plant by SHIGENAGA.[194] Tissue cultures have been used for this purpose on many occasions. By means of phase-contrast cinemicrography, the detailed events within such cells under experiment can be recorded. The agent used can either be incorporated in the tissue culture medium, as in the study by HUGHES and FELL[188] on the effects of mustard gas, or the cultures can first be grown under normal conditions and the substance dissolved in a suitable saline solution can be added thereto while a cell is under observation (HUGHES[195 201]). By this means one can study the effects of a rapidly penetrating agent on each point in the mitotic cycle. This is of importance where more than one phase is liable to be blocked, because the effect on the later stages is never seen unless the earlier sensitive periods are passed without hindrance.

In Table VII, the effects are given of a number of inhibitory substances on the several phases of mitosis in chick cells in culture. A rather miscellaneous group of agents have the property of preventing cells from entering division, and have either no effect on the course of mitosis in a cell in which prophase has begun, or block the later stages to a much smaller extent. This information by itself is hardly sufficient to suggest any features of the metabolism of the cell which may be affected by these substances, and which could thus be regarded as specially important for the entry of cells into mitosis. However, evidence from other sources may relate to this question.

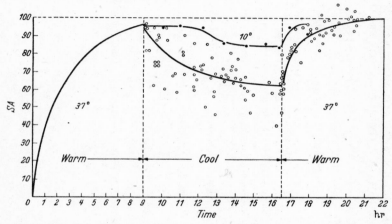

Figure 64 Uptake of K[42] by culture of embryo chick tissue, and reversible loss of isotope on cooling the culture. At 10° C. (●) and at 5° C. (O). Ordinate: relative specific activity of culture. From WESSON *et alii*[202] (*By courtesy, J. gen. Physiol.*).

A number of agents both inhibit cells in tissue culture from entering mitosis, and also allow potassium to escape from the erythrocytes of those mammals which have a high content of this ion (WILBRANDT;[196] DAVSON;[197 198] MAIZELS[199]). Thus both effects are exerted by sodium fluoride, by iodoacetate, by hypotonic saline, and by isotonic non-electrolytes. Neither effect is provoked by cyanide or urethane (DAVSON and DANIELLI;[200] HUGHES[201]). Moreover, it has been shown by WESSON *et alii*[202] that potassium is reversibly lost from cells in tissue culture into the surrounding medium at temperatures below 15° C (Figure 64); in the same way when stored human blood is cooled to 5° C., there is a comparable migration of this ion (HARRIS;[203] DANOWSKI[204]). SPEAR[204a] in 1926 showed that on re-incubation of tissue cultures after chilling for four hours at 0·5° C., the number of mitoses present decreased during the next two hours; this suggested that 'the initiation of mitosis

185

TABLE VII. SHORT-TERM EFFECTS OF VARIOUS AGENTS ON MITOSIS IN CHICK TISSUE CULTURES STUDIED MAINLY IN LIVING MATERIAL (DATA FROM HUGHES[201] OR FROM UNPUBLISHED WORK)

Agent	Concentration in m Mols of added chemicals	Type and degree of effect		
		Pre-prophase	Metaphase	Telophase
Hypertonic saline	(50% Tyrode)	Large inhibition	None	Irregular distribution of chromosomes at anaphase. Occasional inhibition of cleavage, but nuclei reconstruct.
Adenosine, adenylic acids	0·6–1·2	Almost complete inhibition	None	None
NaF	10–15	Complete inhibition	Partial inhibition	None
$CH_2I.COONa$	0·033	Large inhibition	Partial inhibition	Inhibition of nuclear reconstruction, slight
Chloracetophenone (CAP)*	0·065	Partial inhibition	Complete inhibition	Inhibition of nuclear reconstruction, severe
Colchicine†	0·0027	None	Complete inhibition	None
Aminopterin‡	0·5	None	Complete inhibition	Inhibition of Nuclear reconstruction, slight. Inhibition of cleavage, occasionally
Adenine; 2, 6, Diaminopurine§	3·5	None	Nuclear reconstruction directly from metaphase or early anaphase. Inhibition of cleavage almost complete	

* Plate XIV (25); Plate XV (27)
† Plate XIV (23)
‡ Plate XIV (24)
§ Plate XV (26)

has been interfered with'. That reversible migration of potassium across the cell membrane may occur during cell division is shown by the observations of ODDO and ESPOSITO.[204b]

It is desirable to see whether this parallel can be extended further. DAVSON and DANIELLI[200] showed that a number of haemolytic agents in concentrations below the lytic threshold induce an abnormally high permeability of the erythrocyte to potassium, but their effects on mitosis in tissue culture have not yet been investigated. It would also be desirable to examine whether substances which exert an action at other points in the mitotic cycle have any effect on the ionic equilibria of the red cells. Where there is normally a difference in concentration of potassium on either side of the erythrocyte membrane,

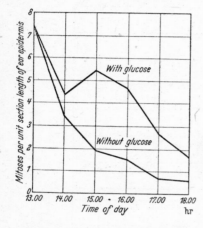

Figure 65 Number of mitoses in the fragments of the ears of mice severed at 13.00 hours, and maintained in physiological salt solutions. From BULLOUGH[208] (*By courtesy, Proc. roy. Soc. B*).

it is believed to be maintained by a metabolic process such as glycolysis which absorbs energy, although the 'pre-haemolytic state' (DAVSON and DANIELLI[200]), is not necessarily related to this. The effect of fluoride on permeability to potassium is probably an indirect one; DAVSON[205] has suggested that intermediate products of glycolysis, accumulating at the cell membrane, may be responsible for the increase in permeability. The effects of iodoacetate and fluoride in preventing the entry of cells into prophase may not be due to the inhibition of glycolysis alone; other agents which exert this effect on the tissue culture are not known to affect carbohydrate metabolism.

In a series of papers, BULLOUGH[206-208] has produced evidence that the entry into mitosis of epithelial cells of the ear of the mouse is dependent on the amount of carbohydrate within the tissues. Once a cell in the epithelium is in prophase, it can continue division even when the ear is severed from the animal and kept in physiological salt solution. If the medium contains glucose, fresh cells can enter mitosis under these conditions (BULLOUGH[208]) (Figure 65). BULLOUGH suggests that cells begin division only when a comparatively high level of energy is available, such as that supplied by aerobic glycolysis. MEDAWAR[209] has found that adult rabbit skin survives in cultivation in the absence of oxygen, but that no cells then enter division.

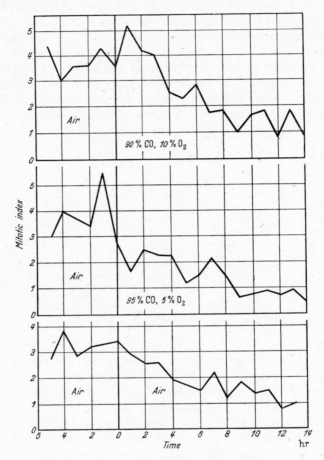

Figure 66 The mitotic index in chick tissue cultures treated with gas mixtures containing carbon monoxide. No immediate effects on growth are detectable. From POMERAT and WILLMER[216] (*By courtesy, J. exp. Biol.*).

The literature on the effects of anaerobiosis on cell division is reviewed by BRACHET.[210] STEINITZ[211] found that when barley seedlings were placed in an atmosphere of nitrogen, mitosis continued for several days, although abnormalities of the chromosomes were then to be seen. Mitosis in the sea-urchin egg can be inhibited at several stages in an atmosphere of hydrogen (HARVEY[212]); but it has not been proved that embryonic cells in tissue culture cannot enter mitosis in the absence of oxygen. LASER[213] found that cultures could grow under these circumstances for several days, but did not specifically examine them for mitoses, while EPHRUSSI *et alii*[214] found that cells would migrate, but would not complete division at an oxygen tension lower than 7 mm of mercury. HARVARD and KENDAL[215] found that although mitosis could occur in cultures at oxygen tensions much lower than this, reducible substances in the medium deprived of oxygen would finally bring the oxidation-reduction potential of the culture to a value below the threshold for growth. Embryonic cells in culture can enter mitosis, in the presence of inhibitors of some stages of glycolysis, such as malonate (POMERAT and WILLMER;[216] HUGHES[201]) and fluoracetate (ALLSOPP and FELL;[217] HUGHES[201]) and respiratory poisons such as carbon monoxide (Figure 66) and hydrocyanic acid (POMERAT and WILLMER;[216] HUGHES[201]). The apparent indifference of the dividing cell in cultures

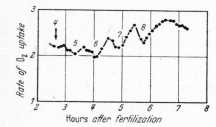

Figure 67 Respiration of eggs of the sea urchin *Psammechinus miliaris* from the 4th to the 8th cleavage. Oxygen uptake measured as rate of movement of the manometer of the Cartesian diver micro-respirometer. From ZEUTHEN[219] (*By courtesy, Biol. Bull.*). Cleavage of the egg occurs near the minima of the curve.

of embryonic tissues to these inhibitors may well be related to the fact that their environment contains an adequate supply of glucose. PACE[218] has shown that the effect of cyanide on respiration in *Paramoecium* depends on the extent to which the respiratory mechanism is saturated with carbohydrate.

Thus the available evidence would not warrant a general statement that cells can only enter mitosis under aerobic conditions. It is probable that the reaction of cells in division to experimental agents is superimposed on the general metabolic pattern of the particular tissue which may vary at different stages of development. ZEUTHEN[219] found that the respiratory rhythm of cell division in echinoderm eggs increases in amplitude after the sixth cleavage (Figure 67). The energy requirements of mitosis at different stages in development may thus be variable.

Adenosine and the adenylic acids at appropriate concentrations prevent the entry of cells into prophase in the whole animal (BULLOUGH and GREEN[220]) and in tissue cultures (HUGHES[221]) where, however, these substances exert no effect at any other point in mitosis.* RUNNSTRÖM

* BERRIAN and DORNFELD[221a] find that the number of mitotic figures in cultivated rat ovaries is significantly reduced by cytidylic, guanylic, and yeast adenylic acids.

and KRISZAT[222] find that adenosine triphosphate increases cytoplasmic rigidity in the egg of *Strongylocentrotus*, and improves the percentage of cleavage in batches of fertilized eggs. Probably in general, purines and their nucleosides and nucleotides may exert either inhibitory or stimulatory (HOPKINS and SIMON-REUSS[223]) effects on growing tissues, depending upon the concentrations applied.

Inhibition of mitosis during prophase

It is rare that cells in mitosis under the influence of chemical agents are held up during prophase. One instance of this is apparently provided by the sea-urchin egg. CLOWES and KRAHL[224] found that fertilized eggs treated with 4, 6 dinitro-o-cresol are arrested at a stage in which the chromosomes can be recognized, the nuclear membrane is still intact, and the asters have just been formed; RUNNSTRÖM[225] [226] found that hydrocyanic acid has a similar effect. Respiration is stimulated by the former agent and depressed by the latter, yet the effect of both on mitosis is similar. SCOTT[227] finds that cyanide inhibits the swelling of the male pronucleus after its fusion with that of the egg.

In a recent review, KRAHL[228] concludes that the tendency of substituted phenols to inhibit sea-urchin eggs in prophase relates merely to the fact that this phase of mitosis is the longest; for the chance of arresting a cell in a particular stage must be proportional to its normal duration where there is no period of special sensitivity during the whole cycle. BLUMENTHAL[229] concluded that the action of cyanides on the fertilized *Arbacia* egg shows no special phase specificity. Prophase in the eggs of *Arbacia* is readily prolonged by irradiation given prior to this stage, during the period of fusion of the male and female pronuclei (HENSHAW;[229a] HENSHAW and COHEN[229b]). Pre-prophase is also a period of special sensitivity of the eggs of *Asterias* to nitrogen mustards (CANNAN, quoted by FRIEDENWALD[229c]).

EPHRUSSI *et alii*[214] claim that at low tensions of oxygen, cells in tissue culture are arrested in prophase. None of the chemical agents applied to tissue cultures by HUGHES[195] [201] [221] have had this effect. ERICKSON and ROSEN[230] find that after treatment of the seedlings of *Zea mais* with the unsaturated lactone protoanemonin, the meristematic nuclei are nearly all either in interphase or early prophase, though a few are apparently in late prophase. No later stages of mitosis are to be seen. According to LOVELESS and REVELL[189] this substance has 'cytological effects similar to the mustards'. D'AMATO[231] refers to other examples of the arrest of plant cells in prophase. However, from the available data, it appears that prophase is the longest phase of mitosis in plant cells (Table III, p 85), and it is possible that arrest at this stage may be related to its duration, rather than to special sensitivity.

Inhibition of the mitotic spindle

A large number of substances are known to interfere with the formation and function of the mitotic spindle. The final effect on the cell is not always the same; if the chromosomes can undergo reconstruction even where their normal distribution by the spindle mechanism has been omitted, then either one nucleus will be formed from the whole double set of chromosomes, or the chromosomes which are scattered throughout the cell may form a number of small nuclei (MISZURSKI and DOLJAN-SKI[232]). If, however, no stimulus to reconstruction occurs in the absence of the normal movements of anaphase, then the cell may remain indefinitely in a condition of arrested 'metaphase'. The paired chromatids may either clump together (Plate XV (23)), or remain discrete. Stages of increasing severity of effect on the mitotic spindle can be distinguished. GAULDEN and CARLSON[191] have shown that a spindle subnormal in size is formed in grasshopper neuroblasts when treated with marginal concentrations of colchicine. In living tissue cultures (HUGHES[201]) when partial metaphase inhibitors such as urethane, cyanide, and fluoride are added to a cell in prophase, the spindle is formed, and usually anaphase ultimately occurs after a much prolonged metaphase, during which the normal random movement of the chromosomes along the spindle is maintained (HUGHES and SWANN[233]). In one cell treated with mustard gas, metaphase was followed for 135 minutes after which anaphase suddenly took place (HUGHES and FELL[188]). More specific inhibitors of the spindle will prevent its formation in a cell treated during prophase and will inhibit the random movement of the chromosomes in a cell in metaphase. Such agents are colchicine, aminopterin, and among sulphydryl reactants, iodoacetamide, and chloracetophenone. Once this random metaphase movement ceases, the cell will never proceed to anaphase. Chloracetophenone will halt the movement of the chromosomes within 30 seconds if added to a cell when anaphase has already just begun; aminopterin acts with nearly the same rapidity (Figure 68); but inhibition during anaphase has not otherwise yet been observed.

Of the substances which act as spindle inhibitors, some are effective at very great dilutions. The classical example of these is the alkaloid colchicine, which LUDFORD[234] found to be effective on cells in mitosis in tissue cultures at a concentration of $10^{-8.4}$ molar. The action of colchicine on dividing cells in the crypts of LIEBERKÜHN was discovered as early as 1889 (PERNICE;[235] EIGSTI et alii[236]). The unrelated compound 1, 4 naphthohydroquinone diphosphate has a similar action at a dilution of the same order (FRIEDMANN et alii[237]). Cells in culture probably are particularly sensitive to metaphase poisons; 2.5×10^{-6} M colchicine is needed for complete inhibition of the spindle in the neuroblasts of the grasshopper embryo (GAULDEN and CARLSON[191]) while the corresponding dose for the staminal hairs of *Tradescantia* is just above 10^{-4} M (NEBEL and RUTTLE[238]). It would be interesting to see whether α nitronaphthalene which is effective on dividing plant cells at $2 \cdot 8 \times 10^{-5}$ M (GAVAUDAN and POUSSEL[239]) would inhibit the spindle in tissue cultures at a greater dilution.

The substance podophyllin, extracted from plants of the genus *Podophyllum* is a mixture which contains two compounds, podophyllotoxin and quercetin, the former of which inhibits the spindle in the egg of

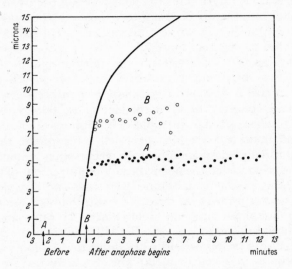

Figure 68 Arrest of chromosome movement during anaphase in cells of chick cultures by A 0·45 millimolar aminopterin, and B 0·07 millimolar chloracetophenone. The continuous curve represents the normal average movement of similar cells in anaphase. In A the agent was added 2½ minutes before anaphase, in B as soon as possible after anaphase began; the movement was arrested within about thirty seconds. In A neither cleavage nor nuclear reconstruction ensued; in B cleavage was irregular, and reconstruction was partially inhibited.

Arbacia at a dilution one hundred times greater than does colchicine (CORNMAN[240]).* In tissue cultures, podophyllin has a marked inhibitory effect on certain tumour cells at concentrations at which embryonic cells are unaffected (ORMSBEE, CORNMAN and BERGER[240a]).

These substances which act as spindle inhibitors at very low concentrations are all of molecular weights of the order of several hundred, but exhibit no more general chemical features in common than do the

* CORNMAN and CORNMAN[241a] have published a detailed study on the effects of these substances on cleavage in a number of marine eggs.

various compounds which exhibit this effect at higher dosages. LETTRÉ and his colleagues in a series of papers[241] have shown that some features are common to the molecules of both colchicine and a few other antimitotic compounds. These, however, are only a small minority of such substances. Nor is much light on the cytological action of colchicine derived from what is known of its various other physiological properties; it provokes haemorrhages in tumours as do bacterial polysaccharides (BOYLAND and BOYLAND[242]), it enhances the effects of adrenaline on the whole animal (RAYMOND-HAMET[243]), it partially inhibits some enzymes, such as xanthine oxidase (KEESER[244]) and interferes at some point in the contraction cycle of striped muscle (LECOMTE[245])*.

The cytological effects of colchicine are not restricted to the inhibition of the mitotic spindle. Mitotic figures are seen in the liver of the adult rat after an injection of colchicine (MISZURSKI and DOLJANSKI[232]); growth in yeast is stimulated by colchicine (RICHARDS[246]), and the chromonemata become more noticeable in the intermitotic nuclei of the cockroach (RIES[247]). Breaks in chromosomes are induced by colchicine in the anthers of *Carthamus* (KRYTHE[249]) and in *Tradescantia* pollen-tubes (EIGSTI[248]). 'Bubbling' at the surface of fibroblastic cells in culture is evoked (MISZURSKI[250]), and perhaps the most important observation of all, BEAMS and EVANS[251] find that eggs of *Arbacia* 20 minutes after fertilization are more readily stratified by centrifugation in the presence of colchicine. Mitosis in some of these eggs was blocked in early anaphase, the dissolution of the asters was observed, and the cleavage of the egg did not occur in their absence.

More comparative studies of the effects of other mitotic inhibitors acting at high dilutions on various types of cell are greatly needed. One should examine their effects both on protoplasmic consistency and on cleavage in a variety of dividing cells. Colchicine has been shown to have no effect on fission in several Protozoa, nor on locomotion and ingestion in *Amoeba* (KING and BEAMS[252]). CORNMAN and CORNMAN[241a] observed that Protozoa multiplied in dishes in which *Asterias* eggs were disintegrating under the influence of podophyllin.

It is of interest that 2-methyl 1, 4 naphthoquinone, which has an inhibitory action on mitosis in tissue cultures (MITCHELL and SIMON-REUSS[253]) has an opposite effect on the *Arbacia* egg, causing parthenogenic activation and cytoplasmic gelation (HALABAN[254]), though the effects on the egg of *Chaetopterus* are again somewhat different (HEIL-BRUNN and WILSON[255]). Among substances which inhibit both mitotic

---

* CORNMAN[245a] has shown that a large excess of carbohydrate can partially neutralize the effect on sea-urchin eggs of colchicine and podophyllotoxin. MURRAY, DE LAM, and CHARGAFF[245b] find that meso-inositol has a specific effect in blocking the action of colchicine on dividing rat fibroblasts in culture.

gelation and cleavage in marine eggs are heparin,* a bacterial poly-saccharide (HEILBRUNN and WILSON[255]) extracts of tissues such as the ovary of *Asterias* (HEILBRUNN *et alii*[256]) and the dye Janus Green B (ALLEN[257]) which is also effective as a blood anticoagulant. These observations are relevant to HEILBRUNN's theory that 'protoplasmic clotting' is involved in cell division (p 140).

The specificity of the action of colchicine on the spindle is illustrated by comparison with substances such as the narcotics which inhibit cells in metaphase at concentrations not much less than those at which their other effects are exerted. Thus colchicine is without influence on cyclosis in *Tradescantia* staminal hair cells (NEBEL and RUTTLE;[238] DERMAN[258]), while this activity in *Elodea* leaves is depressed by chloroform at 0·025 M (MEDES and McCLENDON[259]), a concentration little more than twice that needed to inhibit the spindle in *Allium* root-tips (OSTERGREN[260]) with this narcotic. Again, photosynthesis in *Elodea* ceases when benzene at mitotic-inhibiting concentrations is added. Even I per cent colchicine has little effect on photosynthesis (GAVAUDAN and BREBION[261]).

ÖSTERGREN[260] has shown that in a number of organic compounds, water solubility is inversely proportional to their effectiveness as spindle inhibitors, measured by the greatest dilution at which they act on dividing cells in *Allium* root-tips. Such relationships have been expressed by FERGUSON[262] in physico-chemical terms. Where substances of low water-solubility exert toxic effects, the ratio between their threshold toxic concentrations and their solubility is known as the 'thermodynamic activity' of the compound and varies between 0·1—1·0 for 'unreactive substances of the typical narcotic type', which act in a purely physical manner, while chemical reactions with cell constituents probably occur where the value of the activity coefficient is very low. GAVAUDAN *et alii*[263] have calculated the 'thermodynamic activities' of a number of mitotic inhibitors; the lowest values are those of colchicine and hexa-nitrodiphenylamine.

The action of narcotics on the mitotic spindle is a comparatively recent addition to the list of the inhibitory effects of these substances, and can best be considered in relation to their general subject action within the cell, a subject recently reviewed by McELROY[264] and by DANIELLI.[265] The most significant contribution to this field in recent years has been the discovery that high hydrostatic pressure is able to counteract the effect of some narcotics on bacterial luminescence (JOHNSON *et alii*[266]). This has led to the view that these substances cause a reversible denaturation of enzymic proteins, and that pressure influences this equilibrium in favour of the native form. This theory

---

* Heparin has been found to prevent the agglutination of cytoplasmic particles isolated from lymphocytes (HOSTER *et alii*[257a]).

could be applied to the inhibition of the mitotic spindle either if the orientation and disorientation of the spindle proteins themselves involves a reversible denaturation, or if their state of alignment is under enzymic control. The latter must of necessity be true if SWANN is correct in his thesis (p 126) that the metaphase spindle represents a dynamic equilibrium.

If it were possible to find a suitable example of a mitotic spindle which was insensitive to the effects of hydrostatic pressure *per se* it would be of great value to investigate whether the action of the various agents which affect cells during metaphase could be annulled by pressure, and, if so, whether pressure-sensitivity of the chemical inhibition of the spindle and of bacterial luminescence were correlated. Again, it might be rewarding to seek evidence for cytoplasmic denaturation in the achromatic figure by using KOPAC's method, based on the 'Devaux effect'. Injected oil-drops wrinkle if proteins adsorbed at the oil-cytoplasmic interface are denatured (KOPAC[266a]).

Reversible denaturation of proteins during mitosis has been suggested as the reason for the sensitivity of dividing cells to sulphydryl reactants (RAPKINE[267]), for the number of reactive —SH groups is increased in proteins after denaturation. A number of these substances have been shown to act as metaphase inhibitors. For instance, mitotic arrest at this point was demonstrated by LUDFORD[234] with sodium cacodylate on tissue cultures, and by DUSTIN (P.)[268] with sodium arsenite in the bone marrow of the mouse. HUGHES has shown that the development of the spindle can be prevented when a cell in early prophase in a tissue culture is treated with either iodoacetamide[195] or chloracetophenone.[201] If the development of the spindle involves reversible denaturation of the constituent protein micelles, its sensitivity to sulphydryl reactants would suggest that these agents can act directly upon spindle material. So far, the cytochemical evidence for the presence of free —SH groups in the spindle is restricted to the observations of BRACHET[269] on the reaction of the spermatocytes of *Stenobothrus* with the nitroprusside reagent. On this point he says: 'Au moment des cinèses de maturation, le cytoplasme réagit moins intensement et le fuseau prend un ton plus sombre; si, a cet instant, la cellule est écrasée, on peut retrouver le fuseau a l'état libre et constater qu'il donne une vive réaction.'

On the other hand, CHALKLEY[270] finds that the nucleus of *Amoeba* loses its positive nitroprusside reaction when the nuclear membrane disappears at the end of prophase, and that only 'after fission is complete, and the nucleus is reorganized the reaction can again be evoked in the nucleus'. It would be a notable advance in cytochemistry if there were developed a method for revealing sulphydryl groups of sufficient sensitivity and precision to map out their distribution in a number of dividing cells. There is some doubt whether the method of

CHÈVREMONT and FREDERIC,[271] though adequate for proteins such as keratin, is sufficiently sensitive for this purpose. It is generally true that free —SH groups are abundant in tissues in which cells are frequently dividing; the evidence for this generalization is reviewed by BRACHET.[210]

Other effects of sulphydryl reactants in dividing cells

Metaphase is not the only stage in mitosis which can be blocked by sulphydryl reactants. The effect of iodoacetate in preventing the entry into mitosis of cells in tissue cultures has already been described (p 185); iodoacetamide and chloracetophenone, when added to a culture when anaphase has just begun within a cell, can arrest the further movement of the chromosomes, and at the same time prevent cleavage and the reconstruction of the daughter nuclei. When anaphase and telophase are inhibited by chloracetophenone in this way, bubbling at the surface of the cell begins some minutes after the addition of the agent, and increases in violence to such an extent that the whole cell may be fragmented into blebs, among which the daughter chromosomes are found unchanged still in their early anaphase relationship (Plate XV (27)).

HUGHES[201] has suggested that this blockage of nuclear reconstruction may be due to inhibition of nucleases of the type described by MAVER and GRECO[272] and associated with cathepsin, which is a complex of sulphydryl enzymes. This suggestion, however, leaves unexplained the fact that the formation of the chromosomes in prophase is comparatively insensitive to sulphydryl reactants in the fibroblastic cell, although mitosis can readily be inhibited by such agents at several other points. Inhibition in prophase can result if the action on the cell is sufficiently drastic to arrest cytoplasmic movement, which also ceases in intermitotic cells after prolonged treatment with high concentrations of chloracetophenone.

Chromosomal effects

A number of substances affect the dividing cell primarily by attacking the nucleoproteins and the chromosomes. These include the 'radiomimetic' agents of DUSTIN which cause dividing cells in the mouse to degenerate. Among these are trypaflavine (DUSTIN (A. P.)[273]) the effects of which on tissue cultures have been shown by LETTRÉ and LETTRÉ[274] to be counteracted by nucleic acids, both RNA and DNA, when added to the medium of the culture. Not all the substances which affect the nucleoproteins of the chromosomes induce the breaks and rearrangements which persist in subsequent mitoses after the direct toxic effect has disappeared (LOVELESS and REVELL[189]). Chromosome breaks which do not persist in subsequent cycles of mitosis are provoked by a large number of agents; it has recently been shown that they occur even during the normal germination of the bean (LEVAN and LOTFY[275]). HUGHES and FELL[188] found that when chick tissue cultures were treated with doses of sulphur mustard just sufficient to induce some fragmentation of the chromosomes, the damage to the mitotic spindle and the cleavage mechanism of the cell was then comparatively slight. Metaphase was often prolonged, but in anaphase those chromosomes attached to the spindle then moved at the usual rate. The abnormalities in subsequent divisions of such cells have not yet been examined. Persistent breakage of a chromosome is in itself not necessarily lethal to a cell; HUGHES-SCHRADER and RIS[276] have demonstrated this in their work on the effect of X-rays on Hemiptera such as the coccid bug *Steatococcus* where, thanks to a diffuse attachment to the spindle, chromosome fragments retain their connection thereto. Embryos of this insect were shown to continue their development after X-ray treatment, and many cycles of somatic division occurred with fragmented chromosomes.

The ultimate lethal effects of chromosome breakage in a lineage of cells where centromeres are of the normal type must therefore be due to loss of chromosomal material. Instances are known where early embryonic development is blocked if a chromosome is lacking in the nucleus; POULSON[277] has shown that eggs of *Drosophila* without an X-chromosome do not develop normally beyond segmentation.

A further possibility is that misplaced chromosomal nucleoproteins may exert inhibitory effects within the cytoplasm. This is suggested by the recent observations of MAZIA[278] that development can be blocked when an embryo is treated with the deoxyribonucleic acid of its own species. This was found to occur with eggs both of *Asterias* and the frog, when their own respective DNA was added to the surrounding medium. Foreign DNA was found to have no effect in either instance. BRACHET (private communication), however, has been unable to confirm these observations of MAZIA, though inhibitory effects of constituent molecular units of the nucleic acids, acting either before (p 189) or during (p 198) mitosis, have been described by several authors.

Blockage of the cycle of the deoxynucleoproteins of the cell at a different point is suggested by the work of MARSHAK;[279] MARSHAK and HARTING[280] on the effects of d-usnic acid on the fertilized egg of *Arbacia*. This substance, which is extracted from a lichen, inhibits DN-ase *in vitro* in the presence of cobalt. In the egg, usnic acid prevents the fusion of male and female pronuclei, and also the cleavage of the cell, when it is added subsequent to the prophase of the first mitosis. MAZIA[278] has shown that DN-ase is found within the cytoplasm of the *Arbacia* egg and so the inhibitory effects of usnic acid may possibly be exerted therein. Although the particular observations of these two authors to which reference has just been made are at an early stage, it is clear that they are likely to yield new information of the interrelationships of the nucleus and cytoplasm during mitosis. The importance of this topic needs no emphasis.

Inhibition of cytokinesis

In plants, this stage in the mitotic cycle is highly susceptible to arrest. The phragmoplast, by means of which the new cell wall is formed is an orientated body (p 146) and it is interesting to see that this, like the spindle which precedes it, is sensitive to colchicine; WADA[193] has observed the dissolution of the phragmoplast in the living staminal hair-cell of *Tradescantia* in the presence of this alkaloid. SIMONET and GUINOCHET[281] found that halogenated derivatives of benzene and toluene suppressed cytokinesis in seedlings of *Linum* while nuclear division continued, multinucleate cells were thus formed. These authors refer to this effect as the 'paradichlorobenzene type of response' from the name of the compound which was first found to provoke it, though other workers (GAVAUDAN *et alii*[282]) have found that in the roots of *Triticum* the action of these substances is not entirely restricted to this phase of cell division. KIHLMAN[286] has shown that cytokinesis is suppressed in the meristems of *Allium* roots by treatment with adenine, or with methylated purines. Adenine has a similar effect on chick cells in culture (HUGHES) (Plate XV (2b)). CHALKLEY[287] finds that a variety of agents which interfere with locomotor activity in *Amoeba* prevent the fission of individuals in mitosis, while nuclear division proceeds unhindered. The suppression of cleavage by chemical treatment and the formation of a di-diploid nucleus was first demonstrated by WILSON[288] in 1902, who treated sea-urchin eggs with ether.

However, it has been shown by SHIGENAGA[194] that the formation of the cell plate in *Tradescantia* petal cells is readily disturbed by treatment first with a narcotic and then subsequently with hypotonic sucrose or water. SHIGENAGA's work is a beautiful illustration of the Japanese cytological tradition of work with living material, and the photographs which accompany his paper show very clearly how these treatments can result in several grades of effect. Either a single di-diploid nucleus, or two diploid nuclei may be found within an undivided cell, or an incomplete septum may form between the two daughter nuclei. Since changes in hydration probably occur in both nucleus and cytoplasm during telophase, it may be that the miscellaneous chemical agents which affect this stage of cell division act by interfering with the normal movements of water at this time.

A number of substituted hydroxybenzene derivatives have been shown both to inhibit cell division in marine eggs, mainly of *Arbacia* and also at the same time to stimulate respiration (Figure 69). (The literature in this field has been reviewed by KRAHL[228] and CLOWES[228a].) These effects are fully reversible. Of these substances, 4, 6 dinitro-orthocresol inhibits the *Arbacia* egg in prophase or before (SCOTT[227]), and those of *Cumingia* and *Nereis* at metaphase. In *Asterias* there is no particular point of sensitivity, and after prophase the *Arbacia* egg may be inhibited at any point. Dinitrophenol and halogenated phenols inhibit cleavage in *Arbacia*, though there is no precise point at which mitosis is specially sensitive to interruption (CLOWES *et alii*[283]).

The dual effect of these substances on respiration and cell division are related. They occur at the same time when batches of eggs are treated with increasing concentrations and are believed to be due to the

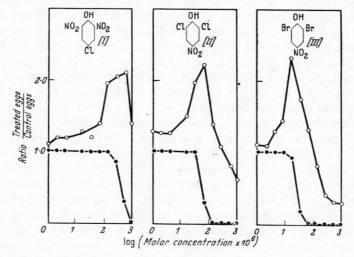

Figure 69 Stimulation of oxygen consumption and block to cell division of fertilized *Arbacia* eggs produced by various concentrations of substituted phenols at 20° C (I). 2, 6-dinitro-4-chlorophenol. (II) 2, 6-dichloro-4-nitrophenol. (III) 2, 6, dibromo-4-nitrophenol. Reagents were added 25 mins. after fertilization. Circles describe oxygen uptake, and dots represent cell division. From KRAHL and CLOWES[291] *(By courtesy, J. gen. Physiol.).*

diversion of oxidative energy from phosphorylative synthesis to the combustion of carbohydrate reserves. Thus LOOMIS and LIPMANN[284] have shown that dinitrophenol can uncouple phosphorylation and oxidation in an isolated enzyme preparation,* and VILLEE *et alii*[285] find that dinitrophenol reduces the uptake of P^{32} and its incorporation into nucleic acids and phosphoproteins in the fertilized *Arbacia* egg.

Comparable effects of dinitrophenols on other cells and tissues are known in which functional activity depending on phosphate bond

*CLOWES[228a] has reported the preparation of cell-free oxidative and phosphorylating systems from the eggs of *Arbacia* in which nitro- and halo-phenols stimulate respiration and inhibit phosphorylation at the same concentrations as with normal fertilized eggs.

energy is depressed, and respiration is stimulated at the same time (McElroy[264]). It is therefore clear that these substances affect cell division only indirectly by interfering with the energy supply at chemical levels below that at which the various visible events of the mitotic process are maintained. Again, d-usnic acid inhibits both cleavage and the uptake of P[32], without any stimulus to respiration (Marshak and Harting;[280] Marshak[279]). This substance must block metabolic pathways at a point different from that affected by the substituted phenols.

It is thus possible to interrupt cell division at a particular phase by agents which act in different ways. For instance, cleavage in the sea-urchin egg is inhibited by high pressure in a direct effect on the egg cortex,* and by dinitrophenols which cut off the supply of energy to the gelating egg proteins. In the absence of evidence from elsewhere, it may not be possible to decide at what levels a 'mitotic poison' is exerting its effect, even if the action is specific on one particular phase of division, for energy requirements may be particularly high in a certain cell at this point. Here is perhaps the most awkward complication of all for those who wish to analyse the nature of mitosis through the experimental treatment of dividing cells.

The best hope of progress in the face of this difficulty is probably to work systematically through a number of substances with definite effects on mitosis, and to test their effects on other features of the activity of the cell. A valuable observation of this kind has been made by Zeuthen[289] who has shown that suppression by colchicine of the achromatic cycle and cleavage in the sea-urchin egg does not abolish the normal waves in the curve of oxygen uptake, measured on the Cartesian diver microrespirometer. These must therefore be related to the nuclear cycle, for the formation of the chromosomes and their reconstruction into nuclei continues in the egg treated with colchicine. It is possible that the uptake of P[32] continues in these circumstances; Skipper et alii[290] have recently shown that the incorporation of formate carbon into nucleic acid purines in the mouse is unaffected by the injection of colchicine. It would not be difficult to suggest a series of such possible lines of inquiry, but to pursue them would need a large amount of co-operation between experts in different techniques.

* The remarkable action of threshold doses of podophyllin in causing regression of the cleavage furrow in sea-urchin eggs in which division is already nearly complete is presumably also a direct effect on the cortical gel (Cornman and Cornman[241a]).

REFERENCES

Nature of the stimulus to mitosis
1 Hammett, F. S., *Amer. J. Roentgenol.*, 43 (1940), 266
2 —, *Scientia*, 5 (1946), 93
3 Cunningham, B. and Kirk, P. L., *J. Cell. Comp. Physiol.*, 20 (1942), 343

[4] RICHARDS, O. W. and CAVANAGH, A. J., in *Essays on Growth and Form*, Ed. by W. E. LeGROS CLARK and P. B. MEDAWAR, Oxford, 1945
[5] MAYER, J., *Growth*, 13 (1949), 97
[6] WEISS, P., in *The Chemistry and Physiology of Growth*, Ed. by A. K. PARPART, Princeton, N.J., 1949
[7] —, *Exper. Cell. Res.*, Suppl. 1 (1949), 475
[8] TYLER, A., *Quart. Rev. Biol.*, 17 (1942), 197, 339
[9] BERRILL, N. J., *Physiol. Rev.*, 23 (1943), 101
[10] NEEDHAM, J., *Biochemistry and Morphogenesis*, Cambridge, 1942
[11] BAKER, L. E. and CARREL, A., *J. exp. Med.*, 44 (1926), 387
[12] FISCHER, A., *Biology of Tissue Cells*, Copenhagen, 1946
[13] GIESE, A. C., *Quart. Rev. Biol.*, 22 (1947), 253
[14] —, *Physiol. Rev.*, 30 (1947), 431
[15] LOOFBOUROW, J. R., *Growth*, Suppl. 12 (1948), 75
[16] THOMPSON, D'A.W., *On Growth and Form*, Cambridge, 1942
[17] JACOBY, F., *Arch. exp. Zellforsch.*, 19 (1937), 241
[18] MEDAWAR, P. B., *Proc. roy. Soc. B*, 129 (1940), 332
[19] FISCHER, A., *Arch. exp. Zellforsch.*, 1 (1925), 369
[20] THIMANN, K. V., in *Currents in Biochemical Research*, New York, 1946
[21] LUDFORD, R. J., *Brit. Empire Cancer Campaign Rep.*, 26 (1948), 89
[22] DARLINGTON, C. D. and MATHER, K., *The Elements of Genetics*, London, 1949
[23] JENNINGS, H. S., in 'The Cell and Protoplasm', *A.A.A.S. Publ. No.* 14 (1940), 44
[24] SWIFT, H. H., *Physiol. Zool.*, 23 (1950), 169
[25] CASPERSSON, T., *Skand. Arch. Physiol.*, 73 (1936), Suppl. 8
[26] — and THORELL, B., *Chromosoma*, 2 (1941), 132
[27] WILLMER, E. N., *Brit. Empire Cancer Campaign Rep.*, 19 (1942), 53; 20 (1943), 60
[28] CLAUDE, A., *Biol. Symp.*, 10 (1943), 111
[29] LIEBMAN, E., *Growth*, 13 (1949), 103
[30] CARREL, A., *Proc. Inst. Med. Chicago*, 8 (1930), 62
[31] SCHAPER, A. and COHEN, C., *Arch. Entw. Mech. Org.*, 19 (1905), 348, quoted by NICHOLSON[35]
[32] STRANGEWAYS, T. S. P., *Tissue Culture in Relation to Growth and Differentiation*, Cambridge, 1924
[33] LORRAIN SMITH, J., *Growth*, Edinburgh, 1932
[34] REIMANN, S. P., *Amer. J. Roentgenol.*, 43 (1940), 275
[35] NICHOLSON, G. W. deP., *Studies on Tumour Formation*, London, 1950
[36] DAWSON, A. B., *Growth*, Suppl. 2 (1940), 91
[37] BLOOM, W., *Physiol. Rev.*, 17 (1937), 589
[38] WEISS, P., *Principles of Development*, New York, 1939
[39] FISCHER, A. and PARKER, R. C., *Proc. Soc. exp. Biol. Med.*, 26 (1929), 583
[40] LITTLE, C. C., in *Genetics, Medicine and Man*, Ithaca, N.Y., 1947
[41] TYLER, A., *Energetics of Embryonic Differentiation*, Paris, 1939
[42] PULLINGER, B. D., *Lancet*, 2 (1949), 823
[43] WOOLLEY, G. W., FEKETE, E., and LITTLE, C. C., *Proc. Nat. Acad. Sci.*, 25 (1939), 277
[44] FEKETE, E., WOOLLEY, G. W. and LITTLE, C. C., *J. exp. Med.*, 74 (1941), 1
[45] WOOLLEY, G. W., FEKETE, E. and LITTLE, C. C., *Endocrinol.*, 28 (1941), 341
[46] —, —, —, *Science*, 97 (1943), 291
[47] — and LITTLE, C. C., *Cancer Res.*, 5 (1945), 321, 506
[48] PARKER, R. C., *J. exp. Med.*, 55 (1932), 713
[49] WHITE, P. R., *Growth*, 10 (1946), 231
[50] —, *J. cell. comp. Physiol.*, 34 (1949), 221
[51] MORGAN, J. F., MORTON, H. J. and PARKER, R. C., *Proc. Soc. exp. Biol. Med.*, 73 (1950), 1
[52] CARREL, A. and EBELING, A. H., *J. exp. Med.*, 38 (1923), 513
[53] —, —, *ibid*, 44 (1926), 261
[54] STERN, E. A., *Culture des Tissus et Cancer*, Paris, 1936
[55] CARREL, A., *Arch. exp. Zellforsch.*, 6 (1928), 70
[56] —, *J. exp. Med.* 15 (1912), 516

[57] CARREL, A., *ibid*, 17 (1913), 14
[58] —, *J. Amer. med. Ass.*, 82 (1924), 255
[59] — and EBELING, A. H., *J. exp. Med.*, 36 (1922), 645
[60] —, —, *ibid*, 36 (1922), 365
[61] —, *ibid.*, 36 (1922), 385
[62] —, *C. R. Soc. Biol.*, 90 (1924), 29
[63] —, *ibid*, 96 (1927), 19
[64] — and EBELING, A. H., *J. exp. Med.*, 44 (1926), 285
[65] DES LIGNERIS, M. J. A., *Arch. exp. Zellforsch.*, 11 (1931), 355
[66] LUDFORD, R. J., *Brit. med. J.*, 1 (1940), 201
[67] FISCHER, A., *Gewebezüchtung*, München, 1930
[68] LIEBMAN, E., *Growth*, 10 (1946), 291
[69] —, *Experientia*, 3 (1947), 442
[70] ROWNTREE, L. G., *Trans. Assoc. Amer. Physicians*, 51 (1936), 148, quoted by TYLER[41]
[71] STERN, K. and WILLHEIM, R., *The Biochemistry of Malignant Tumors*, Brooklyn, N.Y., 1943
[72] FISCHER, A., *Acta physiol. Scand.*, 3 (1941), 54
[73] — and ASTRUP, T., *Pflüger's Arch.*, 247 (1943), 34
[74] LASER, H., *Z. Krebsforsch.*, 39 (1933), 384
[75] BAKER, L. E., *Science*, 83 (1936), 605
[76] FISCHER, A., *Virchow's Arch.*, 279 (1930), 94
[77] —, *J. exp. Med.*, 38 (1923), 667
[78] GUILLERY, H., *Virchow's Arch.*, 275 (1930), 181
[79] ALBERT, A. F. and HECHT, E., *Arch. exp. Zellforsch.*, 14 (1933), 347
[80] SANTESSON, L., *Acta path. microbiol. scand.*, Suppl. 24 (1935)
[81] WILLMER, E. N. and KENDAL, L. P., *J. exp. Biol.*, 9 (1932), 149
[82] BAKER, L. E., *J. exp. Med.*, 69 (1939), 625
[83] — and CARREL, A., *ibid*, 47 (1928), 373
[84] —, —, *ibid*, 48 (1928), 353
[85] CARREL, A. and BAKER, L. E., *ibid*, 44 (1926), 503
[86] FISCHER, A., *Acta physiol. scand.*, 4 (1942), 207
[87] —, *Biol. Rev.*, 22 (1947), 178
[88] HUEPER, W. C. and RUSSELL, M. A., *Arch. exp. Zellforsch.*, 14 (1933), 483
[89] VERNE, J. and VERNE-SOUBIRAN, A., *C. R. Soc. Biol.*, 127 (1938), 1090
[90] HUEPER, W. C., ALLEN, A., RUSSELL, M., WOODWARD, G. and PLATT, M., *Amer. J. Cancer*, 17 (1933), 74
[91] HAMMETT, F. S., *Protoplasma*, 7 (1929), 297
[92] —, *ibid*, 11 (1930), 382
[93] —, *Science*, 83 (1936), 57
[94] VOEGTLIN, C. and CHALKLEY, H. W., *U.S. Publ. Hlth. Reps.*, 2 (1930), 3041
[95] RAPKINE, L., *Ann. physiol. phys. Biol.*, 7 (1931), 382
[96] HAMMETT, F. S. and LAVINE, T. S., *Growth*, 4 (1940), 337
[97] EHRENSVÄRD, G., FISCHER, A. and STJERNHOLM, R., *Acta physiol. scand.*, 18 (1949), 218
[98] FISCHER, A., *Enzymologia*, 14 (1950), 15
[99] —, *Acta physiol. scand.*, 2 (1941), 143
[100] —, *Biochem. J.*, 43 (1948), 491
[101] —, *J. exp. Med.*, 39 (1924), 577
[102] KIAER, S., *Arch. exp. Zellforsch.*, 1 (1925), 115
[103] MOTTRAM, J. C., *Lancet*, 2 (1927), 1232
[104] GEY, G. O. and GEY, M. K., *Amer. J. Cancer*, 27 (1936), 45
[105] CARREL, A. and EBELING, A. H., *J. exp. Med.*, 38 (1923), 499
[106] LANDSTEINER, K. and PARKER, R. C., *ibid*, 71 (1940), 231
[107] FOWLER, O. M., *J. exp. Zool.*, 76 (1937), 235
[108] GAILLARD, P. J., *Protoplasma*, 23 (1935), 145
[109] —, *Hormones regulating Growth and Differentiation in Embryonic Explants*, Paris, 1942
[110] HEATON, T. B., *J. Path. Bact.*, 29 (1926), 293
[111] WALTON, A. J., *J. exp. Med.*, 20 (1914), 554

[112] Trowell, O. A., and Willmer, E. N., *J. exp. Biol.*, 16 (1939), 60
[113] Hoffmann, R. S., *Growth*, 4 (1940), 361
[114] Doljanski, L., and Hoffmann, R. S., *C. R. Soc. Biol.*, 130 (1939), 1246
[115] Hoffmann, R. S., Tenenbaum, E. and Doljanski, L., *Nature*, 143 (1939), 764
[116] —, —, —, ibid, 144 (1939), 1092
[117] Margoliash, E. and Doljanski, L., *Growth*, 14 (1950), 7
[118] Doljanski, L., Hoffmann, R. S. and Tenenbaum, E., *Nature*, 150 (1942), 23
[119] —, —, *Growth*, 7 (1943), 67
[120] Willmer, E. N., *J. exp. Biol.*, 10 (1933), 323
[121] Doljanski, L. and Goldhaber, G., *Proc. Soc. exp. Biol. Med.*, 60 (1945), 132
[122] Medawar, P. B., *Quart. J. exp. Physiol.*, 27 (1937), 147
[123] Ephrussi, B. and Litvac, A., *Arch. exp. Zellforsch.*, 16 (1934), 203
[124] Carrel, A. and Ebeling, A. H., *J. exp. Med.*, 38 (1923), 487
[125] Astrup, T., Ehrensvärd, G., Fischer, A., and Øhlenschlager, W., *Acta physiol. Scand.*, 14 (1947), 195
[126] Fischer, A. and Astrup, T., *Pflüger's Arch.*, 245 (1942), 633
[127] —, —, Ehrensvärd, G. and Øhlenschlager, W., *Proc. Soc. exp. Biol. Med.*, 67 (1948), 40
[128] Astrup, T., Fischer, A. and Volkert, M., *Acta physiol. scand.*, 9 (1945), 134
[129] —, —, ibid, 9 (1945), 183
[130] —, —, ibid., 11 (1946), 187
[131] Astrup, T., Fischer, A. and Øhlenschlager, W., ibid, 13 (1947), 267
[132] White, P. R., and Lasfargues, E., *Proc. Soc. exp. Biol. Med.*, 71 (1949), 479
[133] Fischer, A., *Tissue Culture*, Copenhagen, 1925
[134] Hammarsten, E., *J. exp. Med.*, 43 (1920), 243
[135] Jacoby, F., Trowell, O. A. and Willmer, E. N., *J. exp. Biol.*, 14 (1937), 255
[136] Tompkins, E. R., Cunningham, B. and Kirk, P. L., *J. cell. comp. Physiol.*, 30 (1947), 1
[137] Willmer, E. N., in *Essays on Growth and Form*, Ed. W. E. Le Gros Clark and P. B. Medawar, Oxford, 1945
[138] Horsfall, F. L., *Fed. Proc.*, 8 (1949), 518
[139] Luria, S. E., *Science*, 111 (1950), 507
[140] des Ligneris, M. J. A., *Arch. exp. Zellforsch.*, 18 (1936), 456
[141] Davidson, J. N. and Waymouth, C., *Biochem. J.*, 38 (1944), 39
[142] Brachet, J., *Soc. exp. Biol.*, Symposium No. 1 (1947), 207
[143] Claude, A., *Science*, 90 (1937), 213
[144] —, *Proc. Soc. exp. Biol. Med.*, 39 (1938), 398
[145] —, *Science*, 91 (1940), 77
[146] Tennant, R., Liebow, A. A. and Stern, K. G., *Proc. Soc. exp. Biol. Med.*, 46 (1941), 18
[147] —, Stern, K. G. and Liebow, A. A., *Cancer Res.*, 2 (1942), 218
[148] Nilsson, R., *Arch. Mikrobiol.*, 12 (1941), 63 (quoted in *Chem. Abst.*, 36 (1942), 5486)
[149] Commoner, B., *Quart. Rev. Biol.*, 17 (1942), 46
[150] Warburg, O., *Pflüger's Arch.*, 154 (1913), 599
[151] Hopkins, F. G., *The problem of specificity in biochemical catalysis*, reprinted in *Hopkins and Biochemistry*, Ed. J. Needham and E. Baldwin, Cambridge, 1949
[152] Banga, I., *Z. physiol. Chem.*, 249 (1937), 183
[153] Claude, A., *Amer. J. Cancer*, 30 (1937), 742
[154] Kabat, E. A. and Furth, J., *J. exp. Med.*, 71 (1940), 55
[155] Stern, K. G., *Symp. quant. Biol.*, 7 (1939), 312
[156] —, *Ann. Rev. Biochem.*, 9 (1940), 1
[157] —, *Biol. Symp.*, 10 (1943), 291
[158] Schneider, W. C., and Hogeboom, G. H., *Cancer Res.*, 11 (1951), 1
[159] Claude, A., *Science*, 97 (1943), 451
[160] —, *J. exp. Med.*, 84 (1946), 61
[161] Chantrenne, H., *Biochem. Biophys. Acta*, 1 (1947), 437
[162] Jeener, R and Brachet, J., *Acta Biol. Belg.*, 1 (1941), 476

[163] SHAVER, J. R. and BRACHET, J., *Experientia* 5 (1949), 235
[164] BRACHET, J., *Bull. Soc. Chim. Biol.*, 32 (1950), 443
[165] —, *Growth*, Suppl. 12 (1947), 309
[166] MOOG, F. and STEINBACH, H. B., *J. cell. comp. Physiol.*, 25 (1945), 133
[167] —, —, *ibid.*, 28 (1946), 209
[168] BRACHET, J., *Ann. New York Acad. Sci.*, 50 (1950), 861
[169] —, *Pubb. Staz. Zool. Napoli*, 21 (1949), 77
[170] CLAUDE, A., *Adv. Protein Chem.*, 5 (1949), 423
[171] CASPERSSON, T. and SCHULTZ, J., *Proc. Nat. Acad. Sci.*, 26 (1940), 507
[172] WEISS, P., *Science*, 106 (1947), 511
[173] JEENER, R. and SZAFARZ, D., *Arch. Biochem.*, 26 (1950), 54
[174] WEISS, P., *Quart. Rev. Biol.*, 25 (1950), 177
[175] PETERMANN, M. L., ALFIN-SLATER, R. B. and LARACK, A. M., *Cancer*, 2 (1949), 510
[176] BRACHET, J., *Embryologie Chimique*, Paris, 1947
[177] CLAUDE, A., *Ann. New York Acad. Sci.*, 50 (1950), 854
[178] CARREL, A., in Foreword to R. C. PARKER's *Methods of Tissue Culture*, New York 1938
[179] KNIGHT, B. C. J. G., *Vitamins and Hormones*, 3 (1945), 105
[180] CLAUDE, A., *A.A.A.S. Conference on Cancer* (1945), 223
[181] HOPKINS, F. G., *Proc. roy. Soc.* B, 116 (1934), 426

Inhibitory studies on mitosis

[182] DUSTIN, P., *Arch. Med. Belg.*, 3 (1946), 157
[183] —, *Sang*, 21 (1950), 297
[184] AUERBACH, C. and ROBSON, J. M., *Nature*, 154 (1944), 81
[185] —, —, *Proc. roy. Soc. Edin.* B, 62 (1946), 211
[186] —, —, *ibid*, 62 (1947), 271
[187] DARLINGTON, C. D. and KOLLER, P. C., *Heredity*, 1 (1947), 187
[188] HUGHES, A. F. and FELL, H. B., *Quart. J. micr. Sci.*, 90 (1949), 37
[189] LOVELESS, A. and REVELL, S., *Nature*, 164 (1949), 938
[190] COMANDON, J. and DE FONBRUNE, P., *C.R. Soc. Biol.*, 136 (1942), 410, 423, 460, 746 and 763
[191] GAULDEN, M. E., and CARLSON, J. G., *Genetics*, 32 (1947), 87
[192] WADA, B., *Cytologia, Tokio*, 9 (1939), 460
[193] —, *ibid*, 11 (1940), 93
[194] SHIGENAGA, M., *ibid*, Fujii Jub., 1 (1939), 464
[195] HUGHES, A. F., *J. Roy. micr. Soc.*, 69 (1949), 215
[196] WILBRANDT, W., *Arch. ges. Physiol.*, 243 (1940), 519
[197] DAVSON, H., *J. Cell. Comp. Physiol.*, 10 (1937), 247
[198] —, *Biochem. J.*, 33 (1939), 389
[199] MAIZELS, M., *ibid*, 29 (1935), 1970
[200] DAVSON, H. and DANIELLI, J. F., *ibid*, 32 (1938), 991
[201] HUGHES, A. F., *Quart. J. micr. Soc.*, 91 (1950), 251
[202] WESSON, L. G., COHN, W. E. and BRUES, A. M., *J. gen. Physiol.*, 32 (1949), 511
[203] HARRIS, J. E., *Biol. Bull., Wood's Hole*, 79 (1940), 373
[204] DANOWSKI, T. S., *J. Biol. Chem.*, 139 (1941), 693
[204a] SPEAR, F. G., *Arch. f. Exp. Zellforsch.*, 7 (1928), 484
[204b] ODDO, A. M., and ESPOSITO, M., *J. gen. Physiol.*, 34 (1951), 285
[205] DAVSON, J., *J. Cell Comp. Physiol.*, 18 (1941), 173
[206] BULLOUGH, W. S., *J. exp. Biol.*, 26 (1949), 83
[207] —, *J. Endocrinol.*, 6 (1950), 350
[208] —, *Exp. Cell Res.*, 1 (1950), 410
[209] MEDAWAR, P. B., *Quart. J. micr. Soc.*, 88 (1947), 27
[210] BRACHET, J., *Embryologie Chimique*, Paris, 1947
[211] STEINITZ, L. M., *Amer. J. Bot.*, 30 (1943), 622
[212] HARVEY, E. B., *Biol. Bull., Wood's Hole*, 52 (1927), 147
[213] LASER, H., *Biochem. Z.*, 264 (1933), 72

[214] EPHRUSSI, B., CHEVILLARD, L., MAYER, A. and PLANTEFOL, L., *Ann. physiol. phys. biol.*, 5 (1929), 642

[215] HAVARD, R. E. and KENDAL, L. P., *Biochem. J.*, 28 (1934), 1121

[216] POMERAT, C. M. and WILLMER, E. N., *J. exp. Biol.*, 16 (1939), 232

[217] ALLSOP, C. B. and FELL, H. B., *Exp. Cell Res.*, 1 (1950), 590

[218] PACE, D. M., *Biol. Bull., Wood's Hole*, 89 (1945), 76

[219] ZEUTHEN, E., *ibid*, 98 (1950), 144

[220] BULLOUGH, W. S. and GREEN, H. N., *Nature*, 164 (1949), 795

[221] HUGHES, A. F., *Exp. Cell. Res.*, 1951, In press

[221a] BERRIAN, J. H., and DORNFELD, E J., *J. Exp. Zool.*, 115 (1950), 513

[222] RUNNSTRÖM, J. and KRISZAT, G., *Exp. Cell Res.*, 1 (1950), 284, 497

[223] HOPKINS, F. G. and SIMON-REUSS, I., *Proc. roy. Soc. Lond.*, B 132 (1944), 253

[224] CLOWES, G. H. A. and KRAHL, M. E., *Science*, 80 (1934), 384

[225] RUNNSTRÖM, J., *Protoplasma*, 10 (1930), 106

[226] —, *Biol. Bull., Wood's Hole*, 69 (1935), 351

[227] SCOTT, A., *ibid*, 99 (1950), 362

[228] KRAHL, M. E., *ibid*, 98 (1950), 175

[228a] CLOWES, G. H. A., *Ann. N.Y. Acad. Sci.*, 51 (1951), 1409

[229] BLUMENTHAL, R., *Physiol. Zool.*, 3 (1930), 539

[229a] HENSHAW, P. S., *Amer. J. Roentg.*, 43 (1940), 899

[229b] — and COHEN, I., *ibid*, 917

[229c] FRIEDENWALD, J. S., *Ann. N.Y. Acad. Sci.*, 51 (1951), 1432

[230] ERICKSON, R. O. and ROSEN, G. U., *Amer. J. Bot.*, 36 (1949), 317

[231] D'AMATO, F., *Caryologia*, 1 (1949), 327

[232] MISZURSKI, B. and DOLJANSKI, L., *Amer. J. Anat.*, 85 (1949), 523

[233] HUGHES, A. F. and SWANN, M. M., *J. exp. Biol.*, 25 (1948), 45

[234] LUDFORD, R. J., *Arch. exp. Zellforsch.*, 18 (1936), 411

[235] PERNICE, B., *Sicil. Med.*, 1 (1889), 265

[236] EIGSTI, O. J., DUSTIN, P. and GAY-WINN, N., *Science*, 110 (1949), 692

[237] FRIEDMANN, E., MARRIAM, D. H., and SIMON-REUSS, I., *B. J. Pharm. Chemother.*, 4 (1949), 105

[238] NEBEL, B. R. and RUTTLE, M. L., *J. Hered.*, 29 (1938), 3

[239] GAVAUDAN, P. and POUSSEL, H., *C.R. Soc. Biol.*, 138 (1944), 246

[240] CORNMAN, I., *Biol. Bull., Wood's Hole*, 93 (1947), 192 and 214

[240a] ORMSBEE, R. A., CORNMAN, I., and BERGER, R., *Unio intern. contra Cancrum*, 6 (1949), 657

[241] LETTRÉ, *Die Naturwiss.*, 33 (1946), 75

[241a] LETTRÉ, I. and CORNMAN, M. E., *Ann. N.Y. Acad. Sci.*, 51 (1951), 1443

[242] BOYLAND, E. and BOYLAND, M. E., *Biochem., J.*, 34 (1940), 280

[243] RAYMOND-HAMET, —, *C.R. Soc. Biol.*, 118 (1935), 1292

[244] KEESER, E., *Arch. exp. Path.*, 197 (1941), 187

[245] LECOMTE, J., *Arch. int. Pharm.*, 78 (1949), 440

[245a] CORNMAN, I., *J. Cell Comp. Physiol.*, 35 (1950), 301

[245b] MURRAY, M., DE LAM, H., and CHARGAFF, E., *Exp. Cell Res.*, 2 (1951), 165

[246] RICHARDS, O. W., *Anat. Rec.*, 70 (1937), 87

[247] RIES, E., *Die Naturwiss.*, 27 (1939), 505

[248] EIGSTI, O. J., *Genetics*, 25 (1940), 116

[249] KRYTHE, J. M., *Proc. Ned. Akad. Wetensch.*, 7 (1941), 283

[250] MISZURSKI, B., *Exp. Cell Res.*, Suppl. 1 (1949), 450

[251] BEAMS, H. W. and EVANS, T. C., *Biol. Bull., Wood's Hole*, 79 (1940), 188

[252] KING, R. L. and BEAMS, H. W., *J. cell comp. Physiol.*, 15 (1940), 252

[253] MITCHELL, J. S. and SIMON-REUSS, I., *Nature*, 160 (1947), 98

[254] HALABAN, A., *Biol. Bull., Wood's Hole*, 97 (1947), 240

[255] HEILBRUNN, L. V. and WILSON, W. L., *ibid*, 97 (1947), 242

[256] HEILBRUNN, L. V., WILSON, W. L. and HARDING, D., *ibid*, 99 (1950), 340

[257] ALLEN, R. D., *ibid*, 99 (1950), 353

[257a] HOSTER, M. S., McBEE, B. J., ROLNICK, H. A., VAN WINKLE, Q., HOLSTER, H. A., *Cancer Res.*, 10 (1950), 530

[258] DERMAN, H., *J. Hered*, 29 (1938), 210

[259] MEDES, G. and McCLENDON, J. F., *J. Biol. Chem.*, 42 (1920), 541

[260] ÖSTERGREN, G., *Hereditas*, 30 (1944), 431

[261] GAVAUDAN, P. and BRÉBION, G., *Rev. Trav. Toxic. Pharm. Cell.*, 2 (1946), 37

[262] FERGUSON, J., *Proc. roy. Soc. Lond.* B, 127 (1939), 387

[263] GAVAUDAN, P., POUSSEL, H. and DODÉ, M., *C.R. Soc. Biol.*, 138 (1944), 267

[264] McELROY, W. D., *Quart. Rev. Biol.*, 22 (1947), 25

[265] DANIELLI, J. F., *Cell Physiology and Pharmacology*, Amsterdam, 1950

[266] JOHNSON, F. H., BROWN, D. E., and MARSLAND, D. A., *J. Cell Comp. Physiol.*, 20 (1942), 269

[266a] KOPAC, M. J., *Ann. N.Y. Acad. Sci.*, 51 (1951), 1541

[267] RAPKINE, L., *Ann. physiol. phys. Biol.*, 7 (1931), 382

[268] DUSTIN, P., *Nature*, 159 (1947), 794

[269] BRACHET, J., *Arch. Biol.*, 51 (1940), 151

[270] CHALKLEY, H. W., *Protoplasma*, 28 (1937), 489

[271] CHÈVREMONT, M. and FREDERIC, J. *Arch. Biol.*, 54 (1943), 589

[272] MAVER, M. E. and GRECO, A. E., *Biol. Chem.*, 181 (1949), 861

[273] DUSTIN, A. P., *C.R. Soc. Biol.*, 93 (1925), 465
—, *Arch. exp. Zellforsch.*, 22 (1939), 395

[274] LETTRÉ, H. and LETTRÉ, R., *Die Naturwiss.*, 33 (1947), 283

[275] LEVAN, A. and LOTFLY, T., *Hereditas.*, 36 (1950), 470

[276] HUGHES-SCHRADER, S. and RIS, H., *J. exp. Zool.*, 87 (1941), 429

[277] POULSON, D. F., *ibid.*, 83 (1940), 271

[278] MAZIA, D., *Growth*, 13 Suppl. (1949), 5

[279] MARSHAK A., *Biol. Bull.*, *Wood's Hole*, 97 (1949), 223

[280] — and HARTING, J., *J. cell comp. Physiol.*, 31 (1948), 321

[281] SIMONET, M. and GUINOCHET, M., *C.R. Soc. Biol.*, 130 (1939), 1057; 131 (1939), 222

[282] GAVAUDAN, P., GAVAUDAN, N., and DURAND, J., *C.R. Soc. Biol.*, 130 (1939), 1443

[283] CLOWES, G. H. A., KRAHL, M E. and KELTCH, A. K., *Biol. Bull.*, *Wood's Hole*, 69 (1935) 341

[284] LOOMIS, W. F. and LIPMANN, F., *J. Biol. Chem.*, 173 (1948), 807

[285] VILLEE, C. A., LOWENS, M., GORDON, M., LEONARD, E. and RICH, A., *J. Cell Comp. Physiol.*, 33 (1949), 93

[286] KIHLMAN, B., *Hereditas*, 36 (1950), 103

[287] CHALKLEY, H. W., *Ann N.Y. Acad. Sci.*, 51 (1951), 1303

[288] WILSON, E. B., *Arch. EntwMech.*, 13 (1902), 353

[289] ZEUTHEN, E., Symposium on *Sub-microscopical Structure of Protoplasm*, Pub. d. Staz. Zool. Napoli., 23 (suppl.), In press

[290] SKIPPER, H. E., MITCHELL, J. H., BENNETT, L. L., NEWTON, M. A., SIMPSON, L., EIDSON, M., *Cancer Res.*, 11 (1951), 145

[291] KRAHL, M. E., and CLOWES, G. H. A. *J. gen. Physiol.*, 20 (1936), 173

6

OUTLOOK

PERHAPS it may be allowed that the absence of a complete and unified synthesis of mitosis in the foregoing pages is not wholly due to the shortcomings of the authors' presentation of the subject. Much still remains to be elucidated before it will be possible to construct one, and the student entering this field need fear no lack of problems. There are indeed, as Dr Johnson said of Spain, parts that have not been perambulated.

Not all the unexplored regions of the subject are inaccessible; there are some which happen merely to be off the main tracks of investigation trodden by those who follow particular ideas, or exploit favourable sources of material. These highways may perhaps be classified in the following fashion.

Cytogenetical—The underlying theme of the majority of papers in cytology for most of the last 50 years has been the correlation of the experimental study of inheritance with the behaviour of the chromosomes within the cell. Indeed, cytology is sometimes equated with cytogenetics. Somatic mitosis is only one of many topics in this subject, and in these pages no attempt has been made to discuss any of the others, full though they are of detailed observations on the cell. The cytoplasmic aspects of mitosis however tend not to be included.

Comparative—Two main objectives may be discerned in studies of this kind on the dividing cell. One is the classical aim of all comparative anatomy, that of revealing evolutionary relationships; while the other seeks a closer understanding of the common themes of mitosis and meiosis by revealing the variations upon them found in different organisms.

Physiological—Under this category we can include all those lines of research which deal in such a variety of ways with the living cell. For several reasons, marine eggs, chiefly of Echinoderms, have been used in the great majority of experimental studies on dividing cells, and recent developments in several fields such as in microscopy and the use of trace elements have shown that much still remains to be done with this material. Other cells in which more detail can be seen in life are less readily accessible to experimental analysis, though considerable development is possible both in the methods of observing and in the technique of experimentation on many types of living cell.

Cytochemical—Due to the prominence of the developments in this subject in recent years, it is often thought of as the most modern branch of cell biology, though its roots go back for more than a century, as BAKER[1] has made clear in an interesting historical survey. The development of staining techniques in the later nineteenth century was preceded by MIESCHER's pioneer work on the nucleic acids, and for more than a decade it was hoped that differences in the staining reactions of cell components could be directly interpreted in chemical terms (HUGHES[2]). High hopes and sceptical reaction have marked the progress of cytochemistry and even now the list of substances which can be identified with reasonable probability within components of the cell is still very small. In general, the difficulties increase as the localization of smaller molecules and groups is attempted, and at present the identification of atoms other than by isotopic methods is virtually impossible. Yet until methods are found adequate for tracing the movements of calcium, for instance, within a cell during mitosis it will not be possible to test so interesting a theory as that of HEILBRUNN on the nature of the mitotic stimulus.

Although it would not be true to state that these four general headings of research have been pursued in isolation from each other, this tendency has been a strong one. The distribution of our present knowledge in the subject is partly determined by the restriction of some lines of inquiry to a few favourable sources of material. Thus much of what is known about the cytoplasmic events in mitosis refers to marine eggs, and the nature of the stimulus to enter division has mainly been studied in tissue cultures.

If evolutionary development had provided the Echinoderms with a few large chromosomes, it is probable that our knowledge of the nuclear and the cytoplasmic aspects of mitosis would be more coherent. SCHRADER[3] says that 'it is a striking fact that our knowledge of chromosome structure and behaviour is far in advance of what we know about the rest of the mitotic figure', and although there has been recent progress in the study of the achromatic figure, it is certainly true that the relations of the two sets of events is still largely obscure. We are, for example, wholly ignorant at present of the nature of the actual stimulus which sets off the movement of the chromosomes in anaphase. In watching a living cell through mitosis, metaphase often passes rather slowly, and one awaits the relief of the sudden and unheralded moment when all the chromosomes move together. At such times, this question suggests itself with peculiar insistence. In MICHEL's memorable film of Orthopteran spermatogenesis, shortly before anaphase it can be seen that the mitochondrial investment of the spindle bulges at the equator towards the cell surface. Then anaphase begins, the mitochondria retreat, and soon the cleavage furrow appears at the site where this material has touched the cortical layer. Clearly these events must all be interrelated, though we yet know nothing of how this is achieved.

The attempt is often made to bridge such gaps by a broad appeal to theory and generalization. It may not be amiss briefly to consider this tendency. It is difficult to resist the impression that the elaboration of theories in cytology is sometimes carried to great lengths. DARLINGTON,[4] for instance, in his 'balance theory of mitosis' gives a graphical representation of the charges with which he endows centrosomes and centromeres during mitosis and meiosis, though without an actual scale in millivolts. Within recent years, the nucleic acids have proved a favourable subject for exercises of this kind, the scope of which has not been restricted to this planet alone. The question at issue is not whether truths beyond the immediate reach of observation can be apprehended by imaginative inference, but whether such theories have been found to serve as a useful basis for further research, and to stimulate fresh inquiry into particular aspects of cell division. It is doubtful whether a survey of the progress of cytology would uphold such a claim, though it might be urged that it is the experimenter who has subsequently failed to play his part in testing these hypotheses. In practice, however, the wider is their scope, the less readily can they be tested by a specific inquiry. Anything in the cell could be explained by a general appeal to the nucleic acids, as readily before an experiment as after it.

The generalizing impulse is often expressed in another way. There is a strong tendency to assume that observations made in a specially favourable material must be everywhere valid in virtue of their clarity and precision. If there are discordant results elsewhere, they can be brushed aside as unimportant exceptions. Examples of this are by no means uncommon; two may perhaps be quoted. CLEVELAND[5] in describing some of his very remarkable observations on the cytology of the flagellates parasitic on termites, claims that they apply also to cellular organisms: 'The close similarity between the behaviour of these hypermastigote centrioles, and the centrioles of other cells leaves no room to doubt the general application of the observations on these flagellates to mitosis in both animals and plants.'

Again, LOVELESS and REVELL[6] in surveying methods of research on the effects of mutagenic chemicals make the statement:

> By the use of the precise techniques that had previously been devised for the detection and quantitative estimation of X-ray effects, they (geneticists and cytologists) have shown that certain classes of these compounds are mutagenetic agents, for they can cause heritable nuclear changes that are demonstrably similar to those induced by X-rays. Consequently they have used as experimental materials those, such as *Drosophila* and the classical cytological objects, which were best suited to the application of these techniques, and they have felt justified in doing this by their confidence that their results could in general be extrapolated to other cellular systems.

It is difficult to see more in the last sentence than a declaration of faith in the sense in which St. Paul defines the word (Hebrews XI. 1).

When two authors generalize in this way from two different points in the same field, a controversy may develop, in which each may well be right as far as his own observations are concerned. WHITE[7] puts the point very well in a comment on a debate concerning the state of the chromosomes in telophase: 'The protagonists on both sides of this polemic seem to have tacitly assumed that whichever opinion was true must also be true in all types of cells.'

Those who do this run the risk of neglecting the counsel which in the sister field of genetics was given by BATESON,[8] and which surely is just as relevent to cell biology: 'Treasure your exceptions! . . . Keep them always uncovered and in sight. Exceptions are like the rough brickwork of a growing building which tells that there is more to come and shews where the next construction is to be.'

Mitosis seems to me to be a supreme example in science of diversity within a unity. It can hardly be doubted that the cycle of the formation and dissolution both of the chromosomes and of the spindle are basically similar throughout all the varying divergencies of detail which accompany these events in different organisms. Probably insufficient notice has been taken of these differences, though studies such as those of the SCHRADERS' have shown how revealing these aberrant features can be. It would be desirable to extend such investigations from the purely descriptive level and to combine the second and third of the above categories, and thus to begin the comparative physiology of cell division. Here lies a potential approach of great power to the analysis of mitosis, which could be pursued consciously if we attempted to define what basic factors in addition to the visible events in nucleus and cytoplasm are common to mitosis, wherever the process is found.

In recent years much has been learnt from the detailed study of individual types of cells with various techniques, but it has yet to be shown how far these findings may be applied elsewhere. Above all, we need to know more about the physiology of mitosis in the plant cell; it would be particularly desirable to study topics such as the proteins of the chromosomes, the growth of the orientation of the spindle, and the cytoplasmic events during cytokinesis such as the changes in permeability of the cell membrane. Experience in other aspects of cell physiology has already shown the need for the student to surmount the conventional academic divisions of biology, which in this field have unquestionably impeded its progress.

REFERENCES

[1] BAKER, J. R., *J. Quekett., micr. Club.*, Ser 4, 1 (1943), 256
[2] HUGHES, A. F., *International Revue of Cell Biology* (in the press)

[3] SCHRADER, F., *Biol. Bull.*, 67 (1934), 519
[4] DARLINGTON, C., *Proc. roy. Soc. Lond.* B, 121 (1936), 264
[5] CLEVELAND, L. R., *Science*, 81 (1935), 598
[6] LOVELESS, A. and REVELL, S., *Nature*, 164 (1949), 938
[7] WHITE, M. J. D., in *Cytology and Cell Physiology*, Ed. by Bourne, G., 1st ed., Oxford, 1942, p 152
[8] BATESON, B., *William Bateson, Naturalist*, p 324, Cambridge, 1928

NAME INDEX

SUBJECT INDEX

DATE DUE

APR 1 0 '84			
FEB 2 5 1997			